D1188145

AUTOMOBILE GUIDE

by Frederick E. Bricker

THEODORE AUDEL & CO.

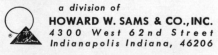

a division of
HOWARD W. SAMS & CO., INC.
4300 West 62nd Street
Indianapolis Indiana, 46206

Foreword

The modern automobile is a complex combination of systems, each designed for maximum efficiency and for compatible relationship with all the others. Each system must be maintained in first-class operating condition, or it may affect the operation of the other related systems.

This book was prepared to guide the mechanic, operator, and owner in understanding the way in which an automobile works and to provide information on the repair that every car needs from time to time. It is the belief of the writer that if the average person understands the operating principle of a device, he will be able to repair it more rapidly and with greater accuracy. This idea is followed in the text. Stress is placed on the explanations of how and why certain units operate as they do. Typical examples of repair procedures are explained; and where applicable, trouble symptoms, their probable cause, and their possible remedies are listed. These lists should be of great help in diagnosing and correcting troubles that occur in any make or model of automobile.

Full use of illustrations is made to supplement the text and to make the explanations as clear as possible. Cutaway and ex-

Foreword

ploded views show the actual construction features of various units, while other illustrations show the actual repair being made.

Special thanks are due every major automobile manufacturer for their cooperation in supplying information on their particular cars. Without their help this book could not have been compiled. Thanks are also due Mr. Frank D. Graham, the author of the original AUDEL Automobile Mechanics Guide.

FREDERICK E. BRICKER

Contents

Contents

Contents

CHAPTER 1

Troubleshooting

In every car ever built, the engine and chassis parts are subjected to abrasive and corrosive wear, heat, vibration, and other factors that cause constant deterioration. In time, hard starting or failure to start, poor engine performance, low gas mileage, and other minor or more serious troubles may result from wear, broken parts, or changes in adjustments.

A car's trouble symptoms may be simple and have an easily identified source; or they may be complex—for example, loss of engine power resulting from a *combination* of ignition-system troubles.

One can save much time, wasted effort, and money by using a *planned procedure* for troubleshooting that will:

1. Quickly isolate the system responsible for the complaint.
2. By elimination, determine the particular part or adjustment responsible for the trouble.

The clues for troubleshooting are provided by the performance of the engine or other components and the appearance and *variation* of parts from the manufacturer's specified wear limits or adjustments.

When using the troubleshooting check lists, it will be helpful to keep the following points in mind:

1. Any troubleshooting check list can only tell *what* to check. A knowledge of engine components, systems, and functions, plus some practical experience is necessary if one is to know *how* to do the job.
2. When troubleshooting, always check the obvious first—is the ignition on, car out of gas, overheated?
3. Don't quit too soon. Find and fix the cause of the trouble, not just a symptom. For example, replacing a battery without finding and fixing a low-drain short in the wiring that caused the battery to become discharged is only a temporary and expensive solution.

The remainder of this chapter lists the most commonly experienced troubles. Their most probable causes are listed under each symptom in the order in which they most frequently occur.

Once the probable cause has been identified, refer to the index to locate the chapter covering the particular component or function. Individual chapters in this book cover specific details on the repair and adjustment procedures for American cars produced in the last ten years.

1. STARTER DOES NOT CRANK AND STARTING RELAY DOES NOT "CLICK"

PROBABLE CAUSE:
(a) Neutral (or parking) starter switch on cars equipped with automatic transmission. Gear-shift lever not in Neutral (or Park).
(b) Loose or broken battery- or starter-cable connections or an undercharged battery.

(c) Defective starter solenoid or remote switch (relay).

(d) Defective ignition starter switch or loose connections.

2. STARTER DOES NOT CRANK BUT STARTING RELAY DOES "CLICK"

PROBABLE CAUSE:

(a) Loose or broken battery- or starter-cable connections or an undercharged battery.

(b) Starter drive gear and flywheel ring gear locked.

(c) Loose starter mounting bolts.

(d) Water in cylinders or engine locked.

3. STARTER ROTATES BUT DOES NOT CRANK ENGINE

PROBABLE CAUSE:

(a) Starter drive improperly adjusted.

(b) Starter drive stuck or broken.

4. ENGINE CRANKS TOO SLOW TO START

PROBABLE CAUSE:

(a) Undercharged battery.

(b) High resistance in battery or starter cables due to corrosion, dirt, or loose connections.

(c) Defective starter.

(d) Oil of too high viscosity (in cold weather) or upper cylinder gum and sludge condition. Oil contaminated with permanent antifreeze.

(e) Mechanical causes—high engine friction from tight bearings or similar causes.

5. **ENGINE CRANKS NORMALLY BUT DOES NOT START**

It is first necessary to determine whether the electrical or the fuel system is the cause of the trouble. Make certain that the car is not out of gas (don't trust the gauge), then proceed as follows: Disconnect the high-tension cable at any spark plug. Place an adaptor in the cable terminal (a paper clip will do). Hold the adaptor about ¼ of an inch from the engine block or the manifold. Have someone turn on the ignition and crank the engine. No spark or a weak spark from adaptor to ground indicates that the trouble is in the ignition system. A good spark indicates that the trouble is probably with the fuel system.

5A. **ENGINE CRANKS NORMALLY, BUT DOES NOT START—HAS NO SPARK OR A WEAK SPARK (from test)**

PROBABLE CAUSE:
(a) Burned, pitted, or dirty ignition points.
(b) Points not opening—worn cam rubbing block or weak point-spring tension.
(c) Distributor cap cracked or has corroded terminals or carbon tracks in the cap.
(d) Distributor rotor burned, cracked, broken, or excessively worn.
(e) Defective condenser or coil.
(f) Moisture in distributor cap or on high-tension cables.
(g) Loose or broken primary-wiring connections.
(h) Defective ballast resistor on cars having twelve-volt systems.

There are two more electrical possibilities to consider before troubleshooting the fuel system. Although a plug cable may provide a good spark against the block, the spark plugs may be fouled or have incorrect gap settings. Therefore, check the spark plugs for the correct gap and good condition. The car may have an electric fuel pump installed. These pumps have wiring connections that can become loose or can break, and electrical contact points that can pit, corrode, or fail. Remember to check these possible electrical troubles when troubleshooting the fuel system.

5B. ENGINE CRANKS NORMALLY AND HAS A GOOD SPARK, BUT DOES NOT START

PROBABLE CAUSE:

(a) Clogged fuel lines or screens.
(b) Choke sticking shut.
(c) Fuel pump inoperative or not delivering sufficient fuel.
(d) Fuel-pump sediment bowl not seated against its gasket (leaking air).
(e) Carburetor float valve stuck or set at wrong level.
(f) Air leaks at intake manifold or carburetor gaskets.
(g) Low compression from worn rings, burned or sticking valves, blown head gasket, etc.
(h) Valve tappets too tight.
(i) Valves out of timing.

6. HARD STARTING

First determine whether the engine is hard to start at all times, only when cold, only when hot, or only on quick restart. As a rough rule (to which there are a number of exceptions), hard starting only when the engine is cold often indicates electrical trouble, while hard starting when the engine is hot or on quick restart indicates fuel-system troubles. Regardless of the condition under which hard starting occurs, if the engine cranks slowly, check the reason for this first.

PROBABLE CAUSE:

(a) Loose or corroded battery or ground cables or connections.

(b) Battery undercharged or of low capacity.

(c) Defective starting motor, solenoid, or relay circuit.

(d) Loose starting-motor mounting bolts.

(e) Engine oil viscosity too high.

(f) Ignition problems (see Spark Test). Spark plugs fouled or improperly gapped. Ignition points pitted, corroded, or with improper gap. Weak condenser. Loose primary wiring connections causing high resistance. Weak coil. Corrosion or poor connections in the high-tension cables.

(g) Fuel-system problems. Partial clogging of fuel lines or filters. Choke sticking shut or inoperative automatic choke on cars so equipped. Carburetor float valve sticking. Improper idle speed or mixture adjustment. Fuel pump providing insufficient pressure or fuel volume. Air leaks. Vapor lock when engine is hot. Improper synchronization of carburetors on multiple carburetor installations.

(h) Low engine compression, which may be caused by any of the following: a blown or leaking head gasket; worn piston rings with or without worn or out-of-round cylinders; burned or sticking valves; excessive clearances between valve stems and guides; air leaks (loss of vacuum) at intake manifold or carburetor gaskets. *Note: Low compression is more likely to cause hard starting when the engine is hot than when the engine is cold.*

7. ENGINE STALLS

PROBABLE CAUSE:
(a) Fuel-system problems: wrong idle or mixture adjustments; choke not operating properly; carburetor float setting incorrect; defective fuel pump; dirt or water in fuel system.
(b) Ignition-system problems: bad or improperly gapped points; defective coil or condenser; worn distributor rotor or defective ignition wiring.
(c) Insufficient valve lash.

8. ENGINE MISSES

There are many possible causes for engine missing. Six conditions of engine missing have been selected that can easily be identified. It is useful to determine which type of missing is involved, since this information will help determine the system responsible for the troubles.

8A. STEADY MISSING AT ALL ENGINE SPEEDS

PROBABLE CAUSE:
(a) Ignition difficulties are usually responsible. Check: plug gap and condition; plug cables, especially the terminal ends; distributor cap, rotor, and contacts.
(b) Low compression.

8B. UNEVEN MISSING AT ALL ENGINE SPEEDS
(Most often caused by fuel-system troubles.)

PROBABLE CAUSE:
- (a) Dirt or water in fuel system, clogged fuel filter, sticking choke, sticking float valve.
- (b) Ignition-system troubles: malfunction of plugs, points, coil, condenser, or cables.
- (c) Excessive back pressure caused by exhaust-system restrictions such as crimped exhaust or tail pipes, rusted muffler baffles, etc.
- (d) Air leaks at carburetor or intake-manifold gaskets.

8C. ENGINE MISSES ONLY AT IDLING SPEED

PROBABLE CAUSE:
- (a) Ignition point gap too close (excessive dwell time).
- (b) Improper idle speed or mixture adjustment. Dirty carburetor.
- (c) Air leaks in fuel-intake system.
- (d) Manifold heat-control valve stuck open.
- (e) Other ignition troubles, such as: defective coil, condenser, rotor, cap, wiring or plugs.
- (f) Low compression.
- (g) Improper valve lash.

8D. ENGINE MISSES ONLY AT HIGH SPEED
(This complaint is most often traced to ignition troubles.)

PROBABLE CAUSE:
- (a) Spark plug condition and gap, or plugs of improper heat range.

(b) Poor condition or alignment of ignition points, or wrong gap setting, causing dwell to be incorrect. Improper timing.

(c) A weak coil, condenser leaky or loosely connected, worn distributor shaft bearings, or distributor poorly grounded.

(d) Fuel-pump pressure low or restrictions in fuel lines or filters.

(e) Carburetor power valve sticking or not operating properly.

(f) Dirty or clogged air cleaner causing reduced air intake at the time of high air-intake requirement.

(g) Gas-tank vent clogged.

(h) Sticking valves.

(i) Overheated engine.

8E. STEADY MISSING ONLY DURING ACCELERATION

PROBABLE CAUSE:

(a) Dirty or fouled spark plugs or cracked insulators.

(b) Trouble with points, condenser, coil, or plug cables.

(c) Weak fuel pump.

(d) Carburetor troubles.

8F. MOMENTARY MISSING (FLAT SPOT) DURING ACCELERATION (Usually caused by carburetor troubles.)

PROBABLE CAUSE:

(a) Defective accelerator pump. Low float-level setting.

(b) Choke sticking (cold engine).

(c) Manifold heat-control valve stuck open (cold engine).

(d) Low fuel-pump pressure or volume.

(e) Ignition defects: fouled spark plugs or incorrect gap, weak coil, high resistance in plug cables.

9. INSUFFICIENT POWER OR POOR HIGH-SPEED PERFORMANCE

PROBABLE CAUSE:

(a) *Fuel-system troubles*
   (1) Air cleaner dirty; restriction in fuel lines or filters.
   (2) Fuel-pump pressure and/or volume low.
   (3) Choke partially closed or carburetor linkage does not allow throttle to be opened fully.
   (4) Carburetor power circuits or high-speed jets not functioning properly.
   (5) Uneven synchronization of multiple carburetors.

(b) *Ignition-system troubles*
   (1) Improper ignition timing, weak coil, or leaky condenser. Points burned or improperly gapped. Mechanical or vacuum advance mechanisms not functioning properly. Ignition polarity reversed.
   (2) Spark plugs fouled or improperly gapped, or plugs of wrong heat range.

(c) *Mechanical causes*
   (1) Low compression caused by: incorrect valve lash or timing; worn or sticking valves; excessive valve-stem-to-guide clearance; leaking head or manifold gaskets; worn piston rings; etc.
   (2) Manifold heat valve stuck closed.

(d) *Overheating*
   (1) Loose or broken fan belt; leaks at radiator hoses

or clamps; water pump defective; radiator or cooling system partially clogged; thermostat defective.

(2) Carburetor air-to-fuel mixture wrong; automatic choke stuck.

(3) Excessive friction. Friction may be in the engine or anywhere in the drive train back to the wheels at the ground; tight engine bearings (especially connecting-rod bearings); excessive expansion, resulting in decreased clearances and increased friction; oil viscosity too high; clutch or propeller-shaft misalignment; improperly adjusted or lubricated wheel, pinion, differential, or transmission bearings; brakes dragging; underinflated tires; front end out of alignment.

10. COOLING-SYSTEM TROUBLES

High engine temperature is the major clue that indicates cooling-system troubles.

PROBABLE CAUSE:
(a) Loss of coolant, either external or internal.
(b) Reduction in air flow.
(c) Reduction of heat transfer because of clogging of the radiator or deposits in the water jacket.

Coolant loss not evident

PROBABLE CAUSE:
(a) Loose, worn, or broken fan belt.
(b) Defective radiator pressure cap.
(c) Defective thermostat or one installed upside down.

(d) Partially clogged radiator. Check for cool spots, which indicate clogging.

(e) Defective water pump.

(f) Deposits in water jackets.

Coolant loss evident

PROBABLE CAUSE:

(a) Cracked or leaking radiator hose or loose hose connections.

(b) Radiator leaks.

(c) Leaks at welch (freeze) plugs.

When there is a *gradual* loss of coolant, but no evidence of external leaks, suspect internal coolant loss. Look for water in the lubricating oil. If water is present in the oil (more than normal condensation), check for a leak in the head gasket or for a cracked block. When the coolant contains permanent-type (ethylene glycol) antifreeze, internal coolant leaks will quickly cause the buildup of gum, sludge, and lacquer deposits that can ruin the engine.

11. ELECTRICAL CHARGING-SYSTEM TROUBLES

The battery, generator, and regulator work together in the charging system and all three elements must be considered when troubleshooting the charging system. For example, when the battery is almost completely discharged, the regulator can no longer control the generator output so that the battery may be recharged.

PROBABLE CAUSE:

(a) *Generator fails to charge*
    (1) Fan belt loose or broken.

    (2) Brushes sticking or generator defective.

    (3) Regulator defective.

    (4) Lead connections reversed.

(b) *Low generator charging rate*

    (1) Slipping fan belt.

    (2) Faulty regulator setting or defective regulator.

    (3) Defective generator.

    (4) Excessive resistance in the charging circuit caused by loose connections, poor ground, or defective wiring.

(c) *Excessive generator charging rate*

    (1) Faulty regulator setting or defective regulator.

    (2) Defective generator.

    (3) Ground in generator-to-regulator wiring.
(When the car is not equipped with an ammeter, this complaint may be noted by the frequent need to add water to the battery.)

12. EXCESSIVE FUEL CONSUMPTION

The fuel consumption for every car is determined by:

(a) Driving conditions—city or country, low or high speeds, winter or summer.

(b) Driving habits—slow or fast acceleration, low or high speeds.

(c) Mechanical condition of the engine. Determine the actual rate of fuel consumption in order to obtain a basis for comparison for any improvement in economy made by mechanical changes or adjustments.

PROBABLE CAUSE:

(a) Carburetor float valve too high or needle valve not closing fully on its seat.

(b) Fuel mixture excessively rich.

(c) Carburetor power valve not operating properly or jets worn or wrong size.

(d) Defective choke operation.

(e) Partially clogged air cleaner (air-fuel mixture richer).

(f) Spark plugs fouled, wrong gap, or otherwise defective.

(g) Defective ignition breaker points or improper ignition advance.

(h) Incorrect ignition timing.

(i) Low engine compression.

(j) Excessive rolling resistance—dragging brakes, tight bearings, low tires, etc.

13. EXCESSIVE OIL CONSUMPTION

Oil can be lost from an engine through external leaks, internal leaks, faulty accessories, through the valve guides, or past the pistons and rings.

PROBABLE CAUSES:

(a) *External oil leaks*

  (1) Valve-cover or fuel-pump gasket.

  (2) Timing-gear cover.

  (3) Oil-pan gasket or drain plug.

  (4) Front or rear main-bearing oil seals.

  (5) Oil-filter gasket or lines to filter.

  (6) Rear camshaft welch plug.

  (7) Crankcase outlet vent plugged (back pressure forces oil out the breather tube).

(b) *Internal oil leaks*

  (1) Defective positive-crankcase-ventilation valve.

  (2) Leaks past a head gasket separating an internal oil passage and a cylinder.

(c) *Oil losses through the valve guides*
    (1) Excessive valve-stem-to-guide clearance.
    (2) Faulty valve-stem oil seals.

(d) *Oil loss past pistons and piston rings*
    (1) Worn, scuffed, scored, or broken piston rings. Oil rings clogged or stuck in their grooves by deposits. Directional-type piston rings installed upside down. Rings installed in excessively worn piston grooves.
    (2) Cylinder bores worn beyond allowable limits or out-of-round.
    (3) Cylinder block distorted because wrong sequence and/or torque used to tighten cylinder-head cap screws.

14. ENGINE KNOCK OR PING

Normal engine combustion proceeds at a controlled rate for a predetermined time. Combustion knock is abnormal combustion that proceeds at an uncontrolled rate. It is always associated with high temperature. Knock causes high combustion-chamber temperature and pressure as well as a noticeable loss of power. This condition can vary widely in severity from an annoying light ping to a severe detonation or preignition, which can break piston rings, cause scuffing or scoring, or even burn holes through piston heads or otherwise cause complete engine failure.

PROBABLE CAUSE:

(a) *Detonation*
    (1) Fuel mixture too lean.
    (2) Fuel of too low an octane value.
    (3) Overadvanced ignition timing.

      (4) Excessive carbon deposits on pistons and cylinder heads.

      (5) Engine compression increased (by milling cylinder head or using thinner gasket).

(b) *Preignition*

      (1) Carbon deposits that stay incandescent.

      (2) High valve temperatures.

      (3) Hot spots caused by poor cooling, especially in the jacket area around the valves.

      (4) Spark plugs of too high a heat range or with broken or cracked porcelain insulators.

      (5) Detonation or any of its causes.

      (6) Sharp edges in the combustion chamber.

CHAPTER 2

Engine Tune-Up

Wear, heat, and vibration gradually change the clearances between the engine parts and the adjustments within the electrical, fuel, and other systems. These changes cause a gradual falling off of engine performance which may not be noticeable at any given moment because the deterioration has been slow.

Periodic car servicing should include engine tune-ups, preferably every spring and fall, and oftener if necessary or justified by the car's mileage. A good tune-up follows a definite sequence of tests and adjustments that will restore the car's original performance, power, and economy as completely as possible. In addition to improved performance, a good tune-up reduces major repair bills, since minor parts failure or defective adjustments are often caught before major engine trouble can result.

This chapter details the steps to be followed for a satisfactory tune-up. It is important to perform the tests and adjustments in a logical and orderly sequence such as listed here. Failure to follow such a sequence may cause some troubles to be overlooked, make additional work necessary, or make it impossible to correctly perform a check or adjustment. For example, making carburetor adjustments while the ignition timing is incorrect is a waste of time. It cannot be done satisfactorily.

Tuning the modern automotive engine requires the following:

1. A knowledge of how to do the job.
2. Dependable test instruments and equipment, such as a voltmeter, ammeter, compression tester, hydrometer, timing light (or test lamp), tachometer, dwell tester, feeler gauges, and necessary hand tools.
3. Accurate test specifications. Basic tune-up specifications will be found in this book.
4. Quality replacement parts installed in a workmanlike manner.
5. A recommended tune-up procedure.

An engine with poor compression or with uneven compression between cylinders cannot be properly tuned. Therefore, many checks start with a compression test. This test requires that the engine be cranked with the starter at sufficient rpm to indicate the maximum engine compression. This cannot be done if the battery is low in charge; therefore, start the tune-up tests and adjustments in this manner:

1. *Inspect and test the battery*
   (a) Look for a cracked or bulged battery case; acid, dirt, or corrosion on top of the battery; plugged cap vents; loose battery clamp; and loose, corroded, or frayed cables or connections. Clean, tighten, or replace as necessary. A saturated solution of sodium bicarbonate (baking soda) will neutralize acid on battery tops. Be careful not to get this solution in the battery electrolyte.
   (b) Test the specific gravity of the battery electrolyte with a hydrometer—a temperature-corrected reading of less

than 1.215 for a 12-volt battery or 1.220 for a 6-volt battery indicates that the battery should be recharged. (Variation of more than .025 between individual cell readings indicates a defective battery.) When the specific gravity is satisfactory, test the battery capacity under load with a suitable battery-starter tester. See Chapter 4.

2. *Test engine compression*

   Provided the battery has sufficient charge, make an engine compression test as follows:

   (a) Run the engine until normal operating temperature is reached. Shut off the engine, clean the dirt from around spark-plug ports, and remove the plugs. Remove the air cleaner and block the throttle plate wide open.

   (b) Insert the compression tester firmly in a spark-plug hole, and crank the engine with the starter for at least four compression strokes to obtain the maximum compression reading. Record the reading.

   (c) Repeat the test for all cylinders, cranking the engine the same number of strokes for each cylinder.

   (d) Compression should be uniform for all cylinders (less than a 10-lb. variation) and greater than the minimum listed in the car manufacturer's specifications.

Low compression must be corrected before any tune-up can be performed. When the compression is low in only one cylinder, look for valve or ring leakage in that cylinder; if it is low in two adjacent cylinders, suspect a cylinder-head-gasket leak between these two cylinders.

To determine whether the valves or the rings are at fault, squirt about a tablespoon of heavy oil into the combustion chamber. Crank the engine to distribute the oil and repeat the compression test. The oil will stop leakage past the rings temporarily. If the same low reading is obtained, the rings are satisfactory, but the valves are leaking. If the compression reading has increased by more than ten pounds, the rings are leaking.

If, during a compression test, the pressure fails to increase steadily but remains the same during two consecutive strokes, and then increases on later strokes, a valve is sticking.

3. *Visually check electrical connections*

   Make a visual inspection of the battery, starter, generator, voltage regulator, ignition switch, and coil primary wiring and connections. Tighten the connections if required. If any of the cables are frayed or appear doubtful, use a voltmeter to check for excessive voltage drop between the connections.

4. *Make mechanical checks*

   Tighten to the manufacturer's specified torque all:
   (a) Cylinder-head cap screws or bolts(be sure to follow the correct sequence for tightening).
   (b) Intake- and exhaust-manifold bolts. (Look for any external evidence of gasket leaks.)
   (c) Carburetor attaching nuts at the mounting base and any attaching screws at the carburetor air horn.
   (d) Fuel- and vacuum-line connections at the carburetor, fuel pump, and distributor.
   (e) Check the manifold heat-control valve for free operation and free it if it is stuck.

5. *Check fan belt*

   Check belt(s) for fraying, cracks, or glaze, and replace as necessary. Check the fan-belt deflection as recommended by the manufacturer. If the specifications are not available, a deflection of about ⅜″ to ½″ in the center of the longest unsupported section of the belt under moderate hand pressure is usually satisfactory.

6. *Service the air cleaner*

   A partially clogged, dirty air cleaner can reduce the engine air intake to a point where the air-fuel mixture is made richer regardless of the carburetor adjustment. A reduction of air intake will also cause loss of power. Always service the air cleaner as a part of the engine tune-up. Oil-wetted, oil-bath, and dry-element air cleaners require different service procedures. Follow the recommended servicing procedure for the type used. *Caution: If the air cleaner is held to the carburetor air horn by a clamp-and-screw arrangement, do not overtighten this clamp, or the air horn may be distorted enough to cause the choke valve to stick.*

7. *Service the spark plugs*

   When servicing the spark plugs, the spark-plug covers and cables should also be checked. Look for cracks, burns, or other damage to the insulation. Also check the cables for loose connections, both at the plug ends and at the distributor-cap tower.

   Remove the spark plugs and inspect them carefully before cleaning and regapping any serviceable plugs. The condition of the spark plugs can indicate the source of some engine troubles. For example, the wet, black deposits of an oil-fouled plug indicate oil pumping due to worn piston rings, pistons, or cylinders; a soft, dry, black deposit indicates gas fouling caused by excessive fuel in the combustion chambers. Burned plugs may indicate an overheating condition, or they may show that a plug of too hot a heat range is being used in the engine. Clean any serviceable plugs. File the electrode surfaces until they are clean and flat, and until parallel surfaces are obtained between the two electrodes. Adjust the gap to the manufacturer's specifications by bending the outer electrode only. Use a round-wire gauge to check the gap.

8. *Service the distributor*

Remove the distributor cap; clean and inspect the cap and rotor. Make sure that the condenser connections are secure and that the lead is not frayed. Carefully examine the breaker points for burning, pitting, or misalignment, and replace if unserviceable. Check the breaker-point spring tension and correct if necessary. Lubricate the cam with high-temperature grease, and lubricate the other distributor areas specified; *do not overlubricate*. Any lubricant getting on the points will cause arcing and will shorten their life. Set the point gap to the correct specification and check the dwell angle to verify the setting.

9. *Service the fuel system*

Clean the carburetor sediment bowl and any fuel filters or screens. Check the action of the choke. Adjust the linkage, if necessary, on mechanical chokes. For an automatic choke, make sure that the heat-riser tube is not clogged or burned out, and check the settings and action of the choke mechanism. Check the fuel-pump pressure and volume output. If an electric fuel pump has been installed, check the electrical connections and the condition of the contact points.

10. *Make final electrical checks*

If the diagnosis or tune-up indicates electrical trouble, the following electrical checks should be made: Check generator output. When the output is low or unsteady, look for a slipping fan belt, worn or sticking brushes, a dirty commutator, or loose wires. When the voltage reading is high, check the regulator. On the regulator, check the cutout-relay closing voltage and opening current, the voltage regulator, and the current regulator. Check for excessive starting-motor current.

Check the ignition coil for primary and secondary circuit resistance, leakage, and output capacity.

11. *Check valve clearance*

Check the valve-stem clearance with the appropriate feeler gauge and adjust to specifications. Note carefully whether the adjustment is to be made with the engine hot or cold.

12. *Service cooling and exhaust systems*

Check both the radiator and heater hoses for cracks, loose connections, or soft spongy hose. Tighten the hose clamps. Blow debris from the radiator core with an air hose, blowing from the side opposite the normal flow of air. Check the water pump if the engine has been running hot. Check the thermostat and the radiator pressure cap. Check the exhaust manifold, muffler, and tailpipe.

13. *Road test*

The final step in a good tune-up should be a road test, which can be used to verify all the checks and adjustments on the basis of actual performance.

Operate the car at minimum speed in high gear, then accelerate rapidly. The engine should accelerate smoothly and evenly. If the engine misses or hesitates, recheck the electrical system. If there are "flat spots," recheck the ignition timing, which may be overadvanced.

A road test also provides an opportunity to check the brakes, steering, clutch and/or transmission, instruments, and accessories. On completion of the road test, recheck for any oil, water, or fuel leaks, and correct all troubles that may have been found.

CHAPTER 3

Spark Plugs

The fuel charge in the cylinder of an automobile engine is ignited by a spark generated between the electrodes of the spark plug. Efficient engine performance demands that the spark must be adequate at all engine speeds and under all conditions to produce complete and proper ignition of the fuel-air mixture. Proper spark-plug performance is perhaps the most important factor in maintaining good gas mileage and engine efficiency.

SPARK-PLUG CONSTRUCTION

The spark plug has two important functions—to insert the spark into the combustion chamber, and to seal the plug hole so that proper pressures are maintained in the cylinder.

The main parts of a typical spark plug (see Fig. 1) are: the insulator, the shell, the internal seals, and the electrodes. The insulator prevents the high ignition voltage (up to 30,000 volts) from flowing in any direction except across the electrodes within the combustion chamber. Any cracks (either visible or invisible) in this insulator can cause misfiring because the crack becomes a path of low electrical resistance and shorts the high voltage to the shell.

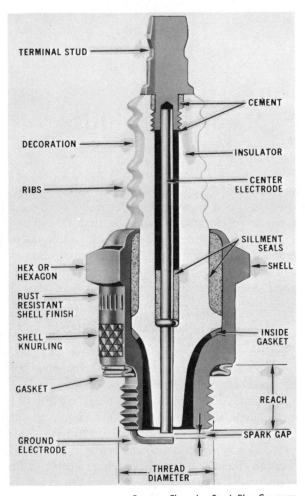

TERMINAL STUD

CEMENT

DECORATION

INSULATOR

CENTER ELECTRODE

RIBS

SILLMENT SEALS

SHELL

HEX OR HEXAGON

RUST RESISTANT SHELL FINISH

SHELL KNURLING

INSIDE GASKET

GASKET

REACH

GROUND ELECTRODE

SPARK GAP

THREAD DIAMETER

Courtesy Champion Spark Plug Company

Fig. 1. Construction features of a modern spark plug.

The shell holds the plug together and acts to connect the ground electrode to the engine through the threads. The gasket seat presses a soft copper washer against a seat on the engine to seal in the compression pressure.

The internal seals are made by a high-temperature, high-pressure cement. They seal the center electrode to the insulator and the insulator to the shell.

The electrodes operate at continuous high temperatures and are surrounded by corrosive gases. Special alloys are used in the electrodes to resist the corrosion and the destructive effects of the spark.

The soft copper washer which seals the spark plug in the engine is designed to be crimped or flattened when the plug is tightened properly. Fig. 2 shows several possible conditions of this gasket when properly and improperly compressed.

Spark plugs wear out, develop troubles, or can be the wrong type for the engine. Most manufacturers recommend replacing spark plugs after 10,000 miles of average operation. Of course, operating conditions can modify this standard. An engine used exclusively for city driving, which means stop-and-go travel, frequent motor starts, and frequent cold-motor operation, may wear out the plugs at 5,000 miles. The plugs in an engine used on the highway may last up to 25,000 miles or more before requiring replacement.

SPARK-PLUG TROUBLES

Spark plug wear is caused by corrosive gases resulting from fuel combustion. These gases attack the electrodes and "eat" them away. The high-voltage spark also corrodes the electrodes and eats the metal away. Both of these factors cause the electrode gap to increase, and the spark has a greater distance to jump.

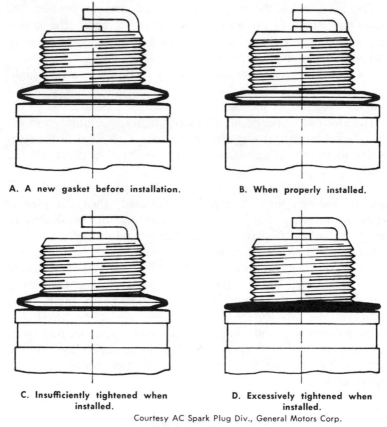

A. A new gasket before installation.

B. When properly installed.

C. Insufficiently tightened when installed.

D. Excessively tightened when installed.

Courtesy AC Spark Plug Div., General Motors Corp.

Fig. 2. The spark-plug gasket.

A much higher voltage is required to cause the spark to jump the wider gap. The ignition system often fails to provide this higher voltage, especially at high speeds, and the spark plug misfires. Cleaning and regapping of the electrodes will cure this condition

Courtesy AC Spark Plug Div., General Motors Corp.

Fig. 3. Electrodes worn too thin for proper regapping.

if there is enough material remaining in the electrodes. The spark plug shown in Fig. 3 illustrates the condition of electrodes worn away enough that the plug cannot be regapped. Such a plug should be replaced. Worn-out plugs cause loss of power, loss of top speed, decreased gas mileage, hard starting, and general sluggish performance. Compare the worn plug in Fig. 3 with the good plug in Fig. 4.

Spark plugs also get dirty. This condition is known as "fouling," of which there are several types.

Oil Fouling

Wet, oily, black deposits (Fig. 5) on the firing end of the plug usually indicate that lubricating oil is leaking into the cylinder.

Courtesy Champion Spark Plug Company

Fig. 4. A normal spark plug after use.

This may occur because of worn piston rings, excessive valve-stem-to-guide clearance, sticking valves, or a faulty fuel pump. Normally, plugs in this condition can be cleaned, regapped, and reinstalled.

If the black deposit is hard and glazed, this indicates that a low-heat-range plug is being used in an oil-burning engine. Either a plug one heat range hotter can be used or the engine should be overhauled.

Gas (or Carbon) Fouling

Excessive fuel in the combustion chamber can cause dry, fluffy, black deposits (Fig. 6) to form on the spark plugs. The excess of

Courtesy AC Spark Plug Div., General Motors Corp.

Fig. 5. An oil-fouled spark plug.

fuel can result from prolonged idling, a faulty automatic choke, or a fuel mixture that is too rich. Use of a cold plug can also cause this type of deposit to form. Cleaning and regapping of the plug will restore engine performance, but the condition may recur. An engine tune-up or hotter type plug will be necessary to eliminate the trouble.

Lead Fouling

Deposits due to the burning of fuel scavengers (such as tetraethyl lead) cause red, brown, yellow, or white colors on the spark-plug electrodes. While these deposits may look bad (Fig. 7), most

Courtesy AC Spark Plug Div., General Motors Corp.

Fig. 6. A gas-fouled spark plug.

of them are not harmful and have little effect on plug performance. If the combustion-chamber temperatures become too high, however these deposits may melt and form a shiny, glazed coating which will act as an electrical conductor and short out the plug. If the plug is not too heavily coated, these deposits can be removed by abrasive cleaning, and the plug can be used again.

SERVICE PROCEDURES

Ideally, spark plugs should be cleaned and regapped every 5,000 miles. Inspection of the plugs while they are removed can

Courtesy Champion Spark Plug Company

Fig. 7. Scavenger deposits.

frequently warn of engine troubles developing or of needed adjustments.

Removing Spark Plugs

1. Remove the plug wires carefully. Grasp the rubber insulator boot and pull it away from the plug slowly—do not jerk it.
2. Use the correct size of deep-socket wrench to fit the plug. The wrong size socket can break the shell or insulator and ruin the plug.
3. Loosen the plugs one turn and use an air hose to blow the dirt away from the plug wells.

41

4. Remove the plugs and gaskets. Inspect each plug as it is removed or keep them in order so that you can identify the cylinder each came from. Trouble in one particular cylinder can be found in this way.

Cleaning Spark Plugs

Clean the top insulator and terminal of each plug. A rag moistened with a cleaning solvent will remove oil and grime. If the electrodes and threads of the plug are oily, clean the plug by brushing it in solvent. Dry the plug thoroughly with compressed air.

There are several approved plug-cleaning machines available. A typical unit is pictured in Fig. 8.

The operation of a typical unit is as follows:

1. Select the correct size of adaptor, place the plug in the adaptor, and the adaptor in position on the cleaner.
2. Hold the plug and adaptor down with one hand.
3. Press the cleaner hood all the way down for 3 to 5 seconds. This action starts the cleaning blast and also covers the top of the plug to protect the operator. Rotate both the plug and adaptor during the cleaning blast.
4. Release the cleaner hood part way to stop the cleaning blast and to allow the compressed-air blast to blow the cleaning compound out of the plug.
5. Remove the plug and examine it for cleanliness. Steps 2 through 4 may have to be repeated to make sure that the entire surface of the insulator is clean and white.

Excessive cleaning can wear away the insulator. Use the cleaning blast cautiously. Fig. 9 shows a spark plug in which the insulator has been partially worn away by excessive blast cleaning.

After the plug has been cleaned, make sure that all the cleaning compound has been removed, especially from the threads. Clean

Fig. 8. A typical spark-plug cleaner.

the threads with a wire brush. Discard any plugs with damaged threads.

Regapping Spark Plugs

The cleaning operation does not always remove all the oxide or scale from the electrodes. Clean the firing surfaces of the two electrodes with a spark-plug or distributor-point file. Widen the gap, if necessary, to insert the file.

The plug should be regapped to the specifications of the car manufacturer (.035″ for most domestic cars). Always use a round-wire type of gauge. The flat feeler gauge does not measure the gap correctly, as shown in Fig. 10.

The side electrode should be adjusted to set the gap. Use the adjusting notch which is part of most spark-plug gapping tools. Never try to adjust the center electrode, because this will break the insulator.

If new plugs are being installed, check the gap setting and adjust to specifications.

Courtesy AC Spark Plug Div., General Motors Corp.

Fig. 9. Insulator tip worn down from excessive blast cleaning.

A. A plain flat feeler gauge cannot accurately measure the true gap width.

B. A round-wire gauge should always be used.

Courtesy AC Spark Plug Div., General Motors Corp.

Fig. 10. Use of the gap gauge.

Installing Spark Plugs

Always use a new gasket on either new or used plugs, except on those plugs which do not use gaskets. An old gasket will not seal properly and will allow gases to blow by.

Make sure that the threads and gasket seats on the engine are clean. Screw the plug in by hand until it is finger tight on the gasket. Then tighten it with a wrench ½ to ¾ of a turn. If a torque wrench is being used, follow the recommended maximum torque shown in Table 1.

Table 1. Maximum Torque Values

Plug Thread	Cast-Iron Heads	Aluminum Heads
10 mm	12 ft-lbs	10 ft-lbs
14 mm	25 ft-lbs	22 ft-lbs
18 mm	30 ft-lbs	25 ft-lbs
⅞"	35 ft-lbs	30 ft-lbs
18 mm taper seat	17 ft-lbs	

Selection of Plugs

To give good performance in a particular engine, spark plugs must operate within a definite temperature range. If the plug temperature is too low, oil, carbon, and scavenger deposits will remain on the insulator and cause fouling and missing. If the plug temperature is too high, the electrodes will wear rapidly and pre-ignition may result. Either of these conditions can prevent the engine from operating at peak performance.

An engine is designed for normal (average) service, and the original spark plugs are selected to operate satisfactorily in this

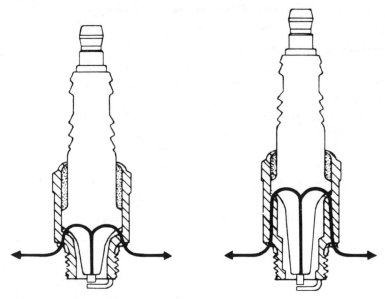

A. A cold type with short heat path.   B. A hot type with long heat path.
Courtesy Champion Spark Plug Company

Fig. 11. Two spark plugs of different heat range.

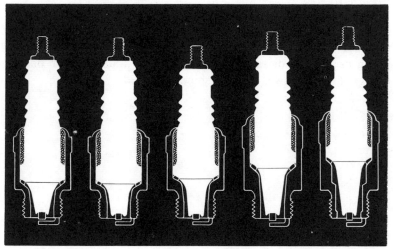

Courtesy Champion Spark Plug Company

Fig. 12. Insulator lengths vary from the cold plug at the left to the hot plug on the right.

type of service. Of course, not all engines are used in this normal service, in which case the spark-plug type must be changed to suit the eventual use of the engine. To suit the requirements of the various types of engine service, spark plugs are manufactured in various "heat ranges."

The term "heat range" is a classification of spark plugs according to their ability to transfer heat from the insulator tip to the cooling medium of the engine. The rate of heat transfer is altered by changing the distance the heat must travel to reach the cooling system. A "cold" plug has a short insulator tip and a thin, short shell, and transfers heat rapidly. A "hot" plug has a much longer insulator tip and a heavy shell so that heat is transferred much more slowly. Fig. 11 illustrates these two types of plugs. Fig. 12 shows a typical range of plugs from cold (on left) to hot (on right).

47

When other than normal operating conditions cause continual carbon or oil fouling, the spark plugs in use are too cold and a type one or two graduations higher (hotter) should be substituted. When preignition or rapid electrode wear is found, a type one or two graduations lower (cooler) should be used.

CHAPTER 4

Storage Batteries

The 12-volt electrical system adopted on late-model cars is used for two main reasons:

1. To provide adequate electrical power to supply the increasing number of electrical accessories used.
2. To make available higher voltages to the ignition system for the new high-speed, high-compression engines.

The advantage of doubling the voltage may be seen if it is realized that, in any direct-current electrical system, the power obtained is directly proportional to the product of current and voltage. Thus, with a 12-volt system, the same amount of electrical power can be delivered with half the amperage, because power is measured in watts, which are simply amperes multiplied by volts. When a generator is required to deliver, say 600 watts, this amount of power can be delivered in many ways, for example, 100 amperes at 6 volts or 50 amperes at 12 volts, since in each case the power obtained will be the same, or 600 watts.

Because it is the current flow in amperes that determines the conductor size, it follows that smaller and more economical wires can be used to deliver the same amount of power in a twelve-volt system that the much larger sizes would deliver in a six-volt system.

It should be noted that with the introduction of the 12-volt electrical system numerous changes had to be made in the electrical accessories. Thus, for example, the battery, starter, generator, the various electric motors, light bulbs, etc., all had to be redesigned to operate at this higher voltage. The electrical circuits—that is, connections to the individual electrical units—will, however, be similar in both voltage systems.

BATTERY FUNDAMENTALS

An electrical battery consists of two or more individual units or *cells* producing electricity by certain chemical reactions. Electrical cells can be classified into one of two groups, namely: *primary* cells and *secondary* cells.

There are a number of different kinds of primary cells, one of the most familiar being the dry cell, such as used in a flashlight. All primary cells become exhausted in converting chemical energy into electrical energy, and they cannot be recharged by an electrical current as can a secondary cell.

Secondary cells, sometimes called accumulators, convert chemical energy into electrical energy. The passing of an electrical current through the cells restores the chemical energy (or *charges* the cells) so that they are ready to supply electric current again when required. There are two types of secondary cells in general use today; these are the *lead-sulfuric acid* type and the *Edison* or *alkaline* type.

The lead-acid cell is made of plates of lead and lead oxide immersed in an electrolyte of sulfuric acid and water. Due to its economical and electrical advantages, the lead-acid storage battery is in general use for many purposes, the most common of which is for starting, ignition, and lighting in the modern automobile. A typical 6-volt automobile battery is shown in Fig. 1.

In automobile installations, several cells are used in groups, or a battery. The number of cells, and their size, depends upon the service required. The usual assembly method is to connect these

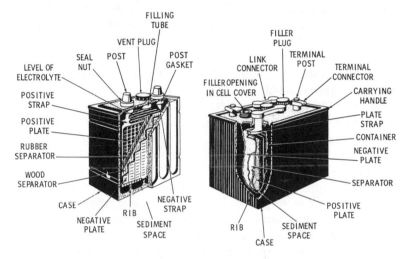

Fig. 1. Construction details of a typical 6-volt lead-acid battery. A 12-volt battery is similar except that it has six cells instead of three.

cells in series—that is, the positive terminal of one cell is connected to the negative terminal of the next cell, and so on, to the end of the row.

With the cells in series, the voltage of the battery is the sum of the voltages of the individual cells. Thus, for example, a typical 12-volt storage battery has 6 cells with 11 plates per cell, and a capacity of 70 ampere-hours at a 20-hour rate, and a rating of 840 watts.

BATTERY CAPACITY RATING

The amount of electricity a battery will deliver within a certain time limit is known as its capacity or *ampere-hour capacity*. The 20-hour rate has been prescribed by the S.A.E. (Society of Automotive Engineers) as an accepted standard for automobile batteries. To measure the capacity, a battery is discharged continuously at the specified rate until the voltage drops too low for efficient use. Thus, a battery that will deliver 3.5 amperes for 20 hours is said to have a capacity of 70 ampere-hours.

This measurement is of particular interest because it indicates what may be expected of a battery in the way of satisfactory performance. The capacity of a battery depends upon the amount of active material that can react with the electrolyte. Obviously, this depends upon the thickness and design of the plates; hence, the number of plates is not always an accurate index of the capacity.

Also, one of the characteristics of a storage battery is that its total ampere-hour capacity is dependent upon the rate of discharge. The lower the rate of discharge, the greater the ampere-hour capacity will be; whereas, the higher the discharge rate, the lower the capacity will be. Thus, a battery having a 70 ampere-hour capacity at a 3.5-ampere discharge rate will ordinarily have a capacity of over 70 ampere-hours at a lower discharge rate.

BATTERY MAINTENANCE

Numerous storage batteries of late construction are of the so-called "dry" type; that is, the electrolyte is provided in separate containers and is added to the battery at the time of installation. This particular feature makes the maintenance of batteries in storage much simpler. In addition, the battery will be fully charged and ready for service immediately after filling.

Care of Dry Batteries

A "dry-charge" battery contains fully charged positive and negative plates, but no electrolyte. The plates are separated by high quality microporous rubber separators.

A dry-charged battery should be stored in a dry place away from excessive heat, and should be kept in its original carton until ready to be put into service. This type of battery will retain its "charged" condition indefinitely if protected from moisture. Three years (36 months) of storage without maintenance usually produces no appreciable deterioration, provided the battery is stored properly.

After electrolyte has been added to a dry-charged battery it becomes a "wet" battery, and should be maintained in the same way as any other wet battery. It may be put into service without an additional charge if it has been stored properly. If one or more cells discharge gas violently after addition of electrolyte, and the specific gravity in any cell drops more than 25 points within 10 minutes, the battery should be charged before being put into service.

Preparing Dry-Charged Batteries for Service

To prepare dry-charged batteries for service, use only approved battery-grade acid electrolyte (1.265 sp. gr. at 80°F.). Care should be exercised in its use to prevent bodily injury or damage to clothing or other material resulting from physical contact with the electrolyte. Electrolyte should be added to dry-charged batteries in a location where water is readily available for flushing in case the electrolyte comes in contact with the body. Prompt flushing with water will prevent serious acid burns.

It is strongly recommended that a person filling batteries with electrolyte wear glasses (preferably safety glasses) to prevent possible damage to the eyes should any spattering of the electrolyte occur. Proceed as follows:

1. Remove the dry-charged battery from its original carton.
2. Remove the vent plugs and discard any seals found in the vent openings.
3. Using a glass or acid-proof plastic funnel, fill each battery cell with electrolyte. *Do not use a metal funnel.* The cell is properly filled when the electrolyte level rises to the split ring at the bottom of the vent well. Do not overfill. In most cases, some electrolyte will remain in the electrolyte container after the battery has been completely filled.
4. After filling the cells, wait five to ten minutes and, if necessary, add additional electrolyte to bring the level back up to the proper point.

Care of Wet Batteries

Batteries in stored new cars, as well as wet batteries in stock, must be given regular attention to prevent sulfation of their plates that may result from inactivity and self-discharge. All automotive-type wet batteries will slowly discharge while standing idle, whether in stored vehicles or in stock, and will self-discharge much faster when warm than when cold.

To minimize the extent of self-discharge, always store batteries fully charged and in the coolest possible place. At frequent intervals, check the level of the electrolyte and add water as required; also check the specific gravity with a hydrometer. A boosting charge at a moderate rate, without excessive overcharge, must be given batteries in storage whenever the specific gravity falls to 1.250, corrected for temperature. Batteries used for display purposes or standing in cars in storage must be treated in the same manner as batteries in stock.

Level of Electrolyte

Water is the only component of the electrolyte which is lost as the result of charging and discharging, and it must be replaced before the electrolyte level falls to the tops of the separators.

If the water is not replaced, and the plates and separators become exposed, the acid may reach a dangerously high concentration that will char and disintegrate the separators and may permanently sulphate and impair the performance of the plates.

Plates cannot take full part in the chemical action unless they are completely covered by the electrolyte. Separators are no longer porous in the area that has dried out as a result of exposure; therefore, the corresponding area of the adjoining plates is rendered inactive and subject to continuous sulfation.

Battery Function

The battery in an automobile has three major functions:

(1) It provides a source of energy for cranking the engine.
(2) It acts as a stabilizer to the voltage in the electrical system.
(3) It can, for a limited time, furnish energy when the demands of the electrical units in operation exceed the output of the generator.

In order for the battery to continue to function, it is necessary that the amount of current withdrawn from the battery be balanced by the current input from the generator so that the battery is maintained in a properly charged condition. If the output exceeds the input, the battery will become discharged and will be unable to supply sufficient energy.

The state of charge of the battery, as well as the temperature of the electrolyte, has an important bearing on its capacity for supplying energy. Battery efficiency is greatly reduced when the temperature of the electrolyte decreases because a low temperature has a decided reducing effect on the electrochemical action. Under high discharge (such as cranking), the battery voltage drops to a lower value in cold temperatures than in warm temperatures.

In extremely cold climates, it is important to keep batteries in a nearly full-charged condition to avoid the possibility of freezing, which will damage any battery.

BATTERY CHARGING METHODS

Because only direct current may be used for charging storage batteries, various types of current converters are used where only alternating current is available. The most commonly used equipment for converting alternating into direct current is the rectifier-transformer combination.

When direct current is available, it is a simple matter to arrange the charging equipment, since all that is necessary is to provide a suitable rheostat to control the charging current and an ammeter to accurately determine the rate of charge. See Fig. 2.

When alternating current only is available, it is necessary to use a rectifier with individual line rheostats and accurate meters. With either AC or DC apparatus, the batteries are charged in series and the charging rates are adjusted to the constant-current rate desired.

Selection of the correct charging equipment depends upon the type, make, and rating of the batteries to be charged, and the type of electrical power available. These factors, together with the number of batteries to be charged simultaneously, will determine the size and type of battery charging equipment that will be required.

There are two separate methods of charging batteries. These differ basically in the rate of charge. In the "slow-charge" method, the battery is supplied with a relatively small amount of current

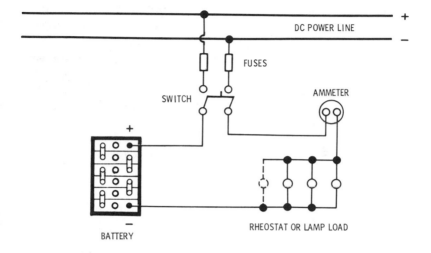

Fig. 2. Wiring diagram for constant-current battery charging when direct current is available.

for a relatively long period of time. In the "quick-charge" method, the battery is supplied with a high current for a short period of time.

The Slow-Charge Method

The slow-charge method, if properly applied, may safely be used under all possible conditions of the battery, provided the electrolyte is at the proper level in all cells. The battery may be fully charged by this method, unless it is not capable of taking a full charge.

The slow battery chargers commonly used in service stations are suitable for charging both 6- and 12-volt batteries on the same circuit. Each 12-volt unit must be considered as equal to two 6-volt batteries, and the charging rate must be adjusted so as not to exceed the amount determined by the smallest 12-volt battery on the line. Safe slow-charging rates are determined by allowing one ampere per positive plate per cell. Thus, the proper slow-charging rate for a battery with 11-plate cells is six amperes.

When putting batteries on the line, connect the positive charger lead to the positive battery terminal, and the negative charger lead to the negative battery terminal. If several batteries are to be charged on the same circuit, the batteries should be connected in series, as shown in Fig. 3.

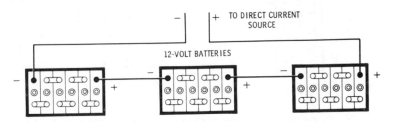

Fig. 3. Wiring diagram of a series hook-up for constant-current battery charging. When charging on a series (constant-current) line, connect the batteries in series and charge at a rate which is safe for the smallest battery. Continued charging at a high rate will result in high temperatures, which should be avoided.

As the batteries approach full charge, each cell will begin to gas or bubble freely. The battery temperatures should not exceed 125°F during charge. If this temperature is reached, the battery should be cooled by reducing the charge rate or removal from the circuit. The battery is fully charged when three successive hourly hydrometer readings show no increase in specific gravity.

The Quick-Charge Method

It should be understood that a battery cannot be brought up to a fully charged condition by the "quick-charge" method. The battery can be substantially recharged or "boosted", but in order to bring the battery to a fully charged condition, the charging cycle must be finished by charging at a low or normal rate.

Used with care, a quick-charger will not damage a battery which is in good condition. A "quick charge" must not be used, however, if any of the following conditions exist in the battery:

1. If the specific gravity readings are not uniform, the low-reading cell may have an internal defect. Quick charging may cause considerable heat to develop, possibly enough to ruin the battery.
2. If the electrolyte is discolored with a brownish sediment, quick charging may produce an internal short and ruin the battery.
3. A sulfated battery will overheat during quick charging. Such a battery requires charging at half the normal "slow-charge" rate for from 60 to 100 hours to reconvert the crystalline lead sulfate into active material.
4. A battery which has been badly overcharged may quickly fail if placed on quick charge.
5. The cell voltages and the color of the electrolyte should be checked a few minutes after the battery has been put on quick charge. If the voltage readings are not uniform within 0.2 volt, or if the electrolyte has become discolored with brownish sediment, the quick charging should be stopped immediately. Charging may be continued by the "slow-charge" method.

A typical fast charger is illustrated in Fig. 4.

Precautions in Battery Charging

A battery charger must be connected in parallel with a battery. The positive terminal of the charger must connect to the positive terminal of the battery. The two negative terminals must also be connected together. With any type or brand of battery charger, the positive terminal is a cable and clamp with red insulation. The negative cable usually has black or green insulation.

If a charger is connected in reverse polarity, the battery can be ruined very quickly, and may even explode due to the extreme heat developed in the electrotype. If the battery is still in the automobile and connected to the electrical system, a reverse-connected charger can ruin a transistor-type regulator and alternator.

Courtesy Allen Electric & Equipment Co.

Fig. 4. The Allen Model 16-90 battery charger. This fast-charge unit is rated at 60 amperes at 12 volts or 100 amperes at 6 volts.

Most modern battery chargers are equipped with a protective device that lights a signal lamp when the charger is connected in reverse polarity. This device also prevents the flow of current until the polarity is correct.

BATTERY TESTING

There are several different ways of testing storage batteries to determine their state of charge, or to locate irregularities and identify worn-out batteries.

Specific-Gravity Test

It is advisable to occasionally check the condition of the battery electrolyte with a hydrometer in order to determine whether the automotive generating system is maintaining the battery in a proper state of charge. This is particularly important during cold weather when the battery must deliver more power.

The hydrometer measures the percentage of sulfate acid in the battery electrolyte in terms of specific gravity. As a battery drops from a charged to a discharged condition, the acid leaves the solution and enters the plates, causing a decrease in specific gravity of the electrolyte. By measuring specific gravity of the electrolyte with a hydrometer, an indication of the approximate state of charge of the battery is obtained.

A hydrometer can be used only if there is sufficient electrolyte above the battery plates to fill the hydrometer tube. **Do not take hydrometer readings immediately after refilling a battery with distilled water.**

To take a hydrometer test, remove the battery filler caps. Draw the electrolyte in and force it out of the hydrometer tube several times to bring the temperatures of the hydrometer float to that of the electrolyte. Then draw in just enough electrolyte to lift the float. Make sure the float is not binding on the side of the hydrometer tube. Read the specific gravity on the float scale.

The specific gravity of the electrolyte varies not only with the percentage of acid in the liquid, but also with a change in temperature. As temperature increases, the electrolyte expands so that the specific gravity is reduced. As temperature drops, the electrolyte contracts so that the specific gravity increases. Unless these variations in specific gravity are taken into account, the reading obtained by the hydrometer may not give a true indication of the state of charge of the battery.

Correction can be made for temperature by adding .004 (usually referred to as 4 "points of gravity") to the hydrometer reading for

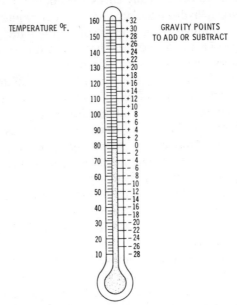

Fig. 5. Hydrometer reading correction chart.

every 10°F that the electrolyte is above 80°F, or subtracting .004 for every 10°F that the electrolyte is below 80°F. (See Fig. 5.)

If the electrolyte temperature is not too far from the 80°F standard or if only an approximate idea of the specific-gravity reading is required, it will not be necessary to make the temperature

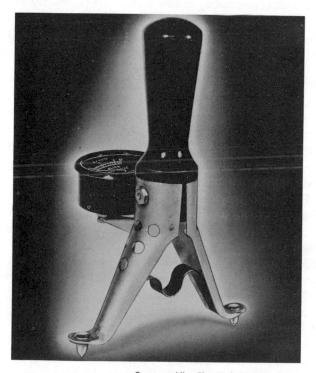

Courtesy Allen Electric & Equipment Co.

Fig. 6. The Allen Model 50-223 cell tester. This type of tester shows individual cell condition under load. The meter reads in both directions from the center so that polarity is not important.

correction. It should be noted that some hydrometers have built in thermometers and temperature-scale correction, which will simplify the operation of obtaining a true specific-gravity reading.

A fully charged battery has a specific-gravity reading of 1.280 to 1.300. A battery that has a specific-gravity reading of 1.250 or less, and all cells reading evenly within 30 points (.030) of each other, requires recharging. A battery that has a specific-gravity reading which varies more than 30 points between any two cells should be replaced and tested for cause of failure.

Voltage Test

The individual-cell tester (Fig. 6) is an inexpensive device which gives a high-rate discharge on each cell separately. To make the battery test, contact the voltmeter prods to the proper cell terminals (red to positive, black to negative), using caution not to connect across more than one cell. The point of the prod will have to be pushed through the sealing compound to make contact with the buried link for each cell reading. The circuit is closed through the fixed resistance of the cell tester, and the voltage of the cell under normal starting-motor load is indicated by the voltmeter.

When using this testing method, the individual-cell readings should not vary more than 0.15 volt between any two cells. A battery showing a variation of more than 0.15 volt between any two cells should be replaced.

High-Rate Discharge Test

Satisfactory capacity tests can be made only when the battery has a specific-gravity reading of not less than 1.215 at 80°F. If the specific gravity is below 1.215, the high-discharge test should not be made.

To make the high-rate discharge test, connect a carbon-pile rheostat in series with an ammeter and the battery as indicated in

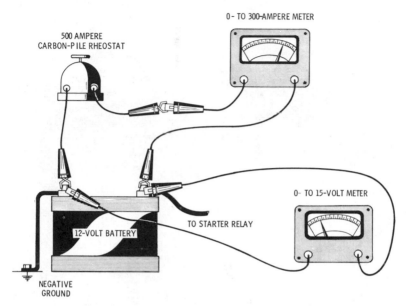

500 AMPERE
CARBON-PILE RHEOSTAT

0- TO 300-AMPERE METER

0- TO 15-VOLT METER

TO STARTER RELAY

12-VOLT BATTERY

NEGATIVE
GROUND

Fig. 7. Connections for a battery-capacity test.

Fig. 7. Be sure that the carbon-pile control knob is rotated to the full-resistance position before connecting.

The voltmeter clips must contact the battery posts only, and not the high-rate discharge tester clips. Unless this is done, the actual battery-terminal voltage will not be indicated. Rotate the rheostat until the ammeter reads three times the ampere-hour rating of the battery (210 amperes for a 70 ampere-hour battery). With the battery under discharge for approximately 15 seconds, read the terminal voltage.

If the terminal voltage reads 9 volts or more (4.5 volts or more for a 6-volt battery), the discharge capacity is satisfactory. If the voltmeter reads less than 9 volts, the battery must be completely

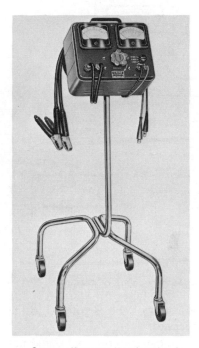

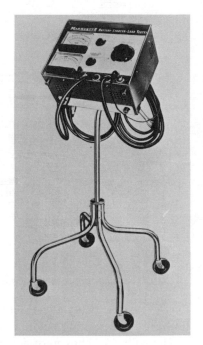

Courtesy Marquette Manufacturing Co.

**Fig. 8. The Marquette Battery-
Starter-Load Tester.**

Courtesy Sun Electric Corp.

**Fig. 9. The Sun Model BST-10
Battery-Starter Tester.**

recharged and tested again. It is important that the rheostat be returned to the starting position immediately after the test to avoid excessive drain on the battery.

Many different discharge testers are available. Figs. 8 and 9 illustrate two of these. The adjustable carbon pile is included in the instrument, and only four cables need be connected.

CHAPTER 5

Distributors

As its name implies, the distributor distributes the ignition spark to the spark plugs at the proper times and in the proper sequence. Its job is very exacting—it must distribute voltages that average 25,000 volts and must do so at very exact time intervals. Slight irregularities in the operation of the distributor can result in very poor engine performance.

GENERAL CONSTRUCTION

The breaker points in the distributor, shown in Fig. 1, open and close the circuit to the primary winding of the ignition coil. At the instant the points close, current begins to flow in the primary circuit and a magnetic field builds up around the primary coil. When the points open, the current flow stops and the magnetic field collapses rapidly. This sudden collapse builds up a very high voltage in the secondary winding of the coil. This high voltage is connected by a wire to the center terminal on the distributor cap. This terminal, in turn, is connected through a rotating contact to the rotor inside the distributor. The rotor turns with the distributor shaft and distributes, in the proper order, the high voltage to the spark plugs.

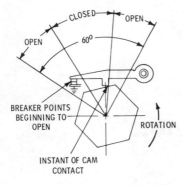

(A) **Points at the instant of opening.**

(B) **Points at maximum separation.**

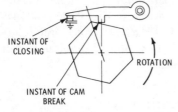

(C) **Points at the instant of closing.**

Fig. 5-1. The cycle of breaker-point action in a six-cylinder engine. An eight-cylinder engine would have an eight-sided cam; a four-cylinder engine a four-sided cam. A change in dwell angle will change the opening time of the points, and this will be reflected in the ignition timing.

Fig. 2 shows a typical distributor for a 6-cylinder engine, while Fig. 3 shows the top view of the breaker plate used in another popular 6-cylinder distributor.

The parts that normally wear and require service are:

1. The breaker points.
2. The rubbing block.
3. The condenser.

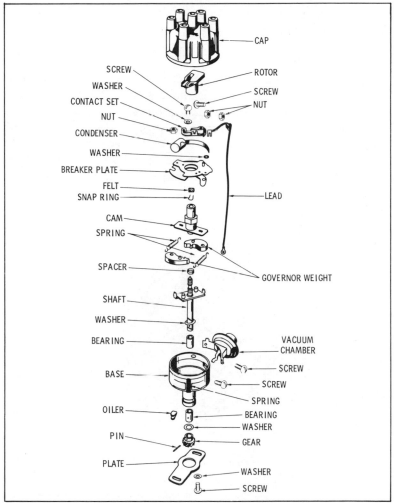

CAP

SCREW
WASHER
CONTACT SET
NUT
CONDENSER
WASHER
BREAKER PLATE
FELT
SNAP RING
CAM
SPRING
SPACER
SHAFT
WASHER
BEARING
BASE
OILER
PIN
PLATE

ROTOR
SCREW
NUT
LEAD
GOVERNOR WEIGHT
VACUUM
CHAMBER
SCREW
SCREW
SPRING
BEARING
WASHER
GEAR
WASHER
SCREW

Courtesy Dodge Div., Chrysler Motors Corp.

Fig. 2. A typical distributor for a six-cylinder engine.

4. The cam.

5. The shaft bearings.

Breaker Points

The breaker points are not subject to mechanical wear because they meet squarely and do not rub together. They are subject, however, to electrical wear. The sparking action at the points, as they open and close the primary circuit, erodes the metal and sometimes causes metal to be transferred from one point to the other. Points that have been in service can be smoothed with an ignition file and left in service. It is not necessary to remove all

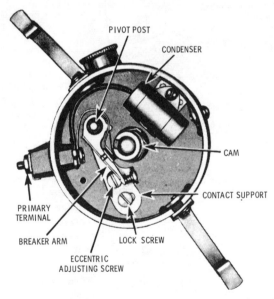

Courtesy Chevrolet Div., General Motors Corp.

Fig. 3. Top view of the breaker plate in a typical six-cylinder distributor.

traces of pits as this only removes too much metal. Simply brighten the surface of the pitted point, and remove the small raised portion from the surface of the opposite point.

Gap Setting—The gap between the breaker points at their widest separation (rubbing block on high point of cam, Fig. 1B) must be adjusted exactly to specifications. Points set too close will tend to burn and pit rapidly, while points set with too much separation will tend to cause ignition failure at high speeds.

A feeler gauge, a dial indicator, or a dwell-angle meter can be used to set the point gap. A feeler gauge should only be used on new points, since the roughness of used points prevents an accurate setting. To set the gap on new points, loosen the lock screw(s) on the contact points, crank the engine until the rubbing block is on a high point of the cam, and insert the correct feeler gauge between the points. Use a screwdriver or appropriate tool to move the movable point back and forth until only a slight drag is felt when the feeler gauge is moved between the points.

A dial indicator can be used to set new or used points, as illustrated in Fig. 4. Clamp the dial indicator to the lip of the distributor and position the lever arm against the back of the movable point with the rubbing block on a cam flat. Set the dial indicator to zero and then crank the engine until the rubbing block is on a high point of the cam. The dial indicator reading is the point gap. Adjust the breaker points until the reading agrees with the specifications.

A dwell meter is an electronic instrument that measures the point gap in terms of the cam rotation angle through which the points remain closed (Fig. 5). Some of the modern distributors have provisions for adjusting the point gap from outside the distributor housing (Fig. 6) without removing the distributor cap. On this type, a small window can be opened in the side of the distributor and a wrench inserted to adjust the gap while the engine

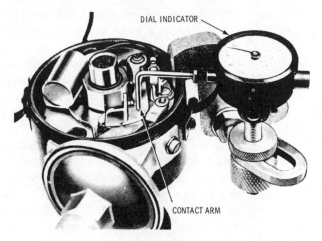

DIAL INDICATOR

CONTACT ARM

Courtesy Dodge Div., Chrysler Motors Corp.

Fig. 4. A dial indicator used to set point gap.

is running. On older distributors, and on those new types without the window, the distributor cap must be removed and the engine cranked with the ignition off.

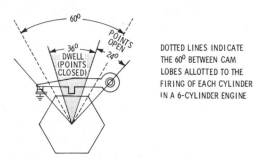

60°

POINTS OPEN

36° DWELL (POINTS CLOSED)

24°

DOTTED LINES INDICATE THE 60° BETWEEN CAM LOBES ALLOTTED TO THE FIRING OF EACH CYLINDER IN A 6-CYLINDER ENGINE

Fig. 5. The meaning of contact dwell.

One lead of the dwell meter should be connected to ground and the other lead to the point terminal on the coil. The meter should be calibrated according to the manufacturer's instructions. Crank the engine, or start it, and adjust the point gap until the meter reading agrees with specifications.

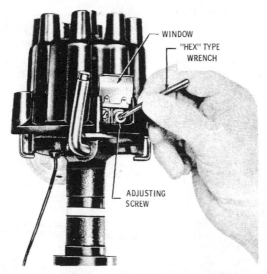

Courtesy Chevrolet Div., General Motors Corp.

Fig. 6. Setting dwell angle on a modern distributor.

Contact Pressure—The contact pressure, or the pressure with which the points are held together when they are closed, should be within the listed specifications. Weak tension will cause point chatter (bouncing) at high speeds, while excessive tension will cause extreme wear of the points, cam, and rubbing block.

Contact pressure is checked by placing the hooked end of a spring-tension scale over the movable breaker arm next to the point, as in Fig. 7. Pull the gauge at a right angle to the movable arm until the breaker points just begin to open. Read the scale. If the tension is not within specifications, adjust the spring tension as follows:

1. Disconnect the coil and the condenser leads at the breaker assembly terminal.
2. Loosen the lock nut holding the end of the spring. Move the spring toward the breaker arm pivot to decrease tension, or in the opposite direction to increase tension.
3. Tighten the lock nut and recheck the spring tension. Repeat the adjustment until the spring tension is correct.
4. Reconnect the coil and condenser leads at the breaker terminal. Tighten the holding nut securely.

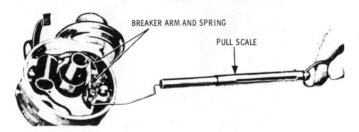

Courtesy Dodge Div., Chrysler Motors Corp.

Fig. 7. Testing breaker-arm spring tension.

Point Alignment—The rubbing block should be aligned so that it strikes the cam squarely. If this is not done, wear will be excessive. The points should be aligned so that they strike squarely over their entire surface (Fig. 8). This is particularly important with the vented type of points. Any misalignment of this type of points will cause premature wear, overheating, and pitting.

Align the points by bending the stationary breaker-point bracket only. *Do not bend the movable arm.* After aligning the points, adjust the gap or the dwell angle.

The Rubbing Block

The rubbing block must follow the cam faces perfectly and must not wear excessively. The cam surface must be lubricated

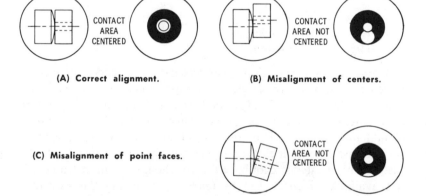

(A) Correct alignment.   **(B) Misalignment of centers.**

(C) Misalignment of point faces.

Fig. 8. Alignment of breaker points.

sparingly with cam lubricant. *Do not use engine oil to lubricate the cam.* On older types of points, the cam lubricant is very important, but the newer points generally have rubbing blocks made of nylon plastic. This material has a very low coefficient of friction and does not wear quickly.

Excessive contact-spring tension has a great effect on the life of the rubbing block. Adjust the spring tension to within specifications for minimum wear on the rubbing block.

When the rubbing block wears down, the points are not opened as widely and the dwell angle increases. When new points are installed, set the gap slightly on the high side (or the dwell angle on the low side) to compensate for the anticipated wear of the rubbing block.

The Condenser

There are three factors that affect condenser performance, and each must be considered when making tests. These are:

1. Capacity value.
2. Low insulation resistance.
3. High series resistance.

Capacity Value—Every condenser has a certain capacity, which is a measure of its electrical capacitance. This capacitance can vary during the life of a condenser and impair the operation of the ignition system. A proper check of the ignition system should include a check of the condenser capacity. Most ignition service instruments include a means for checking capacity. If the instrument in use does not have this function, or if an instrument is not available, a check can be made by replacing the suspected condenser with a new unit of the specified capacitance.

The specified condenser value is critical. The wrong value can cause metal to be transferred from one contact point to the other until the points are almost shorted together. Fig. 9 shows the results of a capacitor of the wrong value.

Low Insulation Resistance—The normal resistance of a good condenser should be several million ohms or more. The measured resistance of a faulty condenser could range from this value down to zero ohms. A low value of resistance in the condenser can upset the ignition system by acting as a shunt across the breaker points. The rapid increase and decrease of the magnetic

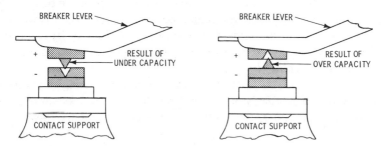

Fig. 9. Pitting of breaker contacts due to condenser of wrong capacity.

field of the coil are slowed, and the output voltage from the coil will be much lower than normal. Most test instruments will measure insulation resistance.

High Series Resistance—High series resistance is usually a result of poor electrical connections within the condenser. The passage of current into and out of the condenser is reduced and again the output voltage from the coil is reduced. Most test instruments will measure series resistance.

The Cam

The distributor cam is pinned to the distributor shaft and must rotate with it. The wear of the rubbing block on the cam tends to round off the high points and reduce the gap setting. This naturally takes a long time, since the cam is made of a very hard, tough metal. If the proper dwell angle and gap setting cannot be obtained at the same time, the cam is worn and should be replaced.

The Shaft Bearings

The distributor shaft has a sleeve-type bearing at the top and bottom. Wear in these bushings will produce side play of the shaft and introduce irregularities in ignition timing. Side play can be checked with a dial indicator clamped to the distributor body with the lever arm contacting a circular portion of the shaft. Move the shaft to and from the indicator in various positions of its rotation. When the side play exceeds specifications, the bearings and/or the shaft must be replaced.

Various specialized tools for removing and replacing distributor bearings are available. For the best results, use the tools approved by the manufacturer for replacing and burnishing the bearings.

DISTRIBUTOR TESTERS

From a diagnostic point of view, the distributor is the heart of the automobile engine and, therefore, must be the subject of careful inspection in any case of poor engine performance.

There are several fundamental tests which must be made on a distributor to determine if it is performing its functions properly. They are:

1. Condenser tests.
2. Electrical resistance test.
3. Breaker-point spring-tension test.
4. Cam-lobe accuracy.
5. Breaker-point alignment.
6. Breaker-point dwell.
7. Breaker-point dwell variation.
8. Centrifugal-advance calibration test.
9. Vacuum-chamber diaphragm test.
10. Vacuum-controlled breaker-plate test.
11. Vacuum spark-advance test.
12. Breaker-plate spring-tension test.

Distributor testers capable of making these tests are available from several manufacturers under various trade names. Fig. 10

Courtesy Snap-on Tools Corp.

Fig. 10. **Distrib-U-Scope** *is typical of the many distributor testers available.*

shows a typical unit. Nearly all of these testers use the stroboscopic principle for one or more of the tests listed above.

A stroboscope is *an electronic instrument by which it is visually possible to stop motion.* Testers using this principle make it possible to see exactly what happens to the moving parts of a distributor and to determine the efficiency of the entire distributor assembly exactly as it is operating on the engine. With this type of tester, of course, the distributor assembly is removed from the automobile and placed in a special holder on the tester.

A variable-speed motor drive in the tester rotates the distributor shaft along with a dial upon which appears segments of light or arrow flashes. (See Fig. 11.) With the proper electrical connections made to the distributor, the light from a neon or similar lamp is controlled by the opening and closing of the point contacts in the distributor. Thus, for a distributor from a 6-cylinder car, the lamp will cause six arrow flashes or segments of light to appear during the time the distributor shaft (and the tester dial) makes one revolution. Each time the lamp flashes, it lights up the segment or arrow for an instant. Each time the flash occurs, however, the segment or arrow will be in a different position around the rim of the dial due to the rotation. This will cause the dial to appear to have six segments or arrows equally spaced around its circumference. A distributor for a 4-cylinder car would cause four segments or arrows to appear, and an 8-cylinder car, eight segments or arrows.

The dial rotates inside a ring on which is inscribed the 360 degrees of a complete circle. This degree ring is adjustable so that the 0° mark can be set directly opposite one of the arrows or the start of one of the light segments that appear when the distributor is under test.

The speed at which the distributor shaft is turned is read on a tachometer and can be adjusted by a speed-regulator knob from 0 rpm to a maximum of 3000 to 4000 rpm or more, depending on the make and model of the tester. Always keep in mind that the distributor-shaft rpm is only one-half the engine rpm. This fact must be taken into account unless the tachometer on the tester is clearly marked as engine rpm.

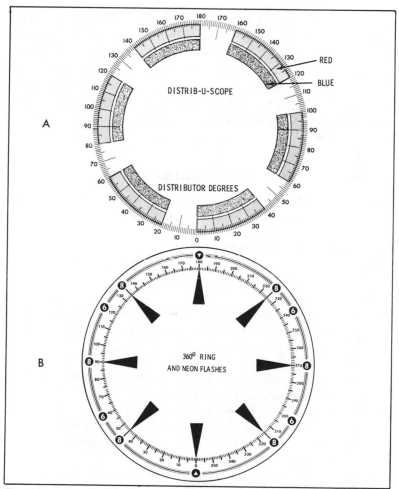

Fig. 11. Typical strobe patterns seen on distributor testers. Uneven synchronization, cam wear, play in the distributor shaft, and point bounce patterns; (A) Snap-On Distrib-U-Scope six-cylinder pattern; (B) Allen-tronic eight-cylinder pattern.

Nearly all distributor testers are similar in general construction to the units just described, but it should be remembered that specific makes and models may differ slightly in some respects. All testers have been designed for accurate results and ease of operation. The final selection of the type of tester best suited for your particular needs is left to your own judgment. A tester fulfilling the requirements of one person will not necessarily meet the needs of someone else.

SUN 500 DISTRIBUTOR TESTER

A typical distributor tester, the *Sun 500*, is shown in Fig. 12. The procedure for using this unit is as follows.

Distributor Visual Inspection

The distributor should be inspected visually before it is placed in the tetser. Examine and note the condition of:

1. The distributor shaft. Check for side clearance and end play.
2. The distributor-shaft bearings and bushings. Check for wear and smoothness of operation.
3. The flexible couplings. Check for wear.
4. Breaker-plate bearings or bushings. Check for wear, smoothness of operation, and lubrication.
5. Cam wick. Check for proper lubrication.
6. Breaker cam. Check for smoothness and lubrication.
7. Insulators, pigtails, and flexible internal leads. Check for breaks, loose connections, etc.
8. Contact points. Check alignment, pitting, and burning.
9. Rubbing block. Check for wear and lubrication.
10. Vacuum-advance linkage. Check for alignment, wear, and binding.

Fig. 12. Sun Model 500 Distributor Tester.

Courtesy Sun Electric Corp.

Distributor Mounting Procedure

Follow this procedure to mount the distributor on the tester.

1. Using the elevation crank, raise the clamp arms high enough to permit the shaft of the distributor being mounted to clear the drive chuck.
2. Position the distributor in the clamp with the vacuum chamber pointing to the right. Tighten the clamp arms securely on the machined surface of the distributor body. If the vacuum advance rotates the entire distributor, first install the proper collet on the distributor.
3. Using the elevation crank, lower the distributor until the gear, or about ¾″ of the tip of the distributor shaft enters the

drive chuck, or until the shaft engages the drive adapter if one is being used. Do not bottom the shaft in the chuck.

4. Tighten the chuck. (For *Delco-Remy* External Adjustment type distributors, approximately center the drive gear between its upper and lower limits of end-play travel before tightening the chuck.) Do not try to raise or lower the distributor after the drive chuck has been tightened.

Condenser Tests

To insure good ignition system performance, condensers should be tested for Series Resistance (which affects coil output); Capacity (which controls point arcing and pitting); and Leakage (which determines whether the condenser insulation can withstand the stress of the ignition system). Condensers that fail one or more of these tests should be discarded.

Procedure—Follow these steps to test a condenser with the *Sun 500* Distributor Tester.

1. Flip the Motor Switch to give the proper direction of distributor rotation. Set the speed to zero rpm.
2. With the condenser test selector switch in the Series Resistance position, connect the condenser test leads together.
3. Turn the condenser calibrate control clockwise from the off position.
4. Allow approximately 30 seconds for the tester to warm up and then adjust the calibrate control until the meter reads on Set Line.
5. Rotate the distributor shaft until the cam holds the breaker points open.
6. Separate the test leads and connect one to the distributor primary terminal and the other to the distributor body. See Fig. 13.

7. With the test selector switch in the Series Resistance position, the meter should read within the black bar at the right end of the scale. Failure to read in this area indicates a faulty condenser.

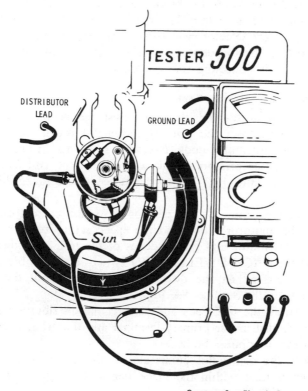

Courtesy Sun Electric Corp.

Fig. 13. One of the condenser test leads from the distributor tester is connected to the distributor housing and the other test lead is connected to the distributor primary terminal to test the condenser.

8. Set the test selector switch in the Capacity position and note the meter reading in microfarads. Compare with the manufacturer's specifications.
9. Set the test selector switch in the Leakage position. The meter should read within the black bar at the left end of the scale. Failure to read within this area indicates a faulty condenser.
10. Set the test selector switch in the Series Resistance position and turn the Condenser Calibrator knob to the off position before disconnecting the test leads.

Distributor Resistance Test

This test indicates the electrical resistance of the distributor primary circuit from the primary terminal through the breaker points to the distributor body. Excessive resistance in any portion of the distributor primary circuit will prevent the coil from performing at full efficiency. Follow this procedure to make this test.

1. With the Motor Switch positioned for the correct direction of distributor rotation and the speed set to zero rpm, clip the distributor and ground leads of the tester together.
2. Set the TACH-DWELL selector switch to the calibrate position and adjust the dwell calibrate knob until the meter reads on the Set line. See Fig. 14.
3. Separate the test leads and connect the distributor test lead to the distributor primary terminal and the ground test lead to the distributor body.
4. With the distributor points closed, the dwell meter pointer should read within the black bar at the right end of the scale. See Fig. 15.

   If the meter reads in the blue area to the left of the black bar, excessive resistance is present in the distributor primary circuit. To locate the source of the excessive resistance, move

Courtesy Sun Electric Corp.

Fig. 14. To calibrate the dwell meter to make a resistance test, the dwell regulator is adjusted until the needle is in the position shown.

the distributor test lead step by step through the distributor circuit toward the ground lead. When the meter indicates less resistance than the previous reading, some measurable resistance exists between the present point of contact of the distributor test lead and its previous point of contact.

NOTE: On distributors which have two sets of breaker points, test the resistance of each set of points by blocking one set open while testing the other.

Breaker-Point Spring-Tension Test

Proper tension of the breaker-point spring is important to obtain normal breaker-assembly life and to maintain full ignition-system efficiency throughout the speed range of the engine. Excessive spring tension can cause rapid rubbing-block, cam, and contact wear. Insufficient spring tension may allow the points to bounce at high speeds, resulting in arcing and burning of the points and causing engine misfiring.

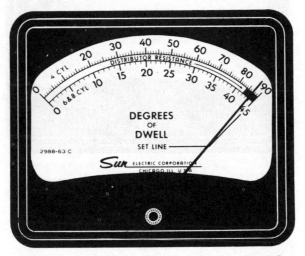

Courtesy Sun Electric Corp.

Fig. 15. The dwell meter pointer in the direction shown indicates a satisfactory resistance condition in the primary circuit of the distributor.

Follow this procedure to test the breaker-point spring tension.

1. Position the lazy hand of the spring-tension gauge on either side of the pointer, depending on whether the gauge will be pushed or pulled to open the points.
2. With the dwell meter calibrated, and the distributor test leads connected to the distributor as for the distributor-resistance

test, place the end of the spring-tension gauge near the contact on the movable arm. See Fig. 16.

3. Slowly pull the spring-tension tester at right angles to the movable arm and gradually increase the pull.

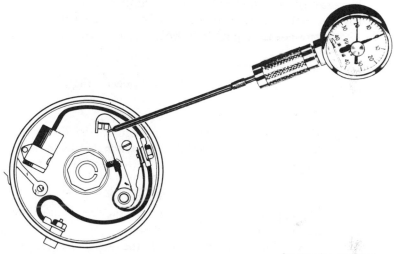

Fig. 16. Correct method of using a spring tension gauge to check the tension of the breaker point spring.

4. Note the reading on the spring-tension scale at the instant the contacts separate. Contact separation will be indicated on the dwell meter by the pointer falling to zero or by the flashing of the arrow on the drive unit. Refer to the manufacturer's test specifications for the correct spring tension for the particular distributor under test.

5. Hold the points open with the spring-tension gauge to the approximate recommended gap and slowly let them close. If the scale reading decreases noticeably from the previous

reading before the points close, it is probable that the pivot requires lubrication as recommended by the manufacturer.

NOTE: On distributors equipped with two sets of breaker points, one set must be held open while testing the other set. A piece of fiber can be placed between the contact points to hold them open.

Cam-Lobe Accuracy Test

The following steps should be followed to check the cam lobes for wear.

1. With the distributor test leads connected to the distributor as before, turn the TACH-DWELL switch to the position which corresponds to the type of distributor being tested (4, 6, or 8 cylinder).
2. Adjust the distributor speed to 1000 rpm.
3. Rotate the degree ring of the tester until the zero on the ring is aligned with one of the arrow flashes.
4. Observe the relative position of all the arrow flashes. All arrow flashes should be evenly spaced around the degree ring within $\pm 1°$. The arrow flashes should be spaced at:

$$90° \text{ for 4-lobe cams}$$
$$60° \text{ for 6-lobe cams}$$
$$45° \text{ for 8-lobe cams}$$

Variations of more than $1°$ from the specified spacing indicates a worn cam or bent distributor shaft.

Breaker-Point Alignment Test

The following steps are necessary to check the breaker points for correct alignment.

1. With the distributor tester set as for the Cam-Lobe Accuracy Test, observe the slight arc appearing between the breaker points. If the points are properly aligned, the arcing will appear in the center of the contacts when viewed from above and from the side.
2. Reduce the tester speed to 200 rpm for the test to follow.

Breaker-Point Dwell Test

Observe the dwell meter and, if necessary, adjust the point spacing until the dwell meter indicates the specific degrees of dwell.

On distributors equipped with dual points, it will be necessary to adjust the dwell on each set individually. To isolate each set for adjustment, the other set can be blocked open by inserting a piece of fiber between the contacts.

Additional information on point dwell and point adjustment is given later in this chapter.

Breaker-Point Dwell-Variation Test

1. While watching the dwell meter, vary the distributor speed from 200 to 1750 rpm. A dwell variation in excess of 2° indicates a worn distributor shaft or bushings.
2. Reduce the speed of the tester to 200 rpm for the next test.

NOTE: If testing a *Loadomatic* type distributor, turn to page 96 for remaining tests.

Centrifugal-Advance Calibration Test

This test is made to determine if the ignition timing conforms to the manufacturer's specified advance curve throughout the operating speed range of the engine. A defective centrifugal-advance unit will cause the engine to be out of time at certain speeds. This always results in a loss of engine performance and, in addition, may cause spark knock and/or overheating.

Perform the following steps:

1. Set the zero of the degree ring in line with the arrow flash that is nearest you.
2. Increase the distributor speed, pausing at each speed specified in the distributor manufacturer's manual to note if the amount of advance indicated by the arrow flash is within $\pm 1°$ (if no range is given) of the specified figure.
3. Momentarily exceed the highest speed specified as a check speed. Then, while returning the distributor speed back to zero, recheck at each test speed to see that the amount of advance at that speed is the same as it was in Step 2, and as specified. Any difference in readings requires correction be made for best engine performance.

    If the advance in both steps 2 and 3 is excessive, the governor-weight springs are weak, or the wrong springs have been installed.

    If the advance is insufficient in Step 2 and excessive in Step 3, the governor weights are sticking and should be freed.

    If the advance is insufficient both on acceleration and deceleration, the governor spring tension is excessive.

Refer to the distributor's manual for the proper service procedure if the distributor fails any of the tests.

Vacuum-Chamber Diaphragm Test

(See page 96 for testing *Loadomatic* type distributors.)

Use the following procedure to test the vacuum-chamber diaphragm.

1. Insert the proper adapter in the vacuum-advance unit and tighten with a wrench to insure a good seal.
2. Attach the vacuum hose to the vacuum-advance unit and seal the hose with a metal clamp.
3. Adjust the VACUUM REGULATOR until the gauge reads 15 inches.
4. Release the vacuum-hose clamp and observe the gauge. The gauge reading will momentarily fall to a lower value.

   If the gauge reading returns to 15 inches within a few seconds, the vacuum chamber is airtight.

   If the gauge reading fails to return to 15 inches, the vacuum chamber can be assumed to be leaky and must be repaired or replaced.

Vacuum-Controlled Breaker-Plate Test

The breaker-plate travel must be smooth and even or the plate will twist, changing the relationship between the cam and rubbing block and causing the dwell angle to change. Any change in dwell angle affects not only the quality of the ignition spark but also affects the timing.

Proceed as follows to check the breaker-plate action.
1. Adjust the speed control to 1000 rpm.
2. Adjust the vacuum to 0 with the vacuum-regulator knob, then increase it to 20 inches while watching the dwell-meter pointer for variations.
3. If the dwell reading varies more than $\pm 2°$ as the vacuum changes from 0 to 20 inches, it indicates worn breaker-plate bushings and bearings, or intermittent distributor resistance. Check the condition of the distributor wiring, which may be broken within the insulation due to flexing.
4. Adjust the vacuum regulator to zero vacuum.

NOTE: This specification applies only to distributors with centrally located breaker-plate bearings.

On *Auto-Lite* distributors, Models IAT, IBP, and IBR which have side-pivoted breaker plates, the dwell will normally vary by more than 2° when the vacuum unit is operated. No definite specifications are given by the manufacturer for the dwell variations of these distributors since the amount of variation varies with the individual distributor depending on the amount of maximum vacuum advance.

Vacuum Spark-Advance Test

The vacuum spark-advance adjusts the spark timing according to the load on the engine to provide peak fuel economy at moderate loads and full power without detonation at heavier loads. While making the test, look in particular for improper calibrations, sticky or erratic breaker-plate action, tilting of the breaker plate, or interference of the condenser with the breaker-plate action.

Proceed as follows:

1. With no vacuum applied to the unit, set the zero of the degree ring in line with one of the arrow flashes. (Distributor speed is 1000 rpm.)
2. Adjust the vacuum regulator to apply the correct amount of vacuum for each specified check point in turn, and note the amount of advance obtained. Compare this amount with the manufacturer's specifications.
3. Momentarily exceed the highest vacuum value specified then reduce it and again note the advance obtained at each specified check point. See Figs. 17 and 18.

If the advance is excessive during both Steps 2 and 3, a weak vacuum-advance spring is indicated.

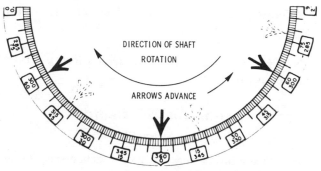

Courtesy Sun Electric Corp.

Fig. 17. Arrows will move in a counterclockwise direction when checking the centrifugal- and vacuum-advance mechanism on a distributor whose shaft rotates in a clockwise direction.

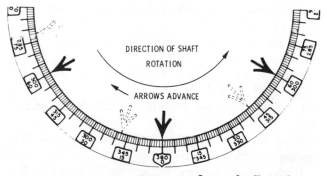

Courtesy Sun Electric Corp.

Fig. 18. Arrows will move in a clockwise direction when checking the centrifugal- and vacuum-advance mechanism on a distributor whose shaft rotates in a counter-clockwise direction.

If the advance is insufficient in Step 2 and excessive in Step 3, or is erratic in both Step 2 and 3, the distributor breaker plate is sticking or binding.

Refer to the distributor manufacturer's manual for the proper service procedure.

NOTE: See page 100 for *Delco-Remy* distributor breaker-plate test.

LOADOMATIC DISTRIBUTORS
(Single Vacuum Chamber)

With the exception of the advance mechanisms, *Loadomatic* distributors are tested in the same manner as shown previously for other distributors.

Vacuum-Chamber Diaphragm Test

1. Insert the proper adapter in the vacuum chamber and tighten to insure a good seal.
2. Leave the test leads connected and the lobe selector switch in the proper position, as before.
3. Attach the vacuum hose to the vacuum unit and seal the hose with the metal clamp.
4. Adjust the Vacuum Regulator until the gauge reads 5 inches.
5. Release the hose clamp and observe the gauge. The gauge reading will momentarily fall to a lower value.

    If the gauge reading returns to 5 inches within a few seconds, the vacuum chamber is air tight.

    If the gauge reading fails to return to 5 inches, the vacuum chamber is leaky and must be repaired.

Breaker-Plate Test

6. Adjust the distributor speed to 1000 rpm.
7. Increase the vacuum from 0 to 5 inches while watching the

dwell meter. If the meter reading varies more than 2°, wear
in the breaker-plate bushing is indicated.

8. Adjust the Vacuum Regulator until the gauge reads zero,
then disconnect the vacuum hose.

Advance Test

9. With the distributor operating at a minimum rpm, place the
zero on the degree ring in line with one of the arrow flashes.

10. Adjust the vacuum-gauge scale to read zero inches and then
connect the hoses as shown in Fig. 19.

11. Adjust the vacuum and distributor speed for each specified
point, in turn, and note the amount of advance obtained.

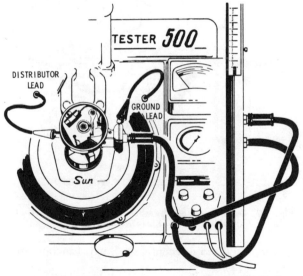

Courtesy Sun Electric Corp.

*Fig. 19. Connections to the distributor to test the vac-
uum chamber diaphragm, the breaker plate action, and
the advance mechanism.*

12. Reduce the vacuum and distributor speed and again note the advance obtained at each specified check point. Consult the manufacturer's service manual for specific adjusting procedures.

LOADOMATIC DISTRIBUTORS
(Dual Vacuum Chamber)

There are two types of dual vacuum-chamber *Loadomatic* distributors—an early type used only on Lincoln in 1953 (Fig. 20),

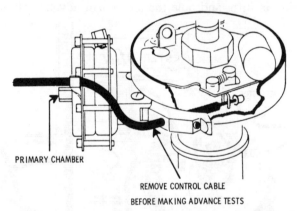

PRIMARY CHAMBER

REMOVE CONTROL CABLE
BEFORE MAKING ADVANCE TESTS

Courtesy Sun Electric Corp.

Fig. 20. Dual vacuum chamber Loadomatic distributor used on 1953 Lincoln automobiles.

and a later type used more recently on Ford, Lincoln, and Mercury products (Fig. 21).

With the exception of the advance mechanisms, *Loadomatic* distributors are tested in the same manner as other distributors explained previously.

Vacuum-Chamber Diaphragm Test

1. Insert the proper adapter into the primary vacuum chamber and tighten to insure a good seal.
2. Leave the test leads connected and the lobe selector switch in the proper position, as before.
3. Attach the vacuum hose to the vacuum unit and seal the hose with the metal clamp.

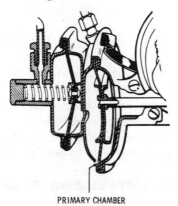

PRIMARY CHAMBER

Courtesy Sun Electric Corp.

Fig. 21. Dual vacuum chamber Loadomatic distributor used on later model Ford, Mercury, and Lincoln products.

4. Adjust the Vacuum Regulator until the vacuum gauge reads 7 inches for the 1953 models or 20 inches for later models.
5. Release the hose clamp and observe the gauge. The gauge reading will momentarily fall to a lower value.

If the gauge reading returns to the original reading within a few seconds, the vacuum chamber is airtight.

If the gauge reading fails to return to the original reading, the chamber is leaky and must be repaired.

Breaker-Plate Test

6. Adjust the distributor speed to 1000 rpm.
7. Increase the vacuum from 0 to 7 inches (or 0 to 20 inches for later models) while watching the dwell meter. If the dwell-meter reading varies more than 2°, wear in the breaker-plate bushing is indicated.
8. Adjust the Vacuum Regulator until the vacuum gauge reads zero, and disconnect the vacuum hose.

Advance Test

9. With the distributor operating at minimum rpm, place the zero of the degree ring in line with one of the arrow flashes.
10. Adjust the vacuum-gauge scale to read zero inches and then connect the hoses as shown in Fig. 19.
11. Adjust the vacuum and distributor speed for each specified check point in turn and note the amount of advance obtained.
12. Reduce the vacuum and distributor speed to zero, pausing at each check point and noting the advance obtained.

DELCO-REMY CENTER-BEARING BREAKER PLATE

Breaker-Plate Spring-Tension Test

This test is made to determine if the breaker plate is free to rotate correctly under the influence of the vacuum spark-control unit. Excessive plate tension may cause sluggish action of the advance mechanism, resulting in erratic timing under changing loads.

To make this test, proceed as follows:

1. Remove the vacuum spark-control unit from the distributor. Replace the small screw finger-tight in the plate to provide an attaching point for the spring-tension scale.

2. With the breaker plate pushed to the full retard position (full travel in the direction of cam rotation), hook the spring-tension scale on the screw, as shown in Fig. 22. Now pull the scale, noting the amount of pull necessary to start movement of the breaker plate.

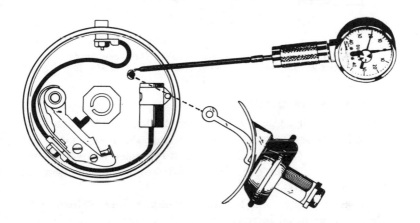

Courtesy Sun Electric Corp.

Fig. 22. Correct method of checking the spring tension of the breaker plate in a Delco-Remy distributor.

The amount of pull, as registered on the spring-tension scale, should not exceed 20 ounces for the type-A plate (Fig. 23), or exceed 15 ounces for the type-B plate (Fig. 24). The tension on a type-A breaker plate may be adjusted by adding or removing shim washers to the tension spring on the underside of the plate. The tension on a type-B breaker plate may be adjusted by stretching or replacing the helical plate-tension spring.

101

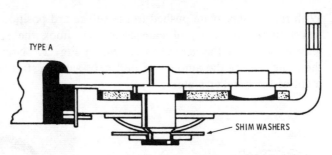

TYPE A

SHIM WASHERS

Courtesy Sun Electric Corp.

Fig. 23. Tension of a type-A breaker plate can be adjusted by adding or removing shim washers to the tension spring.

Distributor Point Dwell

Dwell or dwell angle is the number of degrees* through which the distributor shaft rotates from the time the points close until they open again (See Fig. 25). Thus, dwell angle is inversely proportional to the point gap; that is, increasing the gap decreases dwell, and vice versa.

Insufficient dwell tends to cause ignition failure at high speed, while excessive dwell increases the total average current which the

----

* Some publications of the Ford Motor Company refer to "percent of dwell." The percent of dwell is the relation of the actual dwell as compared to 100% dwell. A 100% dwell for:
> a 4-cylinder engine is 90%
> a 6-cylinder engine is 60%
> an 8-cylinder engine is 45%

Examples of "percent of dwell" are:
> 4-cylinder engine with 60% dwell
>> is 60% of 90° or 54° dwell
> 6-cylinder engine with 60% dwell
>> is 60% of 60° or 36° dwell
> 8-cylinder engine with 60% dwell
>> is 60% of 45° or 27° dwell

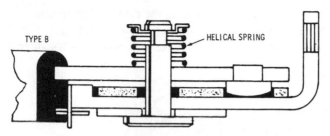

Courtesy Sun Electric Corp.

Fig. 24. Tension of a type-B breaker plate can be adjusted either by stretching or by replacing the helical tension spring.

points must handle, especially at low speeds. Excessive dwell usually leads to a very short point life.

After a distributor is initially timed to any given engine, any change in the dwell will result in a change of timing. This will require retiming the distributor, since the point rubbing block will make contact with the cam at a different place.

When dwell specifications are given with a high and a low limit, set the point dwell to the lower limit when new points are installed, to allow for rubbing block wear.

Contact-Point Gap and Dwell (Cam-Angle Relationship)

If a distributor cannot be adjusted so that the gap and dwell are within specifications at the same time, inspect for the following possibilities:

Improper spring tension or sticky pivot.
Wrong point set installed.
Bent shaft, causing point gap to vary on each cam lobe.
Worn cam lobes or defective cam. (Compare point gap at each cam lobe if in doubt.)

103

Points floating, or not following the cam at high speeds.
Excessive resistance causing false dwell reading.
In practically every case the remedy will be self-evident.

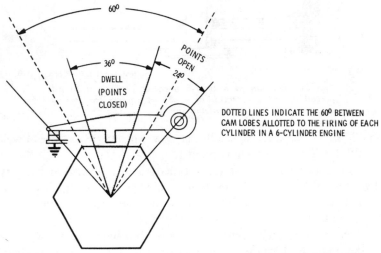

DOTTED LINES INDICATE THE 60° BETWEEN
CAM LOBES ALLOTTED TO THE FIRING OF EACH
CYLINDER IN A 6-CYLINDER ENGINE

Courtesy Sun Electric Corp.

Fig. 25. An illustration of dwell angle.

DELCO-REMY AND HOLLEY DISTRIBUTOR GOVERNOR TEST

Delco-Remy

1. With the distributor mounted in the tester, insert the proper vacuum adapter in the lower fitting on the distributor housing (Fig. 26) and tighten with a wrench to insure a good seal.
2. Turn the Motor Switch to the proper direction of rotation and adjust the speed to zero rpm.
3. Attach the vacuum hose to the vacuum adapter and seal the hose with the metal clamp.

4. Adjust the Vacuum Regulator until the vacuum gauge reads 5 inches.

5. Release the hose clamp and increase the distributor speed until the vacuum gauge reaches a maximum value. This maximum value will vary, depending on the type of centrifugal-valve parts used.

6. After this maximum reading has been reached, slowly decrease the distributor speed until the vacuum gauge falls 0.1 inch from its maximum reading. The speed at which the 0.1-inch vacuum drop takes place will be the no-load governed speed.

Holley

1. With the distributor mounted in the tester, insert the proper vacuum adapter into the lower fitting on the distributor housing (Fig. 27). Tighten the fitting with a wrench to insure a good seal.

2. Turn the Motor Switch to the proper direction of rotation and adjust the distributor speed to zero rpm.

3. Attach the vacuum hose to the vacuum adapter and seal the hose with the metal clamp.

4. Adjust the vacuum regulator until the vacuum gauge reads 4.5 inches.

5. Release the hose clamp. The vacuum reading should now be approximately 2 inches.

6. Adjust the distributor speed to a point well above the desired governing rpm. At this speed, the vacuum gauge should again read the predetermined setting of 4.5 inches if the system is operating properly.

7. Slowly decrease the distributor speed while observing the vacuum gauge. The speed at which the gauge reading begins to fall will be the no-load governed speed.

NOTE: Distributor rpm is one-half the engine rpm. If the factory recommendations call for 3600 rpm no-load governed speed, this will be 1800 rpm on the tester and the governor should be adjusted so that its value will close at this speed. Repeat the above test after each adjustment.

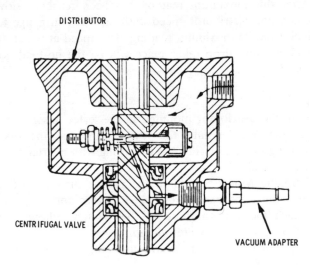

Courtesy Sun Electric Corp.

Fig. 26. Delco-Remy governor.

Transmission and Overdrive Governor Test

The *Sun 500* Distributor Tester can also be used to test transmission and overdrive governors. Proceed as follows:

1. Place the governor drive adapter in the distributor-tester drive chuck and tighten.
2. Place the governor in the clamp and tighten securely.

3. Adjust the elevating control until the governor shaft fits into the slot in the drive adapter.

4. Connect the distributor test lead to the contact terminal on the governor. Connect the ground test lead to the governor body.

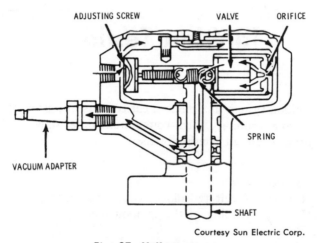

Courtesy Sun Electric Corp.

Fig. 27. Holley governor.

5. Turn the motor drive switch to either right- or left-hand rotation, as indicated by the specifications for the governor being tested.

6. Turn the selector switch to the 8-cyl. position.

7. Use the dwell meter to indicate the "make" and "break" of the governor switch.

8. Check the rpm at "make" and at "break" on acceleration and deceleration, and compare with the manufacturer's specifications for the governor being tested.

CHAPTER 6

Ignition Testing

The ignition system in a modern car consists of a primary (low-voltage) and a secondary (high-voltage) circuit, as shown in Fig. 1. The primary circuit consists of the:

1. Battery.
2. Ignition switch.
3. Primary circuit resistance wire (or resistor).
4. Primary winding of the ignition coil.
5. Breaker points.
6. Condenser.

The secondary circuit consists of the:

1. Secondary winding of the ignition coil.
2. Distributor rotor.
3. Distributor cap.
4. High-tension wires.
5. Spark plugs.

Ignition Switch—The ignition switch on most modern cars serves two purposes. It provides a means of energizing the ignition system, and also of energizing the starter motor. After the engine

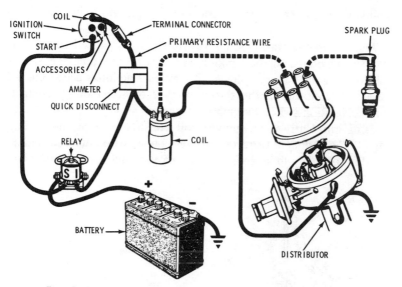

Fig. 1. Typical ignition system for an 8-cylinder engine.

has started, the switch returns to the run position when it is released, disconnecting the starter motor and connecting a resistance in series with the ignition coil and breaker points. This resistance is connected in the circuit on some cars by contacts on the ignition switch. In other cars, the resistance is switched in and out of the circuit by contacts on a relay (usually the starter solenoid) controlled by the ignition switch.

Primary Circuit Resistance Wire (or Resistor)—A resistance wire or an actual resistor is placed in the primary circuit of the ignition system of most makes and models of automobiles. The purpose of this resistance is to limit the amount of current flow through the breaker points at low speeds when they are closed for longer periods of time. This resistance also protects the coil and points when the engine is stopped but the ignition switch has been left on.

During engine starting, this resistance is by-passed to provide increased voltage to the ignition coil during the time the starter has lowered the battery voltage. The by-pass action is accomplished either by contacts on the starter relay (solenoid) or by contacts on the ignition-switch assembly.

Ignition Coil—The ignition coil consists of a primary winding of a few hundred turns of relatively heavy wire plus a secondary winding of many thousands of turns of very fine wire. Both wind-

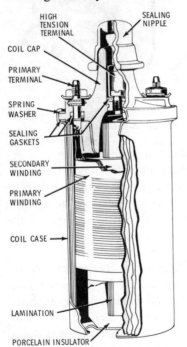

Fig. 2. Sectional view of an automobile ignition coil.

ings are assembled around a soft-iron core and enclosed by a case, one end of which contains the terminals. Fig. 2 shows a sectional view of a typical ignition coil.

Distributor—The distributor performs several functions in the ignition system: (1) It closes and opens the primary circuit to produce the magnetic buildup and collapse. (2) It times these actions so the resultant high-voltage surges from the secondary occur at the right time. (3) It directs the high-voltage surges to the proper spark plug at the proper time. Fig. 3 shows a typical distributor.

Breaker Points—The breaker points are located in the distributor. They are closed by spring pressure and opened by a cam on the distributor shaft. The distributor shaft is rotated by a gear on the camshaft of the engine.

Distributors may have more than one set of breaker points. For example, some distributors have two sets of points connected in parallel (Fig. 4) to provide longer contact closing and higher magnetic strength of the coil.

Other distributors may have two sets of breaker points to provide alternate firing of the cylinders (Fig. 5). Still other distributors are designed for dual ignition systems (Fig. 6).

Condenser—The condenser in a conventional ignition system serves a dual purpose. It protects the contacts by suppressing the arc that results when the points open the circuit to the primary winding of the ignition coil. In addition, the condenser hastens the collapse of the magnetic field, thus increasing the high-voltage output from the secondary of the ignition coil.

Distributor Rotor—The distributor rotor switches the high-voltage surges from the secondary winding of the ignition coil to the proper spark plug at the proper time. The rotor fits on the end of the distributor shaft and is keyed in such a way as to prevent installing it incorrectly. Thus, it rotates with the distributor

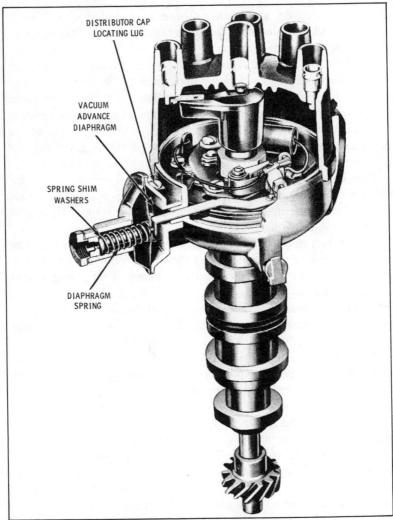

DISTRIBUTOR CAP
LOCATING LUG

VACUUM
ADVANCE
DIAPHRAGM

SPRING SHIM
WASHERS

DIAPHRAGM
SPRING

Fig. 3. A typical automobile distributor.

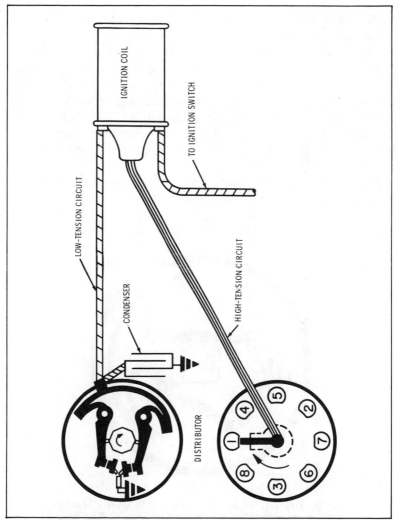

IGNITION COIL

TO IGNITION SWITCH

LOW-TENSION CIRCUIT

CONDENSER

HIGH-TENSION CIRCUIT

DISTRIBUTOR

Fig. 4. Two sets of breaker points connected in parallel.

shaft and is synchronized with the opening and closing of the breaker points.

The high-voltage surges from the ignition coil enter the center terminal of the distributor cap and make contact with the rotor through a carbon-brush arrangement. The surges travel through the rotor to a small metal tip on the outside edge of the rotor. This small metal tip passes very close to, but does not quite touch, the terminals around the inside of the distributor cap. These terminals are connected to the spark-plug wires inserted in the distributor cap.

With this arrangement, and if the ignition system is functioning properly, the metal tip on the rotor is directly under one of the terminals on the inside of the cap at the instant the breaker points open. Thus, the high-voltage surge from the ignition coil enters

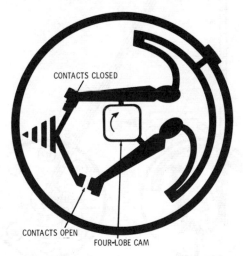

Fig. 5. Two sets of breaker points used with a 4-lobe cam to provide alternate operation in an 8-cylinder automobile engine.

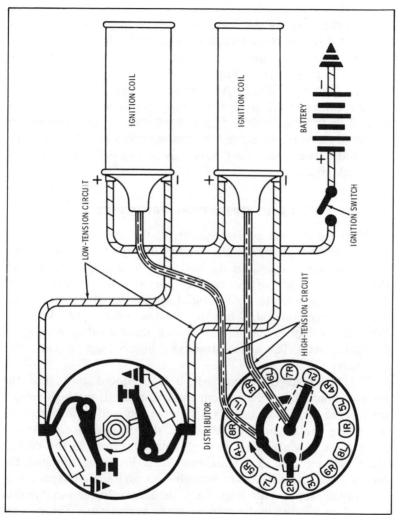

Fig. 6. Dual ignition system for an 8-cylinder engine.

through the center of the distributor cap, through the rotor, jumps the short distance to the terminal under which the metal tip of the rotor is positioned, and travels through the correct high-tension wire to the proper spark plug.

High-Tension Wire—All wiring through which the high-voltage surges travel are heavily insulated to prevent leakage to ground or to other wiring. This type of wire is used between the output of the ignition coil and the center terminal of the distributor cap, and between the outer terminals of the distributor cap and the spark plugs.

BASIC OPERATING PRINCIPLES

When the breaker points are closed, the low-voltage (primary circuit) current flows from the battery, through the ignition switch to the primary winding of the coil, and then to ground through the closed contacts of the breaker points. This primary current flow causes a magnetic field to build up around the primary winding in the ignition coil. When the breaker points open, this magnetic field collapses and moves through the secondary winding of the ignition coil. This action produces a high-voltage current in the secondary.

The high-voltage current, which is produced each time the breaker points open, flows from the coil through the high-tension lead to the distributor cap. The high-tension lead is connected by a rotating contact to the rotor inside the distributor cap. As the rotor turns, it distributes the high-voltage current to the correct spark-plug terminal in the distributor cap. From this terminal, the high-voltage current flows through the high-tension spark-plug wire to the proper spark plug. Thus, the spark plug fires and ignites the fuel-air mixture in the cylinder at the proper time. This process is repeated for every power stroke of the engine.

The demands placed on the ignition system in late-model, high-compression, high-speed engines are enormous. For example, the breaker points in the ignition system of a 6-cylinder engine turning at 3000 rpm will make and break 9000 times every minute, or 540,000 times an hour. Not only must the points make and break at this high rate, but they must do so at very precise times if satisfactory engine performance is to be achieved. Thus, it is apparent that the ignition system must be maintained in first-class operating condition by a thorough systematic and periodic testing and adjustment routine.

TROUBLE ISOLATION

Ignition-system troubles are caused either by a failure in the primary and/or secondary circuit, or by incorrect ignition timing. If an engine trouble has been traced to the ignition system, the trouble can be found by performing a series of tests using individual hand-held instruments, or by using specialized test equipment that has been designed expressly for overall engine analysis and adjustment.

Trouble in the ignition system can usually be isolated to the primary or secondary ignition circuit without the use of instruments, as follows:

1. Remove the coil high-tension lead from the ditsributor cap.
2. Hold the high-tension lead approximately 3/16″ from some convenient point on the motor block or head.
3. Turn the ignition switch on, crank the engine, and check for a spark. If the spark is good, the trouble is in the secondary circuit. If there is no spark, or if it is weak, the trouble is in either the primary circuit, the coil-to-distributor high-tension lead, or the coil.

PRIMARY-CIRCUIT TESTS

A breakdown or loss of energy in the primary circuit can be caused by:

1. Defective primary wiring or corroded and/or loose terminals.
2. Burned, shorted, sticking, or improperly adjusted breaker points.
3. A defective coil.
4. A defective condenser.

A complete test of the primary circuit consists of checking the circuit from the battery to the coil, the circuit from the coil to ground, and the starting ignition circuit. Excessive voltage drop in the primary circuit will reduce the output from the secondary of the ignition coil, resulting in hard starting and poor performance.

When making the following tests, keep in mind that the readings for different makes and models of automobiles may vary somewhat from those given. Always consult the manufacturer's specifications when in doubt.

TEST 1

Connect a voltmeter between the positive battery terminal and the battery-side primary terminal of the ignition coil, as shown in Fig. 7. Observe the meter reading while cranking the engine. The voltage at this point should not exceed 1 to 1.5 volts. (NOTE: The maximum allowable voltage at this point may vary, depending on the make and model of automobile. Always consult the car manufacturer's specifications for the exact voltage.)

Possible Troubles

If the voltage exceeds the specifications, the following are possible troubles:

1. Open circuit from the battery side of the coil to the ignition switch.
2. Ignition switch not closing the circuit to the ignition coil in the start position.

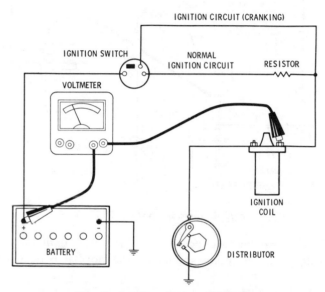

Fig. 7. Ignition System TEST 1.

3. Ground in the circuit from the ignition coil to the ignition switch.
4. Ground in the coil.

TEST 2 (Points open)

Connect the voltmeter between the battery-side primary terminal of the ignition coil and ground, as in Fig. 8. Turn the ignition switch to the ON position, and make sure the breaker points are

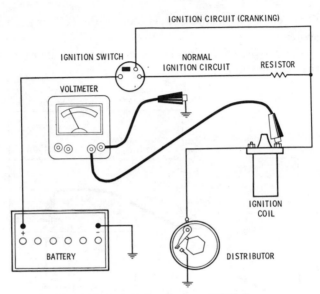

Fig. 8. Ignition System TEST 2.

open. (If the points are closed, jog the starter until they open.) The voltage at this point should be the normal battery voltage.

Possible Troubles

If the voltage is less than the normal battery voltage, the following are possible troubles:

1. Battery not fully charged.
2. Points not open.
3. Ground in the circuit from the ignition coil to the distributor.
4. Ground in the distributor.
5. Ground in the coil.
6. Ground in the circuit to the ignition switch or to the resistor.

TEST 2 (Points closed)

The voltmeter remains connected as in Fig. 8. Close the breaker points by jogging the starter. Turn the ignition switch to ON. The voltage at this point should be between 5 and 7 volts.

Possible Troubles

If the meter reads less than 5 volts, the following are possible troubles:

1. Loose connection from the resistor through the ignition-switch circuit to the battery.
2. Loose connection between the resistor and the ignition coil.
3. The resistor is open or has too much resistance.

If the meter reads more than 7 volts, the following are possible troubles:

1. Loose connection between the ignition coil and the distributor.
2. Resistor out of the circuit because of shorted or incorrect wiring.
3. Resistor has decreased in resistance.
4. Coil primary is open.
5. Breaker points are not closed.

The primary winding of the ignition coil can be checked for an open condition by means of a resistance test. To perform this test, turn the ignition switch off. **(Caution: If the ignition switch is not turned off, the ohmmeter may be damaged.)** Connect an ohmmeter across the primary terminals of the coil. The resistance of the primary winding should be from 0.3 to 9 ohms, the exact value depending on the make and model of automobile.

(Check the manufacturer's specifications for the exact resistance value.) If the resistance reading is infinite, the primary winding is open.

TEST 3

The breaker points are closed as in the last part of TEST 2. Turn the ignition switch ON. Connect the voltmeter between the primary distributor terminal and ground, as in Fig. 9. The meter reading at this point should not exceed 0.2 volt.

Possible Troubles

If the meter reads more than 0.2 volt, the following are possible troubles:

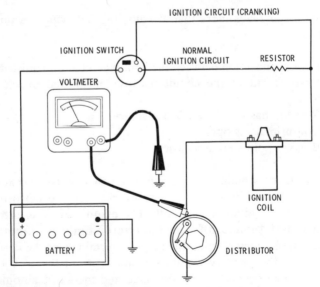

Fig. 9. Ignition System TEST 3.

1. Breaker points not closed.
2. Loose connections in the distributor.
3. Distributor not grounded to the engine.
4. Faulty breaker points.

TEST 4

The breaker points are closed as for TEST 3. Turn the ignition switch ON. Connect the voltmeter between the ignition-switch side of the resistor and the positive battery terminal, in the manner shown in Fig. 10. The meter reading at this point should not exceed 0.7 volt.

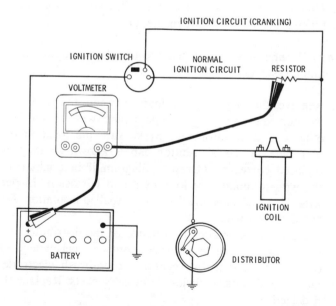

Fig. 10. Ignition System TEST 4.

Possible Trouble

If the meter reads more than 0.7 volt at this point, look for a loose connection or broken wire from the resistor through the ignition-switch circuit to the battery.

SECONDARY-CIRCUIT TESTS

A breakdown or energy loss in the secondary circuit can be caused by:

1. Fouled or improperly adjusted spark plugs.
2. Defective high-voltage wiring.
3. High-voltage leakage across the coil, distributor cap, or rotor.
4. Open secondary winding in the ignition coil.

The following procedure is used to test the secondary circuits of the ignition system:

1. Remove the high-tension lead between the coil and distributor, and remove the spark-plug wires from both the plugs and distributor cap. Make sure the location of each plug wire in the distributor cap is known so they can be replaced correctly. (Draw a diagram if in doubt.) Inspect the wire terminals for looseness and corrosion. Inspect the wires for breaks and cracked or oil-soaked insulation. Replace any defective wires.
2. Clean both the inside and outside of the distributor cap and inspect it for cracks, burned contacts, permanent carbon tracks, and a defective center carbon-brush electrode. Remove any dirt or corrosion from the sockets. Replace the cap if defective.

3. Inspect the rotor for cracks and for burned or pitted contacts. Clean thoroughly. Replace the rotor if it is found to be defective.

High-Tension Wires—The high-tension wires are those from the coil output to the distributor, and from the distributor to the individual spark plugs. On some makes and models of automobiles, these are resistance-type wires designed to help eliminate ignition noise in the car radio.

Either type of wire can be tested with an ohmmeter, the leads of which are connected to each end of the wire being checked. The resistance reading for standard wire should be nearly zero ohms— any reading higher than this value indicates a defective wire which should be replaced. If the resistance reading of a resistance-type wire exceeds 30,000 ohms, it should be replaced.

> **Caution: Do not puncture the insulation of the wire while making a resistance test. To do so may cause separation of the conductor. Measure only from the ends of the wire.**
>
> **When removing the wires from the spark plugs, grasp the molded cap only. Do not pull on the wire because to do so may separate the wire connection inside the cap or damage the weather seal.**

Ignition Coil—To test the secondary winding of the ignition coil, disconnect the high-tension lead from the coil tower. Connect an ohmmeter between the coil tower and either of the primary terminals on the coil. If the resistance reading is infinite, an open secondary winding is indicated. The correct resistance reading will depend on the make and model of automobile, but will range between 5000 and 15,000 ohms. (Check the manufacturer's specifications for the correct resistance.) A reading of less than the specified resistance indicates an internal short within the coil.

Spark Intensity—Disconnect the wire from one of the spark plugs, and check the spark intensity by holding the loose end of the wire approximately 3/16″ from the engine block or head. (To conduct this test, crank the engine with a remote-starter switch.) The spark should jump the gap regularly. Perform the same test with each of the remaining spark-plug wires, one at a time.

If the spark intensity of all spark-plug wires is good, the coil, condenser, rotor, distributor cap, and high-tension wires are probably satisfactory.

If the spark is good at some wires, but poor at others, perform a high-resistance test of the faulty leads.

If the spark is weak or intermittent at all wires, check the ignition coil, distributor cap, rotor, and high-tension wire from the distributor to the coil.

Spark Plugs—Clean, inspect, and gap the spark plugs according to specifications. If specifications are not available, set the gap at .030-.035. Replace any plugs which show signs of excessive wear, corrosion, or deposits.

Ignition Timing—Incorrect ignition timing can cause hard starting, spark knock, loss of power, poor fuel economy, engine overheating, and/or failure to start. Some of the most common causes of incorrect timing are:

1. Timing incorrectly adjusted.
2. Distributor bushing worn, or the distributor shaft worn or bent.
3. Defective vacuum-advance system.
4. Defective centrifugal-advance system (if used).

Any of the above troubles are best detected by using instruments. Specific instructions are given later.

TRANSISTOR IGNITION SYSTEMS

Transistor ignition systems are now available on many new cars as optional equipment. There are also several transistor ignition kits on the market that can be installed in practically any car. This new type of ignition system will no doubt become standard equipment on most cars before many years have passed. The basic principles of operation of all transistor ignition systems are the same, even though their circuits and parts values may differ widely.

The schematic of one type of transistor ignition system is shown in Fig. 11. This system is used on some Fords and Mercurys. The primary of the ignition coil in this system is designed to draw a peak current of 12 amperes (or approximately 5.5 amperes of average current) to provide a high spark-plug voltage at the higher engine speeds.

The transistor in this system acts as a heavy-duty switch, except that it has no moving parts. Consequently, there is practically no time lag in opening and closing the primary circuit. The transistor is connected between the battery and the ignition coil, and is used to make and break the primary circuit of the ignition coil.

The breaker points in the distributor control the transistor. The 8-ohm resistor connected in the wiring harness between the distributor and the transistor, limits the transistor control current (and breaker-point current) to 0.5 ampere. This low current through the breaker points reduces point pitting and increases their life.

The condenser placed across the breaker points in a conventional ignition system is no longer needed in the location of the transistor system. Instead, its value has been increased to 2 mfd and is now located in the amplifier assembly. Here, this condenser performs the function of absorbing the high-inductive energy when the breaker points open. However, it no longer has any effect on the points because it is isolated from them by the transistor.

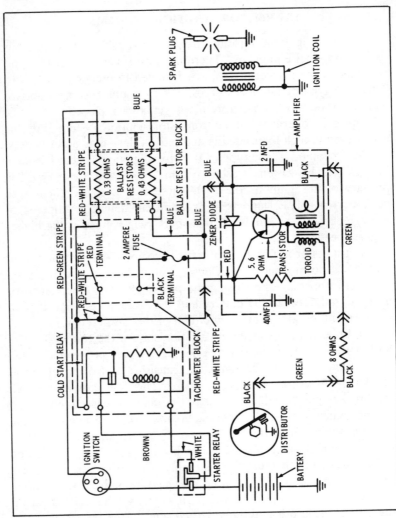

Fig. 11. Transistor ignition system.

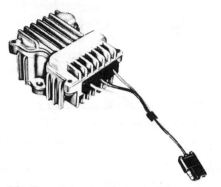

Fig. 12. Transistor ignition amplifier assembly.

The amplifier portion of this system is assembled in a separate unit (Fig. 12) and is mounted under the instrument panel to protect the parts from the engine heat.

The ballast resistors, a tachometer-connecting block, and a cold-start relay are enclosed by a fiber cover and mounted in the engine compartment. A 2-ampere fuse in the lead from the tachometer block to the collector of the transistor in the amplifier protects the transistor from damage if other than normal testing instruments are used.

The contacts of the cold-start relay are normally closed, being opened only during the start cycle. When the starter relay is energized, the cold-start relay is actuated and its contacts open. If, during starting, the available voltage drops below 10.5 volts, the relay contacts will close, by-passing the 0.33-ohm ballast resistor, thus applying full available voltage to the system.

The tachometer block is used to connect a tachometer or dwell meter into the circuit. **Do not connect a tachometer or dwell meter in any other manner. To do so may result in inaccurate readings and possible damage to the transistor.**

The schematic of a slightly different type of transistor ignition system is shown in Fig. 13. This type is available in certain models of the Pontiac Tempest, and features a specially designed distributor, a control unit (ignition pulse amplifier), and a special coil. The other units in the system are standard items as used with conventional ignition systems.

The external appearance of the distributor resembles a standard unit, but the internal construction, as shown in Fig. 14, is quite

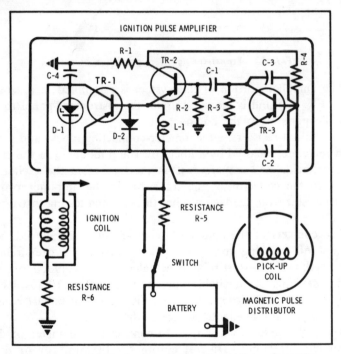

Fig. 13. Schematic of the Pontiac Tempest *transistor* ignition system.

different. An iron timer core and a steel pole piece are used instead of breaker points. These two parts have the same number of projections, or teeth, as there are engine cylinders. The timer core

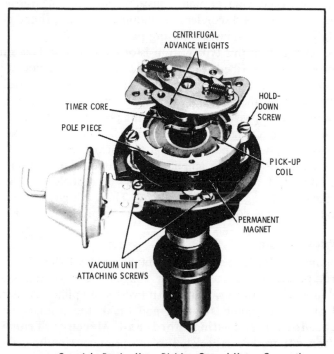

Fig. 14. Internal view of a Pontiac Tempest distributor used with a transistorized ignition system.

rotates inside a magnetic pickup assembly which replaces the conventional breaker plate, breaker points, and condenser.

The magnetic pickup assembly is mounted over the main bearing of the distributor housing, and can be rotated by the vacuum control unit to provide vacuum advance. The timer core can be rotated about the distributor shaft by centrifugal advance weights to provide centrifugal advance.

The electronic control unit consists primarily of transistors, resistors, diodes, and condensers mounted on a printed-circuit board. This unit contains no moving parts.

The operation of this type of transistor ignition system is similar to the one just described, except for the distributor action. In the previous system, breaker points in the distributor control the amplifier unit. In the Tempest system, however, the teeth or vanes on the timer core pass by the teeth on the pole piece. At the instant of their passing, a magnetic path is established between them, causing a voltage pulse to be induced in the pickup coil. This voltage pulse causes TR-3 in the amplifier to conduct. This action turns TR-2 and TR-1 off, which interrupts the current flowing through the primary winding of the ignition coil. Thus, a high-voltage surge is produced in the coil secondary to fire the proper spark plug.

Troubleshooting

Finding trouble in a transistor ignition system follows the same general procedures as used for a conventional ignition system. Keep in mind, however, that the transistor amplifier is used instead of breaker points to make and break the primary circuit.

Procedure for Testing Ford and Mercury Transistor Ignition—If trouble is isolated to the primary circuit, make the following tests to locate the defective item. **Do not use any other procedure or short cut, nor connect test equipment in any other manner than described. To do so may seriously damage the transistor ignition system.**

Remove the cover from the ballast-resistor block and **disconnect the cold-start relay.** Connect a dwell meter to the tachometer block. Connect the red lead to the red terminal and the black lead to the black terminal. Turn the ignition switch on, and observe the dwell-meter reading.

A dwell reading of 0° indicates:

1. Breaker points are dirty or are not closing.

A dwell reading between 0° and 45° indicates:

1. The amplifier and primary circuit are both functioning as they should.
2. The troubles may be in the secondary circuit.

A dwell reading of 45° indicates:

1. No power from the ignition switch.
2. Breaker points are closed and are not opening.
3. Defective amplifier assembly.

To determine which of the three listed items is causing the trouble, use the following procedure:

Disconnect the high-tension lead to the distributor and crank the engine. If the dwell meter reading is 0°, the distributor points are not opening. If 45° dwell is indicated, either the amplifier is defective or there is no power to it from the ignition switch.

Use a voltmeter or test lamp to determine if the transistor in the amplifier is defective. Connect the voltmeter or test lamp between the red-green lead terminal of the ballast resistor and ground. Crank the engine. If a steady voltage is indicated, the trouble is in the amplifier. If no voltage is indicated, there is an open circuit or no power between the ignition switch and the amplifier. This condition could be caused by an open ballast resistor. Replace with a known good resistor and repeat the test.

If the tests indicate a defective amplifier unit, replace with a known good unit and proceed as follows:

Connect the high-tension lead to the distributor. Crank the engine and observe the dwell meter. A reading of less than 45° indicates satisfactory ignition. This means that the amplifier was defective.

If the dwell reading is still 45°, the wiring between the amplifier and coil (through the ballast resistor) is defective. Replace the defective item.

Procedure for Testing Transistor Ignition—If trouble has been isolated to the primary circuit or the ignition system, make the following checks:

Check the pickup coil in the distributor by separating the harness connector and connecting an ohmmeter across the coil. The resistance of the coil should be from 550 to 650 ohms. (Check the car manufacturer's specifications for the particular make and model car being checked to insure the correct resistance value.) If the resistance is infinite, the coil is open. If the reading is below the specified value, the coil is shorted. (The resistance of the coil will increase slightly as the temperature rises.)

The pickup coil may be tested for grounds by connecting the ohmmeter between either coil lead and the distributor housing. The reading should be infinite—if it is not, the coil is grounded.

The centrifugal- and vacuum-advance mechanisms can be checked on a conventional distributor tester (Chapter 5) designed to accommodate this type of distributor.

The primary of the ignition coil can be checked for an open condition by connecting an ammeter across the two primary terminals. An infinite reading indicates an open.

The secondary of the ignition coil can be checked by connecting the ohmmeter from the high-tension center tower to either primary terminal. An infinite reading indicates an open winding.

The repair of the amplifier unit in any transistor ignition system requires special technical knowledge and the use of special instruments. For this reason, repair of these units should be attempted only by qualified persons having the necessary instruments and proper instructions.

IGNITION TIMING

Correct timing of the spark, with relation to the position of the pistons in the cylinders, must be made for efficient engine operation. Most engines have a timing mark or marks (located either on the flywheel or the crankshaft vibration damper) that are used to correctly set the ignition timing. These marks must align properly with a pointer or marks on an adjacent stationary portion of the engine at the instant a spark occurs at the No. 1 spark plug. Fig. 15 shows the timing marks on a typical automobile.

The proper alignment of the timing marks is determined by the gap setting of the breaker points, and the time at which the cam lobes open the breaker points. The gap setting can be adjusted by means of a feeler gauge or a dwell meter, and the opening time can be adjusted by rotating the distributor housing.

Two common methods of setting ignition timing are the test-light method and the timing-light method. With the test-light method, a low-voltage light is connected across the breaker points. The engine is then cranked, with the ignition switch on, until the breaker points just begin to open as the No. 1 piston is in the firing position (both intake and exhaust valves closed and piston near the top of the cylinder). The timing marks should align just as the test light comes on (indicating breaker-point opening).

The second timing method consists of using a timing light connected to the No. 1 spark-plug terminal. The light will flash each time the No. 1 spark plug fires, so that if the light is directed at the flywheel or vibration-damper markings, they will appear to stand still. With this method, the engine is running at idle speed (usually 400 to 500 rpm). Fig. 16 shows a timing light being used on a typical engine.

With either method, the distributor is loosened in its mounting and turned one way or the other until the correct alignment of the timing marks, as specified by the manufacturer, is accomplished.

If the distributor has a vacuum-advance mechanism, it must be disabled before setting the ignition timing with a timing light. This is done by removing the vacuum line from the vacuum-advance unit.

Courtesy Buick Motor Div., General Motors Corp.

Fig. 15. Ignition timing mark and indicator.

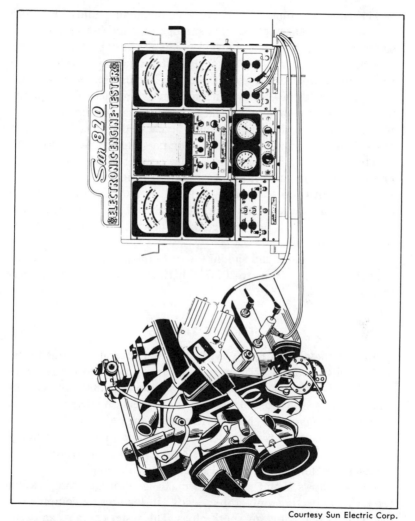

Courtesy Sun Electric Corp.

Fig. 16. A timing light used for setting the ignition timing.

The breaker points should be examined and adjusted before the final timing takes place. If a smudge line appears on the point support and breaker plate, burned points are very probable. Points that have been in service for several thousand miles will have a rough surface, but this does not necessarily mean the points should be replaced with new ones. The roughness on each of the points matches and thus maintains a large contact area. If dirt or scale is present, however, the points should be cleaned with a few strokes of a clean, fine-cut, contact file. Do not attempt to remove all roughness nor try to dress the points down smooth. **Never use emery cloth or sandpaper to clean the points.**

If the points are excessively burned or pitted, they should be replaced. The cause of this condition should be found and corrected. If the cause is not corrected, the new points will also pit and burn in a short time.

The breaker-point gap should be set to the manufacturer's specifications (usually .016″ to .020″) before the final timing adjustments are made.

ENGINE TESTERS

Special engine testers are available from several manufacturers. These units make possible more rapid trouble diagnosis than with the methods previously described. In addition, greater precision of adjustment is also possible which is of great importance in the later model high-speed, high-performance engines.

Most of these units test and make possible precise adjustment on the ignition and carburetion systems, as well as indicating other troubles that hinder the overall efficiency of the engine.

Fig. 17 shows a unit which can make ignition and compression tests by connecting only three leads. It features a compression test without removing any spark plugs. This tester contains an oscil-

Fig. 17. The Dynavision Model 1000 engine analyzer.

Courtesy Marquette Corp.

loscope for viewing the high-voltage secondary patterns of the individual cylinders to permit rapid trouble diagnosis. One roll chart shows the patterns for a properly performing engine; a second roll chart contains up-to-date engine specifications for domestic automobiles.

Another typical engine tester is shown in Fig. 18. This unit also contains an oscilloscope for diagnosing trouble in the ignition system. Tests on the electrical and ignition systems, timing and advance, and cylinder efficiency are quickly, accurately, and easily made with testers of this type.

Many smaller testers are available to perform checks on only certain systems in the automobile. For example, Fig. 19 shows a unit for checking dwell, primary voltages, and engine speeds. This instrument is transistorized, making possible greater accuracy in checking dwell on some of the modern ignition systems.

Another example of a smaller tester is the unit in Fig. 20. This instrument can be used to test the entire ignition system, including the mechanical condition of the distributor. Besides ignition tests, it can also be used to measure the generator voltage and cranking current.

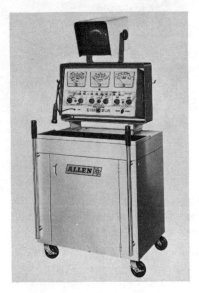

Fig. 18. The Allen-tronic Model PB-881 engine analyzer.

Courtesy Allen Electric and Equipment Co.

IGNITION TESTING WITH A TYPICAL ENGINE TESTER

Testing and adjusting the ignition system of a modern automobile can be made with greater accuracy and speed by using one of the many engine testers now available. In addition to checking the

Fig. 19. The Allen-tronic Model 27-83 engine analyzer.

ignition system, these testers are designed to check other functions of the automobile. These tests will be outlined in other chapters.

The final choice of which tester to purchase is left to the discretion of the user. It will be found that each make has features that may not be found in others. All, however, should perform satisfactorily.

The ignition-system tests described in this section are made with the *Sun 820* engine tester shown in Fig. 21, and are generally representative of the tests that can be made with similar testers of different manufacture.

The Volt-Dwell unit of the *Sun 820* engine tester makes possible both running and static tests on the ignition system and its com-

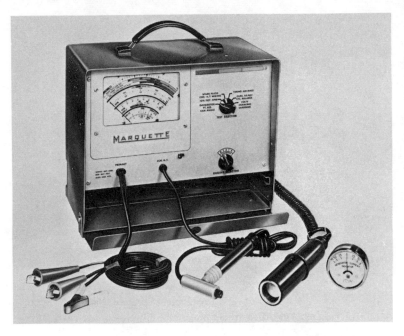

Fig. 20. The Dyna-Tune Model T-200S engine analyzer.

ponents. Before making any of the following tests, the unit must be calibrated according to the procedure outlined in the instruction manual.

Distributor Resistance Test

1. Observe the proper polarity and connect one of the DWELL-COND test leads to the distributor primary lead at the ignition-coil terminal. Connect the other test lead to ground. See Fig. 22.

Fig. 21. The Sun 820 engine tester.

Courtesy Sun Electric Corp.

2. With the engine stopped, but the ignition switch on, observe the dwell meter. If the reading is zero, jog the engine with the starter until the breaker points in the distributor are in the closed position.

3. If the dwell-meter pointer is within the black-bar range, the resistance of the distributor is within normal tolerance.

4. If the pointer is not within the black-bar range, high resistance is indicated in:

   (a) The distributor internal connections.
   (b) The distributor external connections.
   (c) The breaker points.
   (d) The distributor mounting.

To locate the point of high resistance, trace the primary circuit by moving the tester lead step by step through the distributor toward ground.

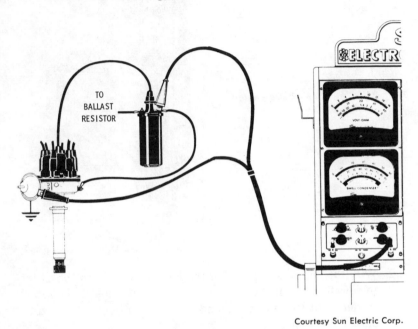

Courtesy Sun Electric Corp.

Fig. 22. Connections for a distributor resistance test.

Dwell Time

1. Set the DWELL selector switch to correspond to the number of cylinders in the engine under test.
2. Connect the Trigger Pickup unit in the circuit of the No. 1 spark plug in the firing order.
3. Turn the CYCLES selector switch to the 4 position (for a 4-cylinder engine).

4. Select the lowest rpm setting that will include the test speed to be used.
5. Start the engine and let it reach its specified idle speed (usually around 500 rpm). Read the dwell time on the 0-60° scale for 6- and 8-cylinder engines and on the 0-90° scale for 4-cylinder engines.
6. If the dwell time is within the tolerance specified by the automobile manufacturer, this indicates that the ignition breaker points are operating normally and have the correct gap setting.
7. If the dwell time is not within specifications, the possible cause of trouble is:

   (a) Incorrect breaker-point gap setting.
   (b) Wrong point assembly.
   (c) Point rubbing block defective.
   (d) Point rubbing block not properly aligned.
   (e) Worn distributor cam.

Dwell Variation

1. Measure and note the dwell time at idle speed.
2. Set the rpm selector switch of the TACH-COMB unit to 5000 rpm, and increase the engine speed to 1500 rpm. Note the dwell reading. Slowly reduce the engine speed to idle while observing the dwell meter. The dwell time should not change more than 3° on most automobiles. If the change is more than 3°, consult the manufacturer's specifications before condemning the distributor.
3. If the dwell variation is within specifications, the distributor is in good mechanical condition.
4. If the dwell variation exceeds the manufacturer's specified limits, the possible trouble is:

(a) Worn distributor shaft.
(b) Loose distributor shaft.
(c) Worn shaft bushing.
(d) Worn breaker plate.

Primary Circuit Test (conventional ignition system only)

1. Turn the selector switch marked VOLT-OHM to the 4-volt position.
2. Observe the proper polarity and connect the voltmeter leads from A to B (Fig. 23) for coils equipped with an external ballast resistor. For coils not equipped with a ballast resistor, connect the voltmeter from A to C.
3. Jumper the primary terminal of the distributor to ground, as shown in Fig. 23. (This jumper makes it unnecessary to spot the engine so that the breaker points are closed. This jumper also eliminates any false readings that might result from defective breaker points, wiring, and connections in the distributor.)
4. Make sure that all the automobile lights and accessories are turned off.
5. Turn the ignition switch on, and observe the voltmeter. Generally, the reading should not be more than 0.5 volt.
6. Test the ignition switch by turning it off and on several times. The voltmeter should read the same each time the switch is turned on.
7. Test all wires for tightness. Move them about and note any change in the meter reading.
8. If the meter reads within specifications, the connections, wiring, and ignition-switch contacts are in satisfactory condition.
9. If the voltmeter exceeds the specified voltage drop, the possible trouble is:

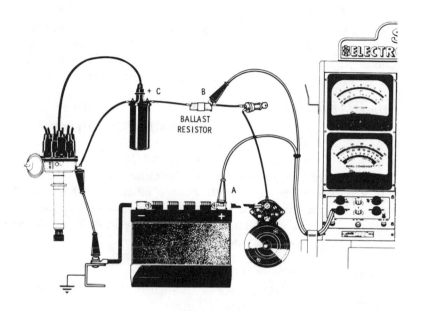

Courtesy Sun Electric Corp.

Fig. 23. Connections necessary to make tests on the primary circuit of the ignition system.

(a) Loose or corroded connections.
(b) Undersize or faulty wiring.
(c) Damaged or worn ignition-switch contacts.

The point of trouble can be isolated by placing the test leads across each connection and wire, in turn. The reading across each connection should be ZERO. The reading across any wire should be in proportion to its length as compared to the length and allowable voltage drop of the entire circuit.

147

Ignition-Coil Resistance Test

If a resistance test is to be made of the coil while it is mounted in the vehicle, the coil must be electrically isolated from the automobile electrical system by disconnecting the coil primary leads and removing the secondary lead from the coil tower.

Primary Resistance Test

1. Turn the VOLT-OHM selector switch to the ×1 position.
2. Connect the test leads together.
3. Adjust the OHM-COIL CALIBRATOR until the pointer of the meter reads zero on the ohmmeter scale.
4. Disconnect the test leads from each other and connect them to the coil primary, one to each terminal, as shown in Fig. 24.
5. Observe the meter reading and compare it with the manufacturer's specifications.

Secondary Resistance Test

1. Set the VOLT-OHM selector switch in the ×1000 position.
2. Calibrate the ohmmeter.
3. Install the Pattern Pickup adapter in the coil tower.
4. Connect one test lead to either of the primary terminals on the coil, and the other test lead to the end of the Pattern Pickup adapter, as shown in Fig. 24.
5. Observe the meter reading and compare it with the manufacturer's specifications.
   NOTE: To test the coil completely, the Ignition Coil Test must also be made.

Coil Primary Ground Test

1. Connect one of the VOLT-OHM test leads to either of the coil primary terminals, and the other test lead to the coil case.

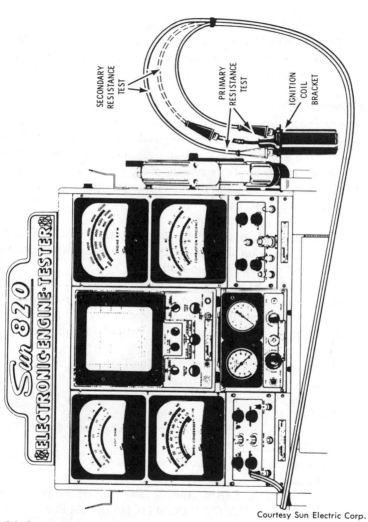

SECONDARY RESISTANCE TEST

PRIMARY RESISTANCE TEST

IGNITION COIL BRACKET

Courtesy Sun Electric Corp.

Fig. 24. Connections necessary for measuring the resistance of the ignition-coil windings.

2. Turn the VOLT-OHM selector switch to the ×1000 position.

3. There should be no reading indicated on the meter. Any meter deflection indicates a grounded primary winding.

Ignition-Coil Test

The Volt-Dwell unit is used in conjunction with the *Sun Scope* to make the ignition-coil test. The leads of the Volt-Dwell unit are connected to the ignition coil and the test results are observed on the Ignition Scope. Tests can be made on 6-, 12- and 24-volt coils. Only one test is made to detect shorts, opens, grounds, and insulation breakdown. Follow this procedure:

1. Place the ignition coil in the coil holder. (NOTE: The coil may be tested on the vehicle by removing both the primary leads and the high-tension lead.)

2. Connect the VOLT-OHM-COIL test leads to the primary terminals of the ignition coil. (See Fig. 25.) Observe polarity.

3. Insert the Pattern Pickup into the secondary coil tower.

4. Connect the ground lead of the Pattern Pickup unit to the vehicle ground.

5. Rotate the OHM-COIL CALIBRATOR fully counterclockwise.

6. Plug the Scope Trigger Pickup jack into the COIL-TEST TRIGGER plug.

7. Turn the test selector knob on the scope unit to the TEST SWEEP position.

8. Turn the frequency selector switch to the 50-500 position.

9. Turn the FINE selector knob fully counterclockwise.

10. Turn the SYNC LOCK control fully counterclockwise.

11. Turn the HORIZONTAL POSITION knob set line to the dot.

12. Turn the PATTERN LENGTH knob set line to the dot.

13. Turn the BRIGHTNESS CONTROL knob fully clockwise.

14. Adjust the VERT POSITION control until the pattern sweep aligns with the zero line.
15. Adjust the FOCUS control to give the sharpest image.
16. Adjust the SCALE ILLUM control to the desired brightness.
17. Turn the COMP VERT SPACING control fully clockwise.
18. Turn the Secondary Vertical Size control to the 40KV position.
19. Turn the Primary Vertical Size control to the 400V position.
20. Turn the Scope selector switch to the SECONDARY DISPLAY position.

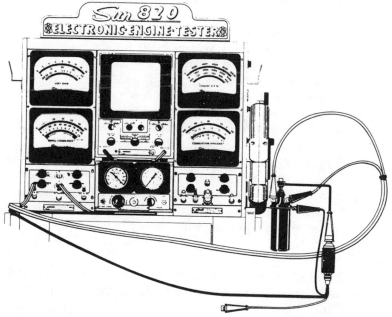

Courtesy Sun Electric Corp.

Fig. 25. Connections for testing the ignition coil.

21. Turn the COIL TEST selector switch to STD COIL for conventional ignition coils, or to TRANS COIL for transistor ignition coils.
22. Adjust the PATTERN LENGTH control until a single, but complete, waveform is expanded across the screen.
23. Rotate the OHM-COIL calibrator clockwise until the highest portion of the waveform reaches 20KV. *Do not exceed 25 KV unless specified by the manufacturer, otherwise the coil may be damaged.*

    NOTE: If the first oscillation of the waveform points down, reverse the test leads to the primary of the ignition coil.
24. Observe the waveform and note the oscillations.
25. If the height of the waveform is 20 KV or more, and the oscillations are similar to those in Fig. 26A, the ignition coil is satisfactory.
26. If the height of the waveform is less than 20KV and few oscillations are seen (Fig. 26B), the ignition coil is defective due to a shorted primary or secondary winding, or due to the breakdown of the internal insulation.
27. If the height of the waveform is 20KV or more, but the pattern is unstable or jittery (Fig. 26C), the ignition coil is defective due to breakdown of the internal insulation.
28. If the waveform is a straight line (Fig. 26D), the ignition coil has an open primary winding.

Condenser Tests

The condenser must have three important characteristics in order to function properly and to assure good ignition. These characteristics are:

1. Minimum series resistance.

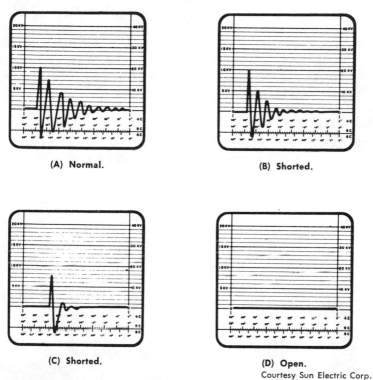

(A) Normal.

(B) Shorted.

(C) Shorted.

(D) Open.
Courtesy Sun Electric Corp.

Fig. 26. Scope patterns of an ignition coil test.

2. Correct capacity.
3. Minimum insulation leakage.

The tests of these condenser characteristics are made with the Tach-Dwell unit which must first be calibrated according to the instructions in the operations manual.

153

NOTE: The ignition condenser can be tested in or out of the vehicle. If the condenser is to be tested while it is in the vehicle, it must be electrically isolated from the rest of the ignition system. To do this, disconnect the wire from the primary terminal of the distributor, and block the breaker points open by placing a piece of fiber between the rubbing block and cam, as shown in Fig. 27.

Condenser Resistance Test

1. Connect one of the DWELL-COND test leads to the primary terminal of the distributor, and the other test lead to ground

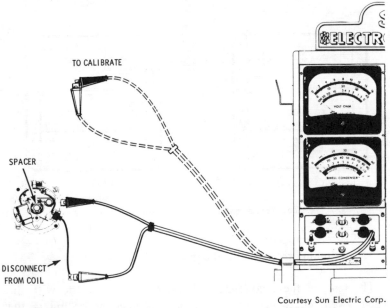

Courtesy Sun Electric Corp.

Fig. 27. Connections of the Tach-Dwell unit test leads to calibrate the unit (dotted lines) and for making condenser tests.

on the distributor housing. If the condenser is removed from the distributor, connect one test lead to the outer case of the condenser and the other test lead to the pigtail.

2. With the COND TEST switch in the SERIES RES position, the meter should read in the Black Bar portion of the meter scale.

3. Move the condenser pigtail. If a deflection of the meter is noted, the pigtail is making poor internal connection and the condenser should be replaced.

4. If the reading is outside the Black Bar, move the test lead from the distributor housing to the body of the condenser. If the reading improves, the condenser is not properly grounded to the distributor housing.

Leakage Test

1. Turn the COND TEST switch to the LEAKAGE position.

2. The meter should now read in the Black Bar portion at the left end of the scale.

3. If the meter reads outside the Black Bar portion, the condenser insulation is leaking and the condenser should be replaced.

Capacity Test

1. Turn the COND TEST switch to the CAP position.

2. Read the RED scale of the meter (0 to 1.0) for the capacity of the condenser in microfarads.

3. If the reading does not indicate a capacity within the tolerances specified by the manufacturer, the condenser should be replaced.

IMPORTANT: If the condenser does not meet the specifications while mounted in the distributor, remove the condenser and retest it. If the condenser tests "bad" in the distributor, but tests "good" when removed, a short or ground in the primary circuit of the distributor is indicated. Suspect the insulation of the distributor primary terminal and the internal circuit of the distributor.

IGNITION SCOPES

An oscilloscope provides a convenient means of observing the performance of an ignition system. A scope does this by displaying an easily interpreted graph-like picture of all phases of the ignition cycle at the instant at which they occur in an operating engine. The displayed picture permits the observer actually to see in detail the results of the many factors which affect the performance of the ignition system. These factors include:

1. Firing-voltage requirements.
2. Spark duration.
3. Coil and condenser action.
4. Breaker-point action.
5. Maximum voltage output of the ignition system.

The following tests and resultant scope patterns are listed for your general guidance only. Specific instructions are given in the instructions manual for the particular engine analyzer being used. The scope patterns shown here are those expected to be seen on the scope screen of the *Sun 820* engine tester.

To interpret the test results obtained with an ignition scope, it is important that the basic scope pattern be thoroughly understood. Study Fig. 28 carefully.

The display visible on a scope screen is usually referred to as a *pattern* or *waveform*. In studying scope patterns, consider them to be graphs of voltage with respect to time. The vertical dis-

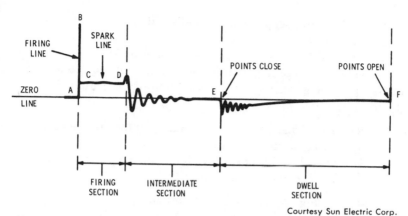

Courtesy Sun Electric Corp.

Fig. 28. Basic secondary waveform obtained at the high-tension tower of the ignition coil.

placement of the scope trace from the zero line (either up or down depending on polarity) represents voltage at any instant along the zero line.

Ignition scopes are designed to display a waveform which is obtained at the high-tension tower of the ignition coil. This secondary waveform contains the most information concerning overall ignition-system operation. Because of the high voltages present in the secondary circuit of the ignition system, the scope screen is calibrated in kilovolts (KV) to permit accurate voltage measurements of the secondary patterns. Each vertical division on the left side of the *Sun 820* scope screen, for example, represents 1 kilovolt (1000 volts); each vertical division on the right represents 2 kilovolts (2000 volts).

Secondary Waveform Interpretation

Each part of the waveform represent a specific phase of operation of the ignition system. For purposes of explanation and better

understanding, the scope pattern is divided into three sections—
Firing, *Intermediate*, and *Dwell*.

The Firing Section—This part of the waveform is called the
firing section because it is during this period that the actual firing
of the spark plug takes place. This portion of the pattern is com-
posed of only two lines:

>*The Firing Line*, a vertical line indicating the voltage required
>to overcome the plug and rotor gaps.
>*The Spark Line*, a horizontal line indicating the voltage re-
>quired to maintain the spark.

Point *A* in Fig. 28 represents the instant at which the breaker
points have separated. The resultant high voltage is indicated by
the vertical rise from *A* to *B*. The height at point *B* shows the
voltage required to fire the plug and rotor gap.

Once the plug fires, there is a noticeable drop in secondary
voltage to point *C*. As the spark continues across the gaps, the
spark voltage remains at a fairly constant lower value until the
spark extinguishes at point *D*.

The Intermediate Section—This part of the waveform immediately follows the firing section, and is seen as a number of
gradually diminishing oscillations which disappear, or nearly so,
by the time the dwell section begins. Starting at point *D*, the remaining coil energy dissipates itself as an oscillating current which
gradually dies out as it approaches point *E*. The oscillations result from the combined effect of the coil and condenser in dissipat-
ing this energy.

The Dwell Section—This part of the waveform represents the
period in the ignition cycle during which the breaker points are
closed. The dwell section starts at point *E* when the breaker points
close. This closure causes a short, downward line followed by a
series of small, rapidly diminishing oscillations. The dwell section

continues until the breaker points open at the beginning of the next waveform (point *F*).

Primary Waveform Interpretation

Since any voltage in the primary circuit of the ignition system will be reflected in the secondary, it is seldom necessary to view the primary pattern for general ignition testing. Most ignition scopes, however, have provisions for viewing the primary waveform when necessary.

Although the primary and secondary patterns resemble each other, it should be noted that the voltage values represented in the primary patterns are much lower than those represented in the secondary patterns. For example, the scales on the Sun 820 ignition scope indicate a maximum primary voltage of either 40 or 400 volts instead of 20,000 or 40,000 volts indicated for secondary patterns.

The primary pattern (Fig. 29) has the same basic sections as the secondary pattern.

The Firing Section—This section displays the series of rapid oscillations occurring in the primary circuit during the time the spark plug is firing. Point *A* in Fig. 29 represents the instant at which the breaker points open.

The vertical rise from *A* to *B*, and the diminishing oscillations which follow, represent the initial and repeated charge and discharge of the condenser and the induced voltage surges in the primary circuit while the spark plug is firing. As the spark jumps the gap and energy is being drained from the coil, the size of these oscillations will decrease until the spark ends (point *C*).

The Intermediate Section—The intermediate section contains a series of gradually diminishing oscillations which disappear, or nearly so, by the time the breaker points close. Beginning with point *C*, the energy remaining in the coil will dissipate itself as an oscillating current which gradually dies out as it approaches point *D*.

The Dwell Section—The breaker points close and cause a faint downward line from point *D* to point *E*. The dwell section is represented by the horizontal line extending from point *E* to point *F*. It is during the dwell section that the breaker points remain closed.

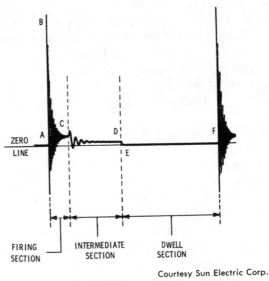

Courtesy Sun Electric Corp.

Fig. 29. Basic primary waveform.

Scope Test Indications

The following indications illustrate only the patterns for those troubles most frequently encountered. The engine speed in each case is 1200 rpm (except where noted otherwise) and the scope display is of the secondary circuits. It must be realized that troubles and defects will vary in severity, which will determine how prominently the trouble will be disclosed by the scope display. It is also true that occasionally two or more troubles may exist at the same time and, in some instances, these troubles may have opposite effects on the scope patterns.

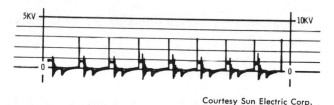

Fig. 30. Normal secondary ignition display for a typical 8-cylinder engine.

A normal display for an 8-cylinder engine is shown in Fig. 30. The waveform as each spark plug fires is displayed, one after the other, to allow comparison between them. Fig. 31 shows the normal display of the coil secondary output.

Fig. 31. Normal ignition coil output display.

Coil Output Voltage at Cranking Speed—The waveform height at the high-tension tower of the ignition coil (with the high-tension lead disconnected) should exceed 20KV. If it does not, the cause may be:

1. A battery not fully charged.
2. A defective ignition circuit.
3. Failure of the ballast-resistor bypass circuit.
4. Insufficient dwell.
5. Excessive distributor resistance.
6. Defective coil or condenser.

If no oscillations are observed following the initial voltage rise, the cause may be:

1. Defective coil or condenser.

Secondary Polarity—If the scope is inverted, as in Fig. 32, the cause may be:

1. Reversed battery polarity.
2. Reversed coil primary connections.
3. An incorrect coil for the vehicle.

Required Firing Voltage—The required firing voltage is the amount of voltage necessary to overcome the rotor and spark-plug gaps to establish a spark across the electrodes of the spark plugs. The condition of the spark plugs and/or secondary circuit, the

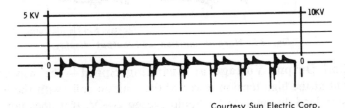

Courtesy Sun Electric Corp.

Fig. 32. Inverted pattern caused by incorrect polarity.

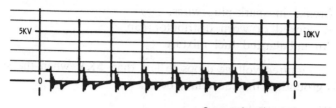

Fig. 33. Firing voltage uniform but high.

temperature, fuel mixture, and amount of compression can affect the amount of firing voltage required. The normal height of the firing lines should be from 5 to 10KV, and uniform.

If the firing lines are uniform but are higher than normal, as in Fig. 33, the cause may be:

1. Worn spark plugs.
2. Too large a rotor gap.
3. A break in the high-tension coil wire.
4. Late ignition timing.
5. A lean fuel mixture.

If the firing lines are uneven, as in Fig. 34, the cause may be:

1. Worn spark plugs.

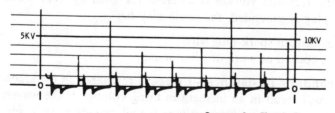

Fig. 34. Uneven firing voltages.

163

2. Breaks in spark-plug wires.
3. A cocked or worn distributor cap.
4. An unbalanced fuel mixture.

If the required voltage drops to less than 5KV when the spark plug is grounded, the cause may be:

1. Worn spark plugs.
2. An engine condition affecting spark-plug operation.

If the required voltage on all cylinders exceeds 5KV when the individual spark plugs are grounded, the cause may be:

1. A broken high-tension coil wire.
2. A wide rotor gap.

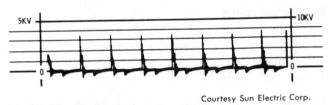

Fig. 35. High secondary resistance affecting all cylinders.

If the required voltage is different for each cylinder when the spark plug is grounded, the cause may be:

1. A broken spark-plug wire.
2. A cocked or worn distributor cap.

Secondary Resistance—Excessive resistance in the secondary circuit will result in an increase in firing voltage. If the waveforms indicate an excessive firing voltage for all cylinders, as in Fig. 35, the cause may be excessive resistance in the:

1. Coil tower.
2. Coil high-tension wire.
3. Rotor.
4. Distributor-cap towers.
5. Radio suppressor.

If the scope display indicates a high firing voltage on one or more cylinders, but not all (Fig. 36), the cause may be excessive resistance in:

1. Distributor cap tower(s).
2. Spark-plug wire(s).
3. Spark plug (fouled).

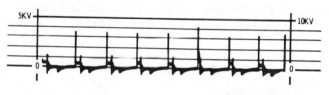

Courtesy Sun Electric Corp.

Fig. 36. High resistance in the secondary circuit affecting one or more cylinders, but not all.

If the spark line appears normal after grounding the spark plug, the cause may be a defective spark plug.

If the spark line on all cylinders is still high after grounding the spark plugs (one at a time), the cause may be defective:

1. Coil tower.
2. Coil high-tension wire.
3. Distributor-cap center tower.
4. Rotor.

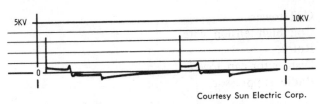

Fig. 37. Waveform indicating a defective ignition coil or condenser.

If the spark line is still high on only one or more of the cylinders after the spark plugs are grounded (one at a time), the cause may be defective:

1. Distributor cap towers.
2. Individual spark-plug wires.

Coil and Condenser—If oscillations are not present in the intermediate sections of the waveforms (Fig. 37), the cause may be:

1. Short in the ignition coil.
2. Leaky condenser.

Breaker-Point Condition and Action—Bouncing of the breaker points will cause a pattern similar to the one shown in Fig. 38. Weak tension in the breaker-point spring will result in a

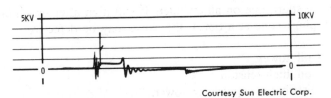

Fig. 38. Scope display showing breaker-point bounce.

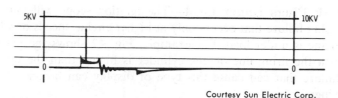

Courtesy Sun Electric Corp.

Fig. 39. Scope display showing effect of weak breaker-point spring tension.

pattern similar to that in Fig. 39. Dirty or burned points will produce a pattern somewhat like the one in Fig. 40.

Secondary Insulation—If the lower excursions of the waveforms of all cylinders are short, intermittent, or absent, such as in Fig. 41, the cause may be insulation leakage in:

1. Distributor cap.
2. Coil tower.
3. High-tension coil wire.
4. Rotor.

If the lower portions of the waveforms are missing from one or more cylinders, but not all, the cause may be insulation leakage in:

1. Distributor cap.
2. Spark-plug wires to the affected cylinders.

Courtesy Sun Electric Corp.

Fig. 40. Abnormal pattern caused by burned or dirty breaker points.

167

Spark Plugs Under Load—The ignition scope will indicate spark-plug failure that occurs only at higher engine speeds or when the engine is under load. For example, Fig. 42 shows the pattern in which the firing line of one cylinder is higher than the others. The failure that can cause this type of display can be one of the following:

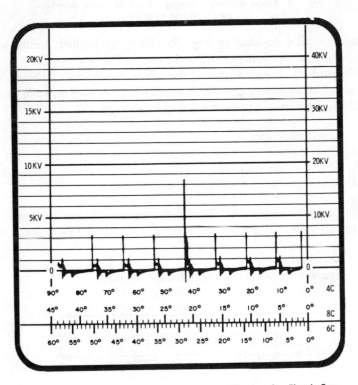

Courtesy Sun Electric Corp.

Fig. 41. The missing lower portions of the waveforms indicate trouble in the secondary insulation.

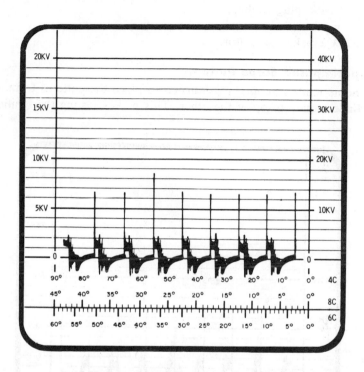

Fig. 42. Scope pattern showing the effect of wide plug gap, open plug resistor, or bad electrodes.

1. A wide plug gap.
2. An open spark-plug resistor.
3. Bad spark-plug electrodes.

If the display shows one or more of the firing lines to be shorter than the others, as in Fig. 43, the cause may be due to:

169

1. Spark plug fouling.
2. Flashover.
3. A cracked insulator.

Superimposed Scope Patterns

Some ignition scopes are designed to place the patterns from all cylinders one on top of the other. This makes testing the ignition

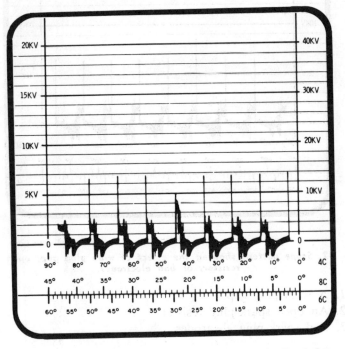

Fig. 43. Scope pattern showing the effect of a fouled spark plug, flash-over, or a cracked insulator.

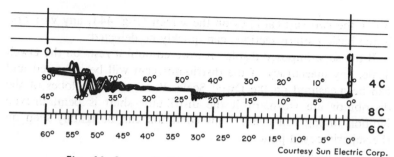

Courtesy Sun Electric Corp.

Fig. 44. Scope display of superimposed patterns.

system for uniformity a much simpler task. By expanding the display horizontally until the waveforms completely fill the span be-

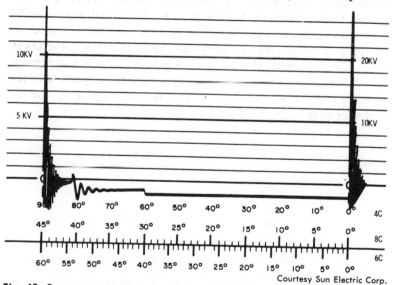

Courtesy Sun Electric Corp.

Fig. 45. Scope pattern showing dwell angle measurement. The dwell angle is read directly on the proper scale, and is where the point-close signal appears. The dwell angle shown here would be 40° for a 6-cylinder engine.

171

tween the two vertical lines on the screen (Fig. 44), any variation in the basic pattern sections can quickly be detected.

If the superimposed display is lowered until it rests on the Dwell Scale, any inaccuracy of the distributor cam will be indicated and can be measured on the Dwell Scale. If one or more lobes of the distributor are worn, or if the distributor shaft is bent, uneven ignition timing will result. This condition can be readily seen on the superimposed patterns.

Dwell Tests

Dwell angle can be accurately measured by using the Dwell Scale near the bottom of the screen. One cylinder pattern is expanded to fill the space between the vertical lines on the scale, and then lowered until it rests on the dwell scale. The dwell angle can be measured directly on the scale. The primary waveform is used for this test to provide greater clarity. As shown in Fig. 45, the Dwell Scale actually consists of three sets of graduations—the upper one for 4-cylinder engines, the second for 8-cylinder engines, and the third for 6-cylinder engines. If the pattern shown is for an 8-cylinder engine, the dwell angle is 30°.

CHAPTER 7

Starters and Generators

The starter and generator on the modern automobile have much in common. Their construction is similar and both utilize the same electrical principles. However, their operation is opposite. The starter converts electrical energy into mechanical motion; the generator converts mechanical motion into electrical energy.

STARTERS

The starter used to crank the engine on all modern automobiles is actually a direct-current (DC) motor capable of developing a high torque (twisting force). The electric current supplied to the starter is furnished by the storage battery.

A cross section of a typical starting motor is shown in Fig. 1. The starter cranks the engine through a pinion gear which is attached to the armature shaft. This pinion gear is brought into mesh with teeth on the rim of the engine flywheel through the action of an overrunning clutch (Fig. 2). With this arrangement, the pinion gear is moved into mesh by a lever actuated by the starter solenoid when the starter button or ignition switch is in the start position. As soon as the engine starts, the speed of the flywheel becomes greater

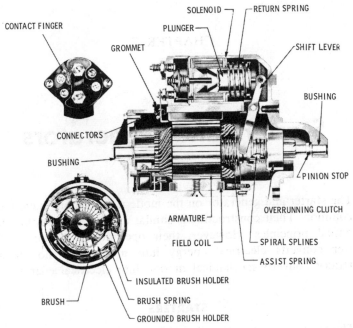

CONTACT FINGER

SOLENOID

RETURN SPRING

PLUNGER

GROMMET

SHIFT LEVER

BUSHING

CONNECTORS

BUSHING

PINION STOP

ARMATURE

OVERRUNNING CLUTCH

FIELD COIL

SPIRAL SPLINES

ASSIST SPRING

INSULATED BRUSH HOLDER

BRUSH

BRUSH SPRING

GROUNDED BRUSH HOLDER

Fig. 1. Starting motor details.

than the speed of the pinion gear, causing the pinion to be pulled out of mesh with the flywheel gear through the action of spiral splines on the armature shaft. The pinion gear will also be pulled out of mesh by the solenoid shift lever whenever the solenoid is de-energized, whether the engine has started or not.

Starter Circuit Tests

Whenever the starter motor turns over slowly, or not at all, or the solenoid fails to engage the starter with the flywheel, excessive resistance in the starter circuit may be the cause.

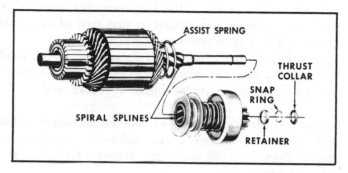

Fig. 2. Armature and overrunning clutch assembly.

The following checks for excessive resistance can be performed with the starter motor on the car.

1. Test the battery and charge it if necessary.

> **CAUTION: To prevent the engine from starting during the following tests, either ground or remove the distributor primary lead. Do not operate the starting motor continuously for more than 30 seconds to avoid overheating.**

While cranking the engine:

2. Measure the voltage drop (V-1) between the positive battery post and the battery terminal of the solenoid, in the manner shown in Fig. 3.
3. Measure the voltage drop (V-2) between the battery terminal and motor terminal of the solenoid.
4. Measure the voltage drop (V-3) between the negative battery post and the starter-motor frame.

175

If the voltage drop in any of the last three checks exceeds 0.2 volt, excessive resistance is indicated in that part of the starting circuit being tested. Locate and correct the cause.

Solenoid Tests—If the solenoid fails to pull in, the trouble may be caused by excessive resistance in the solenoid circuit. To check for this condition, crank the engine as before, and:

1. Measure the voltage drop (V-4) between the battery terminal and the switch terminal of the solenoid. A voltage drop greater than 2.5 volts indicates excessive resistance in the solenoid circuit.

If the voltage drop is less than 2.5 volts:

2. Measure the voltage (V-5) between the switch terminal of the solenoid and ground. The solenoid should pull in with 8.0 volts present at this point.

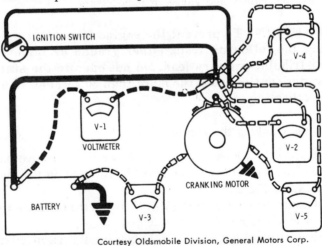

Courtesy Oldsmobile Division, General Motors Corp.

Fig. 3. Starter circuit tests.

If 8.0 volts or more is present and the solenoid does not pull in, remove the starter-motor assembly and check the solenoid. To check the solenoid without removing it from the starter housing, disconnect the strap between the solenoid terminal and the starter.

Complete the following tests as rapidly as possible to prevent overheating the solenoid.
To check the hold-in winding:

1. Connect an ammeter and variable resistance in series with a 12-volt battery and the switch termnial on the solenoid, as shown in Fig. 4.
2. Connect a voltmeter between the switch terminal of the solenoid and ground, as shown.

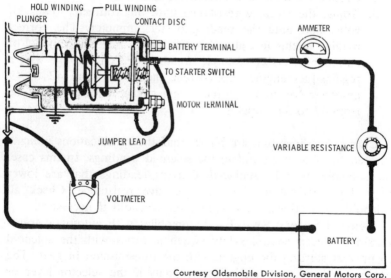

Courtesy Oldsmobile Division, General Motors Corp.
Fig. 4. Testing solenoid windings.

3. Adjust the variable resistance until the voltmeter reads 10 volts, and note the ammeter reading. The correct reading will depend on the make and model of automobile. The service manual should be consulted for the particular automobile under test. For example, the ammeter reading for a 1963 Oldsmobile regular-fuel engine is from 10.5 to 12.5 amperes; for premium-fuel engines the correct reading is 15.5 to 17.5 amperes.

To check both solenoid windings:

1. Connect the voltmeter, ammeter, and variable resistance as in the previous test.
2. Ground the motor terminal of the solenoid.
3. Adjust the variable resistance until the voltmeter reads 10 volts, and note the reading of the ammeter. The correct reading in this test also depends on the make and model of automobile. As an example, for the 1963 Oldsmobile with a regular-fuel engine, the current should be from 42 to 49 amperes; for premium-fuel engines, the reading should be from 47 to 54 amperes.

Current readings that are higher than the specifications indicate shorted turns or a ground in the solenoid windings. In this case, the solenoid must be replaced. Current readings that are lower than the specifications indicate excessive resistance. Check all solenoid connections, then replace the solenoid if necessary.

Neutral Safety Switch—Automobiles with automatic transmissions have a neutral safety switch in series with the solenoid to prevent starting the engine with the transmission in gear. The engine of these cars can be started only if the selector lever or pushbutton is in the neutral or park position.

Bench Test of the Starting Motor

The starter motor on most automobiles must be removed for brush replacement and to correct other troubles that may be present. The procedure for removing the starter varies with different makes and models of automobiles and is included in their service manuals.

Before disassembling the starter motor, remove the cover band and examine the brushes to make sure they are free in their holders. Replace brushes if they are defective or worn beyond their useful limit. Some manufacturers recommend checking the tension of each spring with a pull scale, as shown in Fig. 5. A typical spring tension is from 3 to 3½ lbs. Check the manufacturer's specifications for the exact tension for specific automobiles.

If trouble is still indicated in the starter motor after the brushes have been examined and/or replaced, the unit must be disassembled for further tests. Follow the recommended procedure as outlined in the service manual. This procedure varies for different makes of automobiles.

The following checks should be made on the starter motor after it is removed from the engine.

1. Test the action of the overrunning clutch. The pinion gear should turn freely in the overrunning direction. Check the teeth of the pinion for chips, cracks, and excessive wear. Replace the assembly if necessary. Badly chipped teeth on the pinion gear may indicate chipped teeth on the ring gear. Inspect the ring gear for this condition if the pinion is chipped, and replace if necessary.
2. Check the brush holders to see if they are deformed or bent. Make sure they hold the brushes in the proper position against the commutator. Repair or replace if necessary.

3. Check the fit of the armature shaft in the bushing of the drive housing. The shaft should fit snugly. If the fit is loose, the bushing should be replaced.

Fig. 5. Checking brush spring tension of a starter motor.

4. The overrunning clutch, armature, and field coils should not be cleaned in a degreasing tank or with any grease-dissolving solvents. The clutch mechanism on most starters is permanently lubricated and the solvent will dissolve the grease, leaving the unit without lubrication. The solvent will also damage the insulation on the armature and field coils. It is suggested that all parts, except the clutch, be cleaned in

oleum spirits with a brush. The clutch can be wiped clean with a cloth.

5. Inspect the commutator, and if it is dirty, clean it with No. 00 sandpaper. **Never use emery cloth on the commutator.** If the commutator is worn, pitted or burned, out of round, or has high insulation between the bars, the armature should be placed in a lathe and the commutator cut down.

Fig. 6 shows a tool which can be used for turning down the commutator. To use this instrument, the armature is placed in a vise having soft jaws to prevent damage to the armature laminations. Care must be taken to tighten the vise only enough to keep the armature from turning. The cutting tool

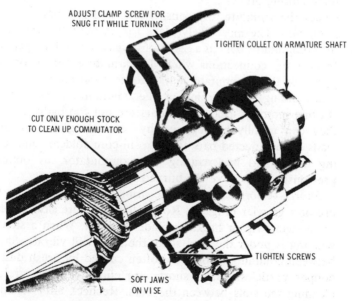

ADJUST CLAMP SCREW FOR
SNUG FIT WHILE TURNING

TIGHTEN COLLET ON ARMATURE SHAFT

CUT ONLY ENOUGH STOCK
TO CLEAN UP COMMUTATOR

TIGHTEN SCREWS

SOFT JAWS
ON VISE

Fig. 6. Turning down the commutator of an armature.

is positioned on the commutator end of the armature shaft as shown in the illustration. The cutter is adjusted to remove only enough stock to clean up the commutator.

After the armature has been turned down, the insulation between the commutator bars may have to be undercut. This can be done with a regular undercutting tool, or with a hacksaw blade if care is taken. The insulation should be undercut approximately 1/32-inch deep and 1/32-inch wide. The slots thus formed should be carefully cleaned out to remove any trace of dirt or copper dust. As a final step in this procedure, the commutator should be lightly sanded with No. 00 sandpaper to remove any burrs left as a result of the undercutting process.

6. Check the armature for opens, shorts, and grounds.

Opens—The most likely place for an open to occur is at the commutator bars as a result of excessive cranking periods. Inspect the connections where the armature conductors are joined to the commutator bars. Loose connections here will cause arcing and burning of the commutator bars as the starting motor is used. If the bars are not too badly burned, they can usually be repaired by resoldering the armature leads in the affected bars (with rosin-core solder), and turning down and undercutting the commutator, as outlined previously, to remove the burned material.

Shorts—Short circuits in the armature are located by the use of a growler (Fig. 7). Rotate the armature slowly, holding a steel strip or hacksaw blade above it. When a shorted winding is under the steel strip, the strip will vibrate. Shorts between commutator bars are often caused by brush dust or copper particles. These shorts are eliminated by carefully cleaning the slots between the bars. Recheck after cleaning, and if the steel strip still vibrates, replace the armature.

Grounds—Grounds in the armature can be detected by means of a 110-volt test lamp and test leads. If the lamp lights when one test prod is placed on a commutator bar and the other test prod is placed on the core or shaft, the

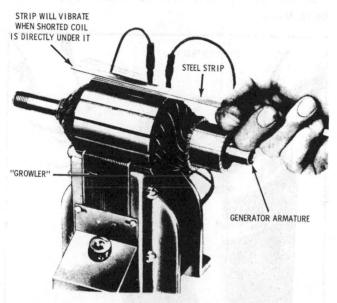

STRIP WILL VIBRATE
WHEN SHORTED COIL
IS DIRECTLY UNDER IT

STEEL STRIP

"GROWLER"

GENERATOR ARMATURE

Fig. 7. Using a growler to test for a short circuit in an armature.

armature is grounded. Grounds are often caused by failure of the insulation brought about by overheating that occurs when the starter motor is used for excessively long cranking periods. Another cause of grounds is an accumulation of brush dust between the commutator bars and the steel commutator ring.

7. The field windings can be checked for an open or a ground as follows:

   Opens—Touch one test-lamp lead to the insulated brush, and the other test lead to the field terminal (Fig. 8). If the lamp does not light, the series field coils are open and should be replaced.

Fig. 8. Testing the field coils for an open.

To check the shunt coil or coils, the ground of each coil should be disconnected. Place the test-lamp leads across the shunt coil to be tested. If the lamp does not light, the coil is open and should be replaced.

Grounds—Disconnect all shunt field coils before making this test. Place one test-lamp lead on the grounded brush or on the case of the starter motor (Fig. 9). Place the other test lead on the connector strap or field terminal. If the lamp lights, a grounded coil is indicated which must be repaired or replaced.

Summary

The following are conditions that may be encountered in the starting motor circuit and the possible causes for such conditions:

1. STARTER FAILS TO OPERATE

Possible Causes:

(a) Weak battery, or dead cell in battery.

(b) Defective ignition switch.

(c) Loose or corroded battery-cable terminals.

(d) Open circuit between the ignition/starter switch and the ignition terminal of the solenoid.

(e) Defective or misadjusted neutral safety switch.

(f) Defective drive unit.

(g) Defective solenoid or solenoid switch.

(h) Defective starting motor.

(i) Armature shaft sheared.

2. STARTER FAILS AND LIGHTS DIM

Possible Causes:

(a) Weak battery, or dead cell in battery.
(b) Loose or corroded battery-cable terminals.
(c) Internal ground in starter-motor windings.
(d) Grounded starter field.
(e) Armature rubbing on pole shoes.

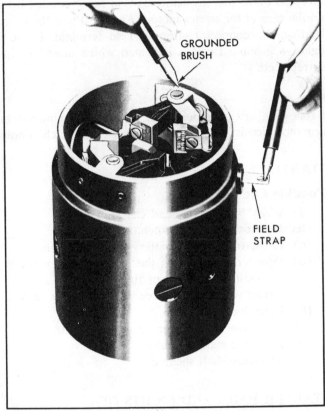

Fig. 9. Testing the field coils for a ground.

3. STARTER TURNS BUT PINION DOES NOT ENGAGE

Possible Causes:
   (a) Broken teeth on flywheel drive gear.
   (b) Armature shaft rusted, dirty, or dry due to lack of lubrication.

4. STARTER PINION LOCKS

Possible Causes:
   (a) Starter mounting bolts loose.
   (b) Armature shaft bent.

GENERATORS

The generating system in the modern automobile consists of three major units—the generator (or alternator for some late model cars), the regulator, and the battery. The generator converts mechanical energy to electrical energy used for ignition, lights, and various accessories. The regulator controls the output of the generator according to the needs imposed upon it. The battery stores electrical power for starting the engine and for operating the various electrical units when the generator is not delivering sufficient output.

A cross-section of a typical generator is shown in Fig. 10. Notice the similarity in construction to the starting motor shown previously. The generator on most automobiles is shunt wound (armature and field connected in parallel), has two brushes, and has a maximum output of approximately 35 amperes. Heavy-duty generators are available on cars having air conditioning or other accessories that require more power than the standard generator can provide.

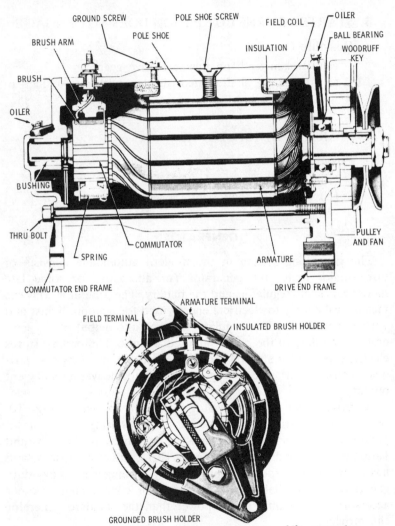

GROUND SCREW

POLE SHOE SCREW

FIELD COIL

OILER

BRUSH ARM

POLE SHOE

INSULATION

BALL BEARING

WOODRUFF KEY

BRUSH

OILER

BUSHING

THRU BOLT

COMMUTATOR

SPRING

ARMATURE

PULLEY AND FAN

COMMUTATOR END FRAME

DRIVE END FRAME

ARMATURE TERMINAL

FIELD TERMINAL

INSULATED BRUSH HOLDER

GROUNDED BRUSH HOLDER

Fig. 10. Cross section of a typical automobile generator.

Generating Circuit

The generator output is controlled by a voltage regulator which means that any trouble occurring in the generating system may be due to either or both of these units. Detailed discussion of regulators will be found later in this chapter, but they are mentioned here with generators since the two are interdependent in the generating system.

A generating circuit may contain one of two different types of voltage regulators. Fig. 11A shows a circuit in which a single-contact regulator is used, while Fig. 11B shows a circuit with a double-contact regulator. These circuits are typical of all generator systems, but small differences may be incorporated in other makes and models. Always check the manufacturer's service data for specific circuits and specifications.

Inspecting and Testing the Generator System

The generator should be inspected and tested at least every 5000 miles for optimum performance. High-speed operation, dusty conditions, high temperatures, and operating the generator at or near full output most of the time are all factors that increase bearing, commutator, and brush wear.

Generator Inspection—The following checks will show if the generator is in need of on-the-car service, or whether it should be removed for repair.

1. Using a light and mirror, inspect the commutator. A low or unsteady output may be caused by a greasy and dirty commutator, by a rough or out-of-round condition, or by high mica (insulation) between the bars. If the commutator bars are burned, an open armature circuit may be the cause.
2. Inspect the commutator end of the generator for thrown

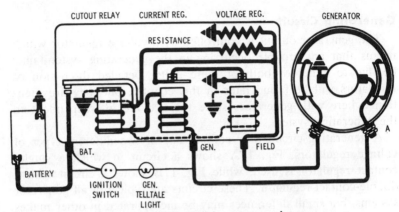

(A) Circuit with a single-contact regulator.

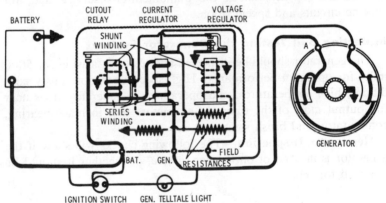

(B) Circuit with a double-contact regulator.

Fig. 11. Examples of an automobile generator circuit.

solder, indicating that overheating due to excessive output has occurred.

Excessive output is the usual result when the generator field is grounded. To determine if this is actually the cause, disconnect the wire at the FIELD terminal of either the generator or regulator and run the engine at medium speed. If the generator output drops off, the regulator is defective. If the output still remains high, the generator field is grounded internally. When a grounded field is found, it is usually necessary to replace the regulator as well as to repair or replace the generator.

3. Check the condition of the brushes. Make certain they are not binding in the brush holders, and that they are seated properly on the commutator with enough tension to give firm contact. Brush leads and screws must be tight. If the brushes are worn to one-half their original length, they should be replaced. This will mean removal of the generator on most automobiles.

4. If the commutator is in bad condition (other than just being dirty) the generator should be removed for repairs. If dirt is the only problem, it can usually be removed without taking the generator from the car. Clean off any grease with a cloth saturated with trichlorethylene or other noninflammable solvent.

5. Check the fan belt for condition and proper tension. Make sure all mounting bolts and brackets are tight. A loose fan belt allows belt slippage, resulting in rapid belt wear and low or erratic generator output. If the belt is too tight, rapid wear of the belt and generator and water-pump bearings will result. If the belt needs adjustment, first loosen and remove it from the generator pulley. Then check the generator bearings for freeness of rotation and side play. Rough or excessively worn bearings should be replaced.

6. Inspect and check all wiring connections at the generator, regulator, charge indicator or ammeter, junction block, and battery to make certain they are clean and tight. Clean any

loose connections before tightening to insure a good contact. Inspect the wiring for broken insulation, broken strands, and loose terminals. Make any corrections necessary to eliminate excessive resistance.

Generator Output Tests—After inspecting the generator, a test of its output should be made.

1. Check the belt tension and adjust as necessary.
2. Disconnect the lead from the FIELD terminal of the regulator and connect a 25-ohm, 25-watt variable resistance between this lead and ground, as in Fig. 12.

   CAUTION: With double-contact regulators, never ground the generator field while the field lead is con-

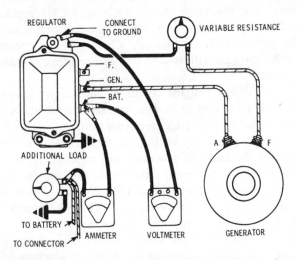

Fig. 12. Connections for checking the output of a generator.

nected to the regulator. To do so will damage the contacts in the regulator.

3. Disconnect the battery lead at the BAT terminal of the regulator. Connect a test ammeter between the BAT terminal on the regulator and the disconnected battery lead (Fig. 12). Make sure the ammeter polarity is correct (negative meter lead to the battery lead, and the positive meter lead to the BAT terminal of the regulator).
4. Connect a voltmeter between the BAT terminal of the regulator and ground. Adjust the variable resistance for maximum resistance.
5. Connect an accurate tachometer between the distributor terminal of the ignition coil and ground.
6. Turn on all lights and accessories to produce a maximum load.
7. Start the engine and gradually increase its speed to the rpm recommended by the manufacturer for this test. Adjust the variable resistance in the field circuit until the voltage reaches but does not exceed 16 volts, or until all the resistance has been cut out of the field circuit. The ammeter should read the rated output of the generator (usually around 35 amperes for standard-duty generators).

CAUTION: Never allow the voltmeter reading to exceed 16 volts. To do so may damage the lights, radio, etc.

8. If the full rated output cannot be obtained at the specified engine speed, the generator should be removed for further testing, and re-installed before making any adjustments on the regulator.

Circuit Wiring Tests—Excessive voltage drop in the charging circuit tends to keep the battery in an undercharged condition. Excessive voltage drop is the result of poor connections or other high resistance, and can be checked by connecting an ammeter and voltmeter as shown in Fig. 13. Proceed as follows:

1. Ground the FIELD terminal of the regulator.

   CAUTION: On double-contact regulators, remove the lead from the FIELD terminal and ground this lead.

2. Turn off all lights and accessories and operate the engine at a speed that will produce a reading of 20 amperes on the ammeter..

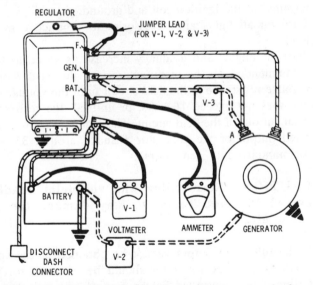

Fig. 13. Ammeter and voltmeter connections for checking generating circuit resistance.

3. Measure the voltage at V-1, V-2, and V-3 (Fig. 13). The V-1 reading plus the -2 reading should not exceed 0.9 volt. The V-3 reading should not exceed 0.3 volt. If the readings exceed these limits, excessive resistance in the circuit is indicated. (NOTE: The readings listed are typical values only. Check the manufacturer's specifications for exact readings of specific makes and models.)

If excessive resistance is found, check the wiring for defects and poor or loose connections. Look especially for poor ground connections, and clean and tighten them.

Generator Bench Tests—If it has been found necessary to remove the generator for further tests or repair, the following procedure may be used to determine the cause of unsatisfactory output before disassembly.

1. Inspect the commutator and brushes as described previously. If these items are satisfactory, and the cause of trouble is not apparent, proceed with the next step.
2. Place a piece of cardboard between the commutator and the grounded brush. Check for grounds by connecting a test lamp between the A (armature) terminal on the generator and the frame of the generator. If the lamp lights, the generator has an internal ground. Locate the ground by placing cardboard under the other brush and checking the brush holders, commutator, and field winding separately.
3. If the generator is not grounded, check the field for an open circuit by placing one test lamp prod on the F (field) terminal of the generator and the other test lamp prod on the insulated brush holder to which the other end of the field winding is connected. Failure of the lamp to light indicates an open in the field winding. If the open is caused by a broken lead

or bad connection, it can be repaired. If the open is inside one of the field coils, however, the coil cannot be repaired but must be replaced.

4. If the field is not open or grounded, check for a short circuit by connecting a 12-volt battery and an ammeter in series with the field coils. Proceed with care since a shorted field might draw enough current to damage the ammeter. Check the manufacturer's specifications for the normal current drawn by a satisfactory field coil. A high current reading indicates a short circuit.

   If a shorted field is found, the regulator must be checked for burned contacts which usually occur when this condition exists.

5. If the cause of trouble still has not been located, the generator must be disassembled for tests on the armature. (For the armature tests, use the same methods as for the starter-motor armature explained previously.)

Polarizing the Generator—It is often necessary to polarize new or rebuilt generators, or generators that have been repaired, before they will start producing an output. The polarizing process merely introduces a small amount of magnetism into the field pole pieces to start the generating action.

On automobiles using Autolite and single-contact Delco-Remy regulators, the generator is polarized by momentarily connecting a jumper between the GEN and BAT terminals on the regulator. For cars with a *Delco-Remy* double-contact regulator, insulate the ungrounded brush in the generator from the commutator before placing a jumper wire between the GEN and BAT terminals of the regulator.

For automobiles with *Ford* or *Bosch* regulators, polarize the generator as follows:

196

1. Disconnect the field and battery wires from the regulator.
2. Momentarily touch the ends of these two leads together.
3. Reconnect the leads to the proper terminals.

Special generator and regulator testers are available from a number of different manufacturers. These units provide a means of rapid and accurate trouble diagnosis of an automobile generating system. When one of these testers is used, the instructions and procedures contained in the operating manual for the tester should be followed very carefully. Fig. 14 shows an example of a commercial unit for performing practically any test on generators,

Courtesy Sun Electric Corp.

Fig. 14. The Sun Model GRT-70 Generator-Regulator Tester designed and built specifically for bench testing.

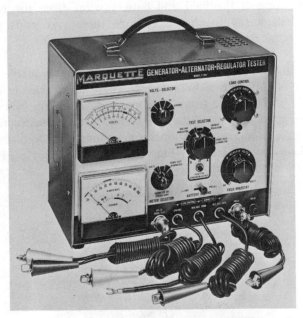

Courtesy Marquette Manufacturing Co.

Fig. 15. The Marquette Model T-201 Generator-Alternator-Regulator Tester.

regulators, and starting motors. Fig. 15 illustrates a smaller portable unit for testing generators, regulators, and alternators.

GENERATOR REGULATORS

A generator regulator performs several functions. It protects the generator from excessive output which might burn up the generator; it protects the electrical components (lights, radio, heater motor, etc.) from damage by excessive voltage; it controls the output of the generator to keep the battery in a fully charged condition; and it regulates the generator output to match the electrical requirements of the automobile.

A regulator contains three major components—a cutout relay, a voltage-regulator relay, and a current-regulator relay. These parts are mounted on a single base plate, with a cover over the com-

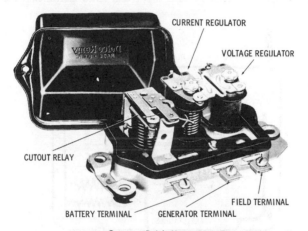

Courtesy Buick Motor Div., General Motors Corp.

Fig. 16. A typical generator regulator showing the major components and terminals.

plete unit (Fig. 16). A circuit diagram of a complete generating system is given in Fig. 17.

Cutout Relay—There is no output from the generator when the automobile engine is stopped. If the battery is not disconnected from the generator during this time, current will flow from the battery through the generator to ground. This would quickly discharge the battery and possibly damage the generator. The cutout relay prevents such a current flow by opening the generator circuit when the engine is stopped or idling. When the engine speed increases, the output voltage of the generator exceeds the battery voltage, and the cutout relay closes the circuit between the generator and battery.

Voltage Regulator—This relay limits the voltage output of the generator to a safe value to protect all the electrical units in the automobile when the battery and electrical load demands are at a minimum.

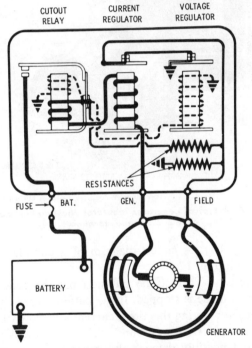

Courtesy Buick Motor Div., General Motors Corp.

Fig. 17. The generating system in a typical automobile.

Current Regulator—This relay protects the generator by preventing it from exceeding its rated output during periods of maximum electrical demands.

Generator Regulator Tests

Five types of original-equipment generator regulators are found on automobiles in use at the present time. They are *Delco-Remy* single- and double-contact types, *Autolite*, *Bosch*, and *Ford*. Each of these units contains a cutout relay, voltage-regulator relay, and a current-regulator relay.

If tests are made on the regulator while it is on the car, the car battery must be adequately charged. In addition, the regulator must be at its normal operating temperature. The regulator temperature can be brought up to normal by running the engine for approximately 15 minutes with the regulator cover in place.

CAUTION: Keep in mind as these test are made that improper connections can damage the regulator, generator, and test equipment.

Cutout-Relay Test—A cutout-relay test indicates the voltage at which the cutout-relay contacts close (cut-in voltage) and the amount of reverse current necessary to cause the contacts to open.

TEST PROCEDURE

1. Connect an ammeter and voltmeter as shown in Fig. 18.
2. Start the engine and let it run until the regulator is at its normal operating temperature.
3. Gradually increase the speed of the engine from a slow idle and note the voltage at which the cutout contacts close. (When the contacts close, the needle of the ammeter will move in a positive direction from zero, indicating that charg-

ing current is flowing.) The voltage reading at the instant just before the contacts close is the cut-in voltage.

4. Gradually decrease the engine speed. The charging current (as indicated on the ammeter) will decrease as the engine speed decreases. The ammeter needle will drop slowly to zero and then deflect in the negative direction. When the contacts open, the needle will swing back to zero. Note the ammeter reading at the instant just before the contacts open.

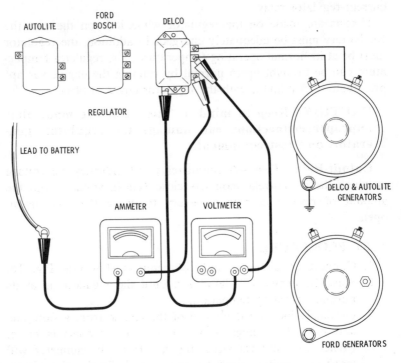

Fig. 18. Test hook-up for checking the cutout relay of a regulator.

This reading indicates the amount of reverse current required to open the contacts.

TEST CONCLUSIONS

1. If the contacts close and open within the specified limits, the cutout relay is operating satisfactorily and the adjustments are correct.

2. If the contacts close and open at other than the specified limits, remove the regulator cover and examine the cutout relay for burned or pitted contacts. If the contacts cannot be cleaned by burnishing (never use abrasives), the regulator must be replaced.

   CAUTION: Always disconnect the battery lead at the regulator before attempting to clean the contacts.

3. If the contacts are in good condition, but they close and open at other than the specified limits, the cutout relay should be adjusted.

ADJUSTMENT

On *Delco-Remy* single contact units (Fig. 19A), turn the adjusting screw clockwise to increase the closing voltage, or counterclockwise to decrease it.

On *Autolite* regulators (Fig. 19B), bend the spring support on the cutout relay down to increase the closing voltage, or up to decrease it.

On *Bosch* and *Ford* regulators (Fig. 19C), bend the tang on the cutout relay up to increase the closing voltage, or bend the tang down to decrease the closing voltage.

The contact-opening current determines if the cutout relay opens at or below the specified maximum value. This specified value may vary from 2 to 9 amperes, depending on the make of

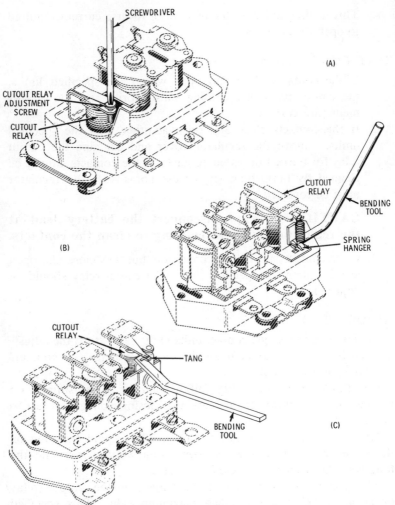

Fig. 19. Regulator cutout-relay adjustment; (A) Delco-Remy single-contact; (B) Autolite; (C) Ford or Bosch.

regulator. If the value is outside the specified limits, the air gap of the cutout relay must be adjusted. Refer to the manufacturer's recommended procedure to make this adjustment.

Voltage Regulator Relay Test—Adjustment of the voltage-regulator relay is seldom necessary if the battery remains charged and does not need more than the normal amount of water added, and lights or radio tubes do not have to be replaced at frequent intervals.

If the above conditions do not exist, however, or if a major tune-up is performed, the voltage at which the voltage regulator operates should be checked. The cover should be on the regulator and the unit at normal operating temperature. The voltage-regulator relay operation and adjustment are affected by temperature. The manufacturer specifies the temperature at which tests are to be made, and lists a correction factor to compensate for temperature variation when making adjustments. It is important that this correction factor be used.

The voltage-regulator relay may be checked with a suitable volt-ampere tester or by use of the many battery-starter-regulator testers on the market. Special fixed and variable resistors, as well as carbon piles, may be used in various hook-ups. Detailed instructions are furnished by the test-equipment manufacturers for the use of their equipment. These instructions should be carefully followed.

Operation of the voltage regulator relay may also be checked with a voltmeter and ammeter connected as shown in Fig. 20.

TEST PROCEDURE

1. Start the engine and turn on a combination of lights and/or accessories to obtain a generator output (as read on the test ammeter) of 10 to 15 amperes.
2. Slowly increase the engine speed from idle to 1600 rpm

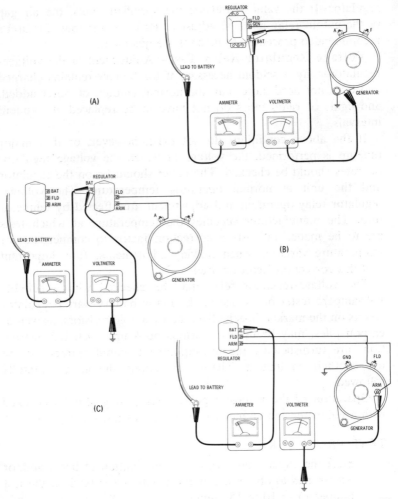

Fig. 20. Voltage-regulator relay test connections; (A) Delco-Remy; (B) Autolite; (C) Ford or Bosch.

for a *Delco-Remy, Ford* or *Bosch* regulator, or 2000 rpm for an *Autolite* unit.

3. The voltmeter reading should increase as the engine speed increases until the voltage regulator starts operating, after which the voltage should remain constant and within specifications.

4. Momentarily increase the engine speed. The voltage reading should remain constant.

5. If the voltage reading is not within the specified limit, or does not remain constant, the regulator needs adjustment or replacement.

ADJUSTMENT

Adjustment of the *Delco-Remy* voltage regulator relay is made by turning the adjusting screw (Fig. 21A) clockwise to increase the voltage limit, or counterclockwise to decrease it. If the screw is turned too far clockwise (voltage limit too high), it must be turned counterclockwise until there is a clearance between the screwhead and the spring support. Carefully bend the spring support up until it touches the screwhead, then readjust the relay by turning the screw slowly clockwise. Always make the final setting by turning the screw clockwise. Recheck the voltage readings with the regulator cover in place.

Adjustment of the *Autolite* voltage-regulator relay is made by bending the spring hanger arm (Fig. 21B) up or down. Bend the hanger arm down to increase the voltage limit, and up to decrease it. Recheck the voltage reading with the regulator cover in place.

Ford or *Bosch* voltage-regulator relays are adjusted by bending the tang (Fig. 21C) up to increase the voltage limit and down to decrease it. Recheck the voltage reading with the cover in place.

Adjustment of the voltage regulator should always be made according to the specifications of the manufacturer.

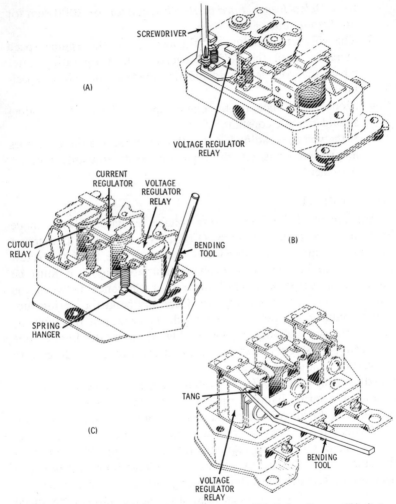

Fig. 21. Voltage-regulator relay adjustment; (A) Delco-Remy; (B) Auto-lite; (C) Ford or Bosch.

Current-Regulator Relay Tests—The current-regulator relay is checked to determine if it is limiting the generator output to the specified rating. The test must be made with the regulator at its normal operating temperature and with the cover in place.

PROCEDURE

1. Connect the voltmeter and ammeter as shown in Fig. 20. Start the engine and run it until the regulator is at its normal operating temperature.
2. Turn on the headlights, all accessories and, if necessary, connect an additional load (carbon pile or bank of lights) across the battery to bring the system voltage to at least 1 volt below the voltage regulator setting.
3. Stop the engine. Restart and increase the engine speed to 1600 rpm for *Ford*, *Bosch*, and *Delco-Remy* regulators, or 2000 rpm for *Autolite* units.
4. Note the ammeter reading. The current output of the generator should be within the specified limits.

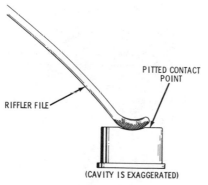

PITTED CONTACT POINT

RIFFLER FILE

(CAVITY IS EXAGGERATED)

Fig. 22. A riffler file can be used to clean pitted areas only.

ADJUSTMENTS

If the current output of the generator is not within specifications, adjustment of the current-regulator relay is made in exactly the same manner as the adjustment on the voltage-regulator relay described and illustrated previously (Fig. 21).

Regulator Contact Service

The majority of generator-regulator troubles are caused by dirty, oxidized, or pitted relay contacts in the regulator. These conditions increase the contact resistance and promote arcing and burning. The regulator must be removed from the automobile if it is found necessary to clean the contacts.

A riffler file can be used to clean out pitted areas on the contacts, as shown in Fig. 22. Crocus cloth can be used for cleaning other areas (Fig. 23). Never use a regular file, sandpaper, emery cloth, or other abrasives that will scratch or gouge the contact surfaces. After cleaning and polishing the contacts, it is important

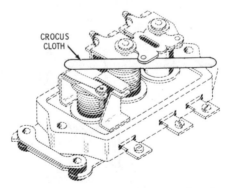

Fig. 23. Regulator contacts can be cleaned and polished with crocus cloth.

to remove all foreign material from their surfaces. Clean the contact surfaces with trichlorethylene and a piece of lint-free tape. Dry the surfaces with a clean strip of lint-free tape.

ALTERNATORS

An alternator is an AC generator used instead of a DC generator in the charging system of some automobiles. The alternator, unlike the DC generator, will deliver an output voltage at a low idle speed and considerably more output voltage at low operating speeds. Thus, an alternator meets the demand of stop-and-go city driving and increased accessory load better than the DC generator.

The output of an alternator is alternating current (AC), which means that half the total output current flows in one direction and the other half flows in the opposite direction. The electrical circuits of the automobile, however, can use only current flowing in a single direction, which means the alternator output must be changed to direct current (DC). This is done by passing the alternating current through diode rectifiers which allow the current to flow in only one direction.

Construction

A typical alternator consists of a stator, a rotor, two slip rings, two brushes, and six diodes. In addition, of course, is the necessary end frames, pulley, fan, etc. A cross-sectional view of an alternator is shown in Fig. 24.

The stator consists of a number of windings wound on the inside of a laminated core that is attached to the frame of the alternator. It is from these windings that the output of the alternator is taken.

The field coil is wound on the rotor, which revolves within the stator. Two brushes, each riding on a slip ring, are located at one end of the rotor shaft. One slip ring is electrically connected to one end of the field coil, and the other slip ring is connected to the opposite end of the coil.

The stator windings are connected to the diodes in such a way that the alternating output of the stator is converted (rectified) to direct current. The diodes also prevent the battery from discharging through the alternator when the engine is stopped. Thus, a cutout relay is not needed.

Servicing Precautions

Greater care must be taken in servicing an alternator system than in servicing a DC generator system. Precautions are:

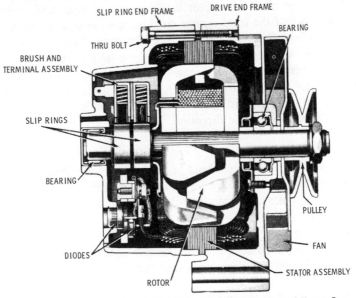

Courtesy Oldsmobile Division, General Motors Corp.

Fig. 24. Cross section of a **Delcotron** *alternator.*

1. Observe correct polarities. Never reverse the battery leads as this may damage the diodes and/or the wiring.
2. Do not short or ground any of the terminals on the alternator or regulator.
3. Do not operate the alternator unless it is connected to a load. If the alternator operates with its output open, extremely high voltages may be produced that are both dangerous and damaging to the alternator.
4. Do not attempt to polarize an alternator. It is not only unnecessary, but may damage the unit.
5. Make sure that any battery charger or booster battery is connected in the proper polarity.
6. Make sure the belt tension is proper. An alternator is more critical in this respect than a DC generator.
7. Do not apply pressure to either of the end frames of an alternator. Apply pressure only to the center portion when applying belt tension.
8. Use only a battery that is known to be good. The lower the charge condition of the battery, the higher the output of the alternator. If the battery is too low and remains so too long, the alternator may be damaged.

On-the-Vehicle Tests

The following tests can be made with the alternator and regulator in the automobile.

Output Test—The output of most alternator charging systems can be checked by using a voltmeter and ammeter connected as shown in Fig. 25. In addition, a tachometer is used to accurately indicate the engine rpm. Connections to some alternator systems cannot be made as shown in Fig. 25. Therefore, the type of system must be determined before the proper connections can be made. Always follow the recommendations of the manufacturer for sys-

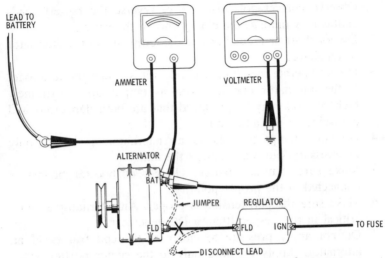

Fig. 25. Meter connections for testing an alternator.

tems that differ from the one shown. The output test most frequently
made is as follows:

1. Connect the positive lead of the voltmeter to the ouput terminal of the alternator, and the negative lead to ground.

2. Disconnect the lead from the output terminal of the alternator (usually labeled BAT). Connect the positive lead of
   the ammeter to the output terminal of the alternator, and
   connect the negative lead to the disconnected lead. Turn on
   the automobile lights and all accessories.

3. Connect a tachometer between the primary distributor terminal and ground.

4. Start the engine and gradually increase its speed to the number of rpm's specified for the particular system being tested
   (usually between 1250 and 2000 rpm).

5. Note the ammeter reading. This is the output current of the alternator and should be within the specified limits for the unit being tested.
6. Note the voltmeter reading. The voltage should be slightly higher than the normal charging voltage (usually from 12.5 to 15 volts for a 12-volt system). If the rated output current is obtained at a voltage between 12.5 and 15 volts, the alternator is operating correctly.

If the rated output cannot be obtained, stop the engine and remove the field connection from the alternator. Connect a jumper from the F to the BAT terminal on the alternator. Restart the engine and see if sufficient output current is now obtained. If it is, the regulator is defective. If the current is still below specifications, the alternator is at fault.

TEST CONCLUSIONS

If the alternator does not meet the output current and/or voltage specifications as listed by the manufacturer, any one of several troubles may exist.

No Alternator Output—Check for:

1. A blown or broken fusible wire in the voltage regulator.
2. A loose alternator drive belt.
3. Worn brushes.
4. Worn slip rings.
5. Open rectifiers (diodes).
6. An open field circuit.
7. An open stator winding.

Low and/or Unsteady Output—Check for:

1. A loose alternator drive belt.
2. Dirty regulator contacts.

3. Worn or defective brushes.
4. High resistance at the battery terminals or at the junction block (if used).
5. An open stator winding.
6. High resistance in alternator body-to-ground lead.

Excessive Charging Rate with a Fully Charged Battery—Check for:

1. An unnecessarily high regulator setting.
2. An improper ground on the regulator base.
3. An open in the voltage-regulator circuit.
4. A stuck contact in the regulator.

Noisy Alternator—Check for:

1. A loose alternator mounting.
2. A damaged rotor or rotor fan.
3. A frayed or worn drive belt.
4. Worn bearings.
5. Interference between the stator leads or rectifiers and the rotor.

Burned Regulator Contacts—Check for:

1. Excessive voltage-regulator setting.
2. Shorted field-coil windings on the rotor.

Stuck Regulator Contacts—Check for:

1. A poor ground connection between alternator and regulator.
2. An open resistor element in the regulator.

Bench Tests

The alternator must be removed from the automobile and disassembled for the following tests.

Stator Tests—To test the stator for opens, connect an ohm-meter or a 12-volt test lamp between one pair of stator leads, as shown in Fig. 26. If the ohmmeter reading approaches infinity or the test lamp does not light, the winding is open. Repeat this test for each of the stator windings.

To test the stator windings for a ground, connect an ohmmeter or the test lamp from any stator lead to ground. If the ohmmeter reads near zero or if the test lamp lights, the stator is grounded.

Testing the stator windings for a short circuit is difficult be-cause of the low resistance of the windings. If the other tests prove normal, and the alternator still does not produce the specified out-put, shorted stator windings may be the cause.

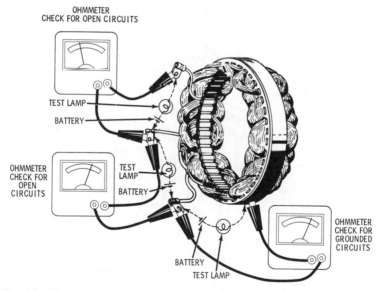

Fig. 26. Connections for testing the stator of an alternator for opens and grounds.

A stator that fails any of the tests just outlined should be replaced.

Rotor Tests—To test the rotor for opens, connect an ohmmeter or 12-volt test lamp to each slip ring, as shown in Fig. 27. If the ohmmeter reading is near infinity or the lamp fails to light, the field winding on the rotor is open.

To test the rotor for grounds, connect an ohmmeter or the test lamp between either slip ring and the rotor shaft, as shown. If the ohmmeter reading is near zero or the test lamp lights, the field coil is grounded.

To test the field coil for a short circuit, connect an ammeter and a 12-volt battery in series with the slip rings. The field current at

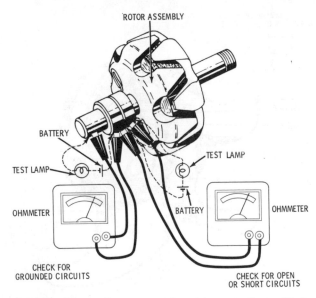

Fig. 27. Connections for testing the rotor of an alternator for opens and grounds.

218

standard temperature should be within the specified range (usually from 1.9 to 2.3 amperes) for the particular unit under test. If the field current is above the specified value, the coil is shorted. If the rotor fails any of the tests just outlined, it should be replaced.

Diode Tests

The rectifiers (diodes) used in the alternator allow current to flow through them in only one direction. This characteristic is used to check their condition. Two methods can be used to test the diodes—the ohmmeter and test-lamp methods.

Ohmmeter Method—The ohmmeter used for this test should employ a 1.5-volt cell. To make the test, disconnect the stator leads and connect the ohmmeter leads across one of the diodes as shown in Fig. 28. Note the ohmmeter reading. Reverse the ohmmeter leads and note the reading. If both readings are the same, the diode is defective. A good diode will give one high reading and one low reading. Test the remaining diodes in the same manner.

Test-Lamp Method—A 12-volt (maximum) test lamp is substituted for the ohmmeter in this test. Disconnect the stator leads and connect the test lamp across one of the diodes in the same manner the ohmmeter was connected in the previous test method. If the test lamp lights in both positions of the test leads, or if it fails to light in both positions, the diode is defective. With a good diode, the lamp will light in one position of the test leads, but will not light when the leads are reversed.

Diode Replacement

To replace a defective diode, it is necessary to unsolder the diode leads. The other diodes must be protected from heat damage during this process. Holding the leads of the defective diode with pliers will usually allow enough heat dissipation to prevent damage to the remaining diodes. The same procedure is used to protect the re-

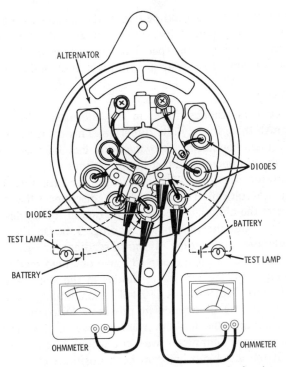

*Fig. 28. Connections for testing the diodes in
an alternator.*

placement while its leads are being soldered. Some alternators require special tools to press individual replacement diodes in position. Still other alternators require the replacement of an assembly unit containing three diodes mounted on a plate. Check the instructions of the manufacturer for removal and replacement procedures. Make certain the correct replacement is made. Positive diodes are usually identified by a (+) or red marking, and a negative diode by a (−) or black marking.

ALTERNATOR REGULATORS

There are three basic types of alternator regulators—the double-contact type (Fig. 29), the single-contact transistorized type (Fig. 30), and the all-transistorized type (Fig. 31). A cutout relay is not

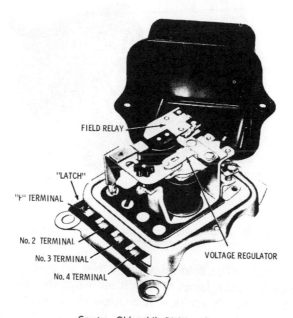

FIELD RELAY

"LATCH"

"F" TERMINAL

No. 2 TERMINAL

No. 3 TERMINAL

No. 4 TERMINAL

VOLTAGE REGULATOR

Courtesy Oldsmobile Division, General Motors Corp.

Fig. 29. A double-contact alternator regulator.

needed because the diodes in the alternator prevent a reverse-current flow. A current regulator is not required either, because the alternator is self-limiting in current output as long as voltage control is maintained.

Relay-Type Regulators

The double-contact and single-contact types of alternator regulators contain two major components—a field relay and a voltage-regulator relay.

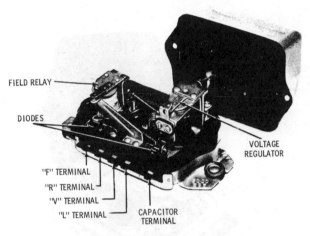

FIELD RELAY

DIODES

VOLTAGE
REGULATOR

"F" TERMINAL
"R" TERMINAL
"V" TERMINAL
"L" TERMINAL

CAPACITOR
TERMINAL

Fig. 30. A single-contact transistorized alternator regulator.

Field Relay—The field relay serves two purposes. It controls the charging-indicator lamp, turning it out when the alternator has an output current. In addition, it controls the amount of current through the field to allow the alternator to start its charging action as soon as the engine starts and to increase this charging action to full output at speeds past idle.

Voltage-Regulator Relay—This relay regulates the output voltage of the alternator to a predetermined value to protect the alternator from an excessive current output.

Courtesy American Motors Corporation

Fig. 31. An all-transistorized alternator regulator.

All-Transistorized Regulators

The all-transistorized regulators do not contain relays or contacts. Instead, transistors control the alternator output. Some regulators of this type provide an output-voltage adjustment. Others are completely sealed and must be replaced if the output voltage is not within the specified limits.

Regulator Servicing

The servicing of alternator regulators is seldom necessary. However, the contacts may need cleaning and the air gap need adjusting from time to time. The voltage setting may also require adjustment due to a variation in electrical load caused by changing weather conditions.

A sooty, discolored condition of the voltage-regulator relay contacts after only a short operating period is normal and does not indicate a need for cleaning. However, they should be cleaned if the output voltage is measured and found to be unsteady. The contacts should be cleaned with a fine grade of silicon carbide paper followed by a bath of alcohol or trichlorethylene to remove the residue. **Never use a file to clean the voltage-regulator relay contacts.**

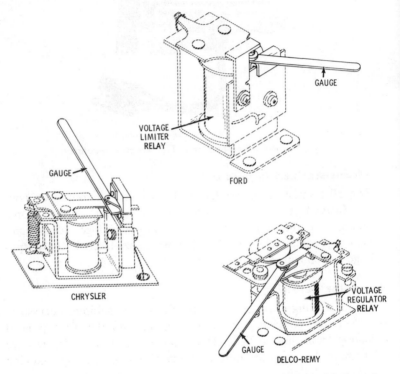

Fig. 32. Checking the contact opening on the voltage-regulator relay.

A fine-cut, thin, flat file can be used to clean the contacts of the field relay. Remove only enough material to clean the contacts. **Never use sandpaper or emery cloth to clean either the voltage-regulator or field-relay contacts.**

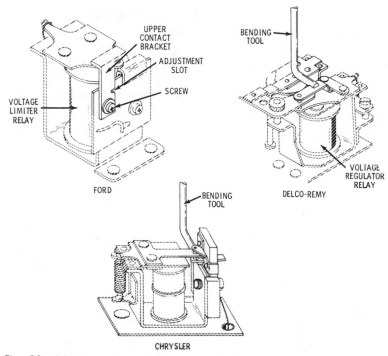

Fig. 33. Adjusting the contact opening on the voltage-regulator relay.

Double-Contact Regulators—Both the voltage-regulator and field-relay require three adjustments—contact opening, air gap, and voltage setting.

The contact opening of the voltage-regulator relay is made by measuring the opening between one set of contacts with the other set just touching (Fig. 32). Adjustments are made either by bending one of the contact arms, or by loosening a screw and adjusting the upper contact as required (Fig. 33). Check the manufacturer's specifications for the correct contact opening.

The air gap of the voltage-regulator relay is checked by measuring the space between the relay armature and core (Fig. 34). If the air gap is not correct, turn the adjusting nut, or loosen the screw holding the contact bracket (Fig. 35), and adjust to obtain the specified gap for the unit being serviced.

The voltage setting of the voltage-regulator relay can be checked by connecting a ¼-ohm resistor and an ammeter in series between the positive terminal of the battery and the BAT terminal of the

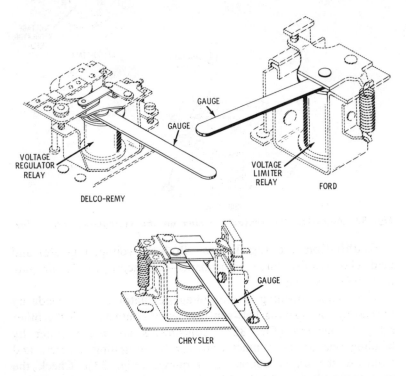

Fig. 34. Checking the air gap on the voltage-regulator relay.

alternator. This resistor will limit the output of the alternator to 10 amperes, which is a requirement for this test. Connect a 50-ohm variable resistor between the F terminal of the alternator and the F terminal of the regulator. Connect a voltmeter between

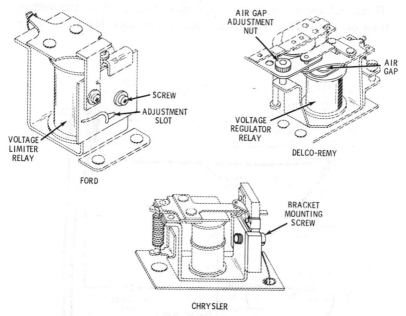

Fig. 35. Adjusting the air gap on the voltage-regulator relay.

the BAT terminal of the alternator and ground. Connect a jumper between the BAT terminal of the alternator and the regulator as shown in Fig. 36.

The alternator must be operated with the cover on for approximately 15 minutes at 1500 rpm in order to bring the surrounding temperature up to the proper level. After the warm-up period, ad-

227

just the 50-ohm variable resistor to its lowest resistance setting and increase the engine speed to 2500 rpm. Note the voltmeter reading at this speed. This reading should be within the voltage range specified by the manufacturer for the particular temperature at which the regulator is operating.

If the voltage is outside the specified range, adjust the voltage setting on *Delco-Remy* units by turning the adjusting screw (Fig.

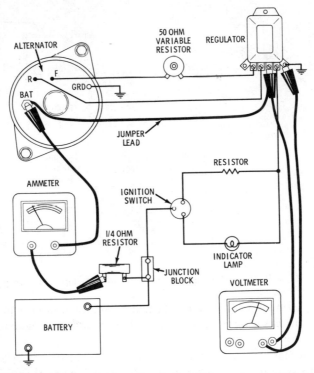

Fig. 36. Connections for checking the voltage setting of the voltage-regulator relay.

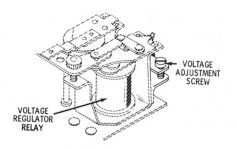

DELCO-REMY

Fig. 37. Adjusting the voltage setting of a Delco-Remy voltage-regulator relay.

37). On *Ford* and *Chrysler* regulators (Fig. 38), adjustment is made by bending the spring hanger down to increase the voltage and up to decrease it. With the engine speed still at 2500 rpm, increase the resistance of the 50-ohm variable resistance. The regu-

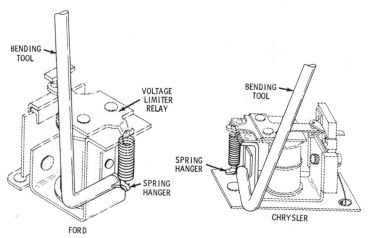

Fig. 38. Adjusting the voltage setting of a Ford and Chrysler voltage-regulator relay.

lator should now be operating with the lower set of contacts closed. Readjust the relay to bring the voltage within the specified range.

NOTE: On Delco-Remy *units, the final setting of the adjustment screws must be made by turning it clockwise to insure that the screwhead is seated against the spring holder. Always take the final voltage reading with the regulator cover in place.*

The field-relay contact opening is measured by inserting a feeler gauge of the correct size between the contacts, as shown in Fig. 39. If adjustment is necessary, gently bend the armature stop, or loosen the screw and raise or lower the stop assembly. (When it is necessary to make an adjustment on a unit having an adjustable

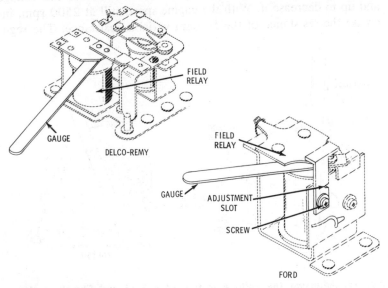

Fig. 39. Checking and adjusting the contact opening of the field relay.

armature stop, the field-relay air gap must be checked and adjusted first.)

The field-relay air gap is checked by measuring the spacing between the armature and the relay core (Fig. 40). If adjustment is

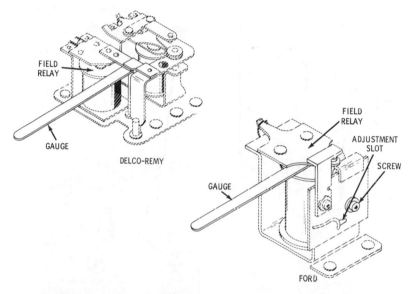

Fig. 40. Checking and adjusting the air gap of the field relay.

necessary, bend the flat contact spring carefully, or loosen the screw and move the contact mounting assembly.

The closing voltage of the field relay may be checked by connecting a 50-ohm variable resistor between the positive terminal of the battery and the coil of the field relay. Also connect a voltmeter between the coil of the field relay and ground. Set the variable resistor to its highest value, and turn the ignition switch off.

Slowly decrease the resistance, and note the voltmeter reading at the instant the field relay closes. This voltage can be set to the specifications of the manufacturer by bending the heel iron of the relay or by bending the spring hanger, in a manner similar to that shown in Fig. 41.

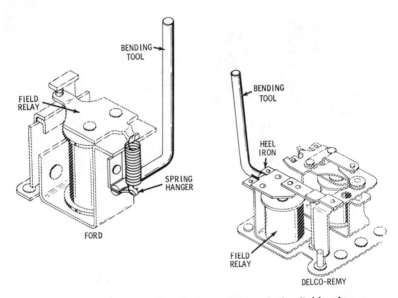

Fig. 41. Adjusting the closing voltage of the field relay.

Single-Contact Transistorized Regulators—To adjust the air gap of a single-contact transistorized type of voltage-regulator relay, press the armature (not the contact) down against the proper size feeler gauge inserted between the armature and relay core. The contacts should just touch under this condition. Adjust, if necessary, by loosening the contact-support bracket screws and moving the bracket up or down.

The field-relay air gap should be checked in exactly the same manner and adjusted by bending the flat contact-support spring to provide the gap specified by the manufacturer.

The contacts of the voltage-regulator may be cleaned when necessary in the same way prescribed for the double-contact regulator.

The diodes in this type of regulator may be checked with an ohmmeter that uses a 1.5-volt cell. Unsolder the diode leads and connect the ohmmeter across them, first in one direction and then with the leads reversed. If both readings approach either zero or infinity, the diode is defective and must be replaced. A good diode will give a high and a low reading for the two ohmmeter connections.

The transistor can be checked by connecting a voltmeter between the F terminal of the regulator and ground. A voltmeter reading of 9 volts or more with the ignition switch on indicates the transistor is satisfactory. If the meter reading is less than 9 volts, either the transistor is defective or a regulator resistor is open. To determine which is defective, remove the regulator cover and hold the contacts of the voltage-regulator relay apart. If the voltmeter now reads more than 9 volts, the transistor is defective and must be replaced. If the meter reading is still less than 9 volts, a resistor is open and must be replaced.

All-Transistorized Regulator—This type of regulator has no moving parts, but some units do provide an output-voltage adjustment. If the output voltage cannot be brought within range with this adjustment, the entire unit must be replaced. If the output voltage of the non-adjustable type is outside the specified range, the unit must be replaced.

CHAPTER 8

Lighting Systems

In general, an automobile lighting system includes those lights required by law, that is: headlights, headlight-beam indicator, taillight, and license-plate light. Included, also, either as new-car equipment or as accessories, are many lamps that add to the convenience, comfort, and safety of driving.

Among these are: parking lights, stop and directional signal and pilot lights, instrument lights, courtesy lights, dome lights, fog lights, glove and luggage compartment lights, etc. The lighting system includes the cables or wires and the various switches, circuit breakers, fuses, etc., that supply and control the lighting current. When working on lights, switches, and wiring harnesses, consult the manufacturer's wiring diagram. A typical diagram is shown in Fig. 1.

HEADLIGHTS

The modern sealed-beam unit has its filaments, reflector, and lens sealed to form a single unit. Such a unit has a glass reflector sprayed with vaporized aluminum. This provides a reflecting surface almost as bright and much less expensive than silver.

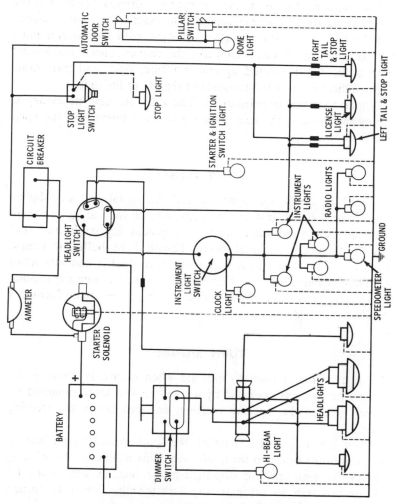

Fig. 1. A typical lighting-system wiring diagram.

The filaments for the upper, or country, driving beam, and the lower, or passing, beam are mounted in exactly the right positions and the lens is fused to the glass reflector, with the interior filled with an inert gas. Thus, sealed like the conventional incandescent lamp bulb, it is protected against moisture, dust, and tarnishing. High efficiency is assured throughout the life of the unit.

Proper focusing is permanent. The only cleaning necessary is wiping the front of the lens. When a filament burns out, the glass unit is replaced.

OTHER LIGHTS

Parking lights, tail lights, directional signal and stop lights, compartment lights, instrument lights, etc., in fact all lights except the headlights (and some special equipment fog lights and spot lights), carry conventional 6- or 12-volt light bulbs or lamps. Some have single contacts, and some have double contacts when two filaments are included. For information concerning the candle-power of the various light bulbs, refer to the manufacturer's specifications.

TURN SIGNAL

A turn signal is used to indicate when a turn is about to be made. The signal is operated by a small control lever mounted on the left side of the steering housing, and just below the steering wheel.

When a turn is to be signaled, the lever should be pushed up for a right turn or down for a left turn. This will cause the parking light at the front and the stop light at the rear, as well as a pilot light on the dash, to automatically flash the direction to be turned at a rate of 80 to 100 flashes per minute.

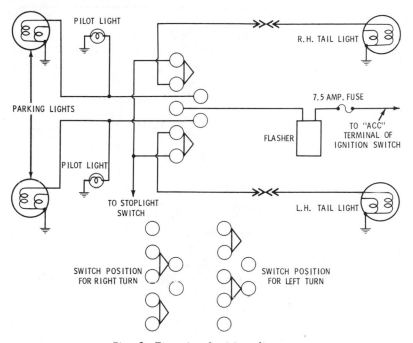

Fig. 2. Turn-signal wiring diagram.

The most common causes of trouble with the turn signals are: defective flasher, burned-out bulbs, blown fuse, and a defective switch.

Troubleshooting

1. If the indicator light in the dash panel burns steadily, or flashes rapidly when a turn is signalled:
   a. Check for a burned out bulb in the parking or stop lamp.
   b. Check for a faulty flasher if both the parking and stop lamps stay on.

237

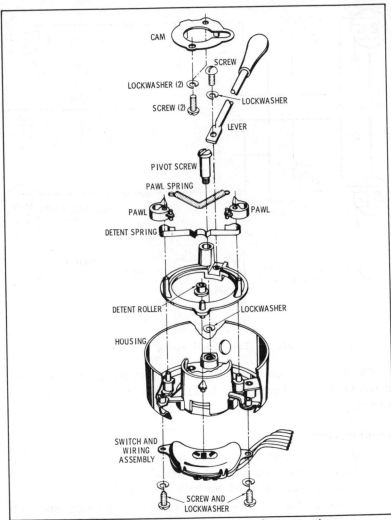

Fig. 3. Details of typical turn-signal construction.

2. If the indicator does not light when a turn is signalled:
   a. Check for a burned out indicator light.
   b. Check for a faulty flasher.
3. If the switch fails to cancel after the completion of a turn, check for worn or broken parts in the switch mechanism (Fig. 3) in the steering column.

HEADLIGHT SWITCH AND CIRCUIT BREAKER

The pull-type headlight switch is conveniently mounted on the instrument panel. The first out position of the knob turns on the parking lights, taillights, and instrument-panel lights; the second position turns on the headlights, taillights, and instrument lights.

On most units of this type, rotating the knob to the left turns on the dome and/or courtesy lights; rotating the knob to the left gradually dims the instrument-panel lights.

Built into the headlight switch is an overload circuit breaker which is an effective safety feature. An overload through this switch, such as that caused by a grounded or short-circuited cable, causes heating of a bimetallic element and separation of the contact points. The points snap apart, interrupting the flow of current.

As soon as the temperature of the bimetallic element falls, the points snap together, again closing the circuit. Thus, this switch acts like a flasher unit, causing the connected lamps to go on and off. The heavier the current flowing through the short or ground, the more quickly the points will separate.

LIGHTING TROUBLES

1. LIGHTS DO NOT BURN

   Possible Cause:

   (a) Burned out bulb or unit.

(b) Defective wiring.
(c) Defective light switch.
(d) Loose connections.
(e) Run-down battery.

2. LIGHTS FLICKER

Possible Cause:

(a) Loose connections.
(b) Poor ground at light socket.

3. BULBS BURN OUT FREQUENTLY

Possible Cause:

(a) Excessive battery voltage.
(b) High charging rate.
(c) Poor ground at light socket.
(d) Short in light circuit.
(e) Incorrect type of bulb.
(f) Corroded battery terminals.

AIMING THE HEADLIGHTS

Proper aiming of the headlights is very critical. If the aim is set too low, insufficient light will be thrown on the road ahead of the car. If the aim is too high, oncoming drivers will be blinded. The headlights on every car are provided with adjustment screws for horizontal and vertical aiming of the high beam lamps. The low beams of sealed-beam units need not be adjusted because they are positioned properly with respect to the high beams during manufacture and can not change. On four-light systems, the low beams are separate lights and must be aimed separately.

AIMING LUGS

Fig. 4. Details of a sealed-beam unit.

Two methods are generally used for headlight aiming. One method uses special aiming equipment which mounts on the headlight lens by means of suction cups and small glass pedestals or alignment points molded into the lens surface. The other method uses the patterns made by the beams themselves on a wall or screen.

Using Aiming Equipment

Sealed-beam headlamp units are provided with aiming lugs (Fig. 4) for the alignment of aiming equipment such as the one shown in Fig. 5. This aimer can be used to correctly aim headlights without turning them on.

The aimer consists of a circular base which attaches to the sealed-beam unit by means of a plunger-operated suction cup. Attached to the front of the base and extending perpendicular to it is an L-shaped arm. When the aimer is mounted on the lamp, this arm points to the center of the car and is parallel to the ground. Mounted in the arm between the base and cross arm is a bubble level which may be adjusted for variations in the floor levelness.

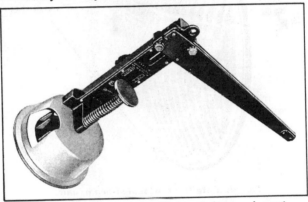

Fig. 5. One type of headlight aiming equipment.

The various manufacturers specify different conditions of vehicle loading during headlight aiming. They may specify that the gasoline tank should be empty, full, or half full; that the driver (or a substitute weight) should or should not be behind the wheel; that the spare tire should or should not be in the trunk. Always follow the vehicle manufacturer's specification and/or state regulations for the conditions of the vehicle.

Always bounce the car several times to allow springs and shock absorbers to settle normally. Remove the headlight trim to expose the adjustment screws (Fig. 6). Install an aimer on each headlight to be aimed. Most manufacturers specify that the inboard pair of four-headlamp cars be aimed first. These sealed-beam lamps have a numerical "1" molded into the lens and have only one filament. They are used in conjunction with the high beam of the outboard lamps for highway driving. The outboard lamps have a "2" molded in the lens and have two filaments—a low beam and a high beam.

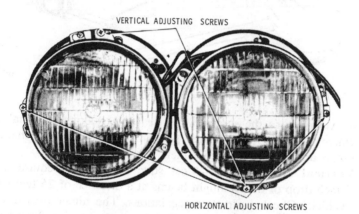

VERTICAL ADJUSTING SCREWS

HORIZONTAL ADJUSTING SCREWS

Courtesy Dodge Division, Chrysler Motors Corporation

Fig. 6. Headlight aiming screws.

Position the aimer over the lens with the aiming lugs engaging the proper points on the aimer. Push the lever that forces the suction cups onto the lens. Mount another aimer on the other lamp of the pair to be aimed. Rotate the crossarms so that they are approximately horizontal and pointing toward the center of the car. Knot both ends of the elastic string provided with the aimers, and stretch it between the two aimers, using the slots provided. The installation should appear as in Fig. 7.

Horizontal Adjustment—Turn the horizontal aiming screw on one lamp until the string is positioned over the crossarm center-

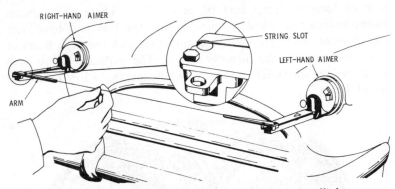

Fig. 7. Aimers and string installed on No. 1 headlights.

line. Always turn the screw *clockwise* while making the final adjustment to insure that all free play in the headlamp mechanism is taken up. Repeat the adjustment on the other lamp.

Vertical Adjustment—Most state regulations require a 2- or 3-inch drop of the headlight beams at a distance of 25 feet from the vehicle. Check your state regulations. The aimer provides an up-and-down adjustment (Fig. 8) to compensate for floor level. On a level floor, both the UP and DOWN view windows will show a zero.

To set the vertical aim of the headlights, set the aimer for a "2" or a "3" in the DOWN window. Turn the vertical aiming screw on one lamp counterclockwise until the bubble is at the end of the level. Then turn the screw *clockwise* until the bubble is centered. Repeat the operation on the other lamp.

The outboard, or No. 2, lamps are aimed in the same manner.

Using a Wall or Screen

There are many ways of aiming headlights by means of a wall or screen. The method described does away with the need for an exactly level floor and establishes beam height correctly regardless of floor slant.

Select a location in which the vehicle can be positioned with the front surface of the headlamps exactly 25 feet from a vertical wall. The wall should preferably be painted white with a nonreflective surface.

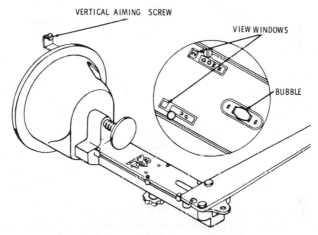

VERTICAL AIMING SCREW

VIEW WINDOWS

BUBBLE

Fig. 8. View windows and bubble level.

Construct two uprights, or stands, exactly alike and 20″ high. Position these on one side of the vehicle and sight across the tops of the two uprights. Have an assistant mark the spot on the wall where the line of vision intersects. Repeat on the other side of the vehicle and draw a line on the wall connecting the two points. This operation establishes a reference line exactly 20″ above the floor (Fig. 9).

Measure the distance from the floor to the center of one lamp. Subtract 20 inches from this dimension and add the difference (dimension "B" in Fig. 10A) to the 20-inch line on the wall. Repeat this operation on the other lamp. Connect these points to form the horizontal center line of the lamps. Draw another horizontal line 2 inches (3 inches in some states) below and parallel to this center line (Fig. 10A). Mark the center line of the front

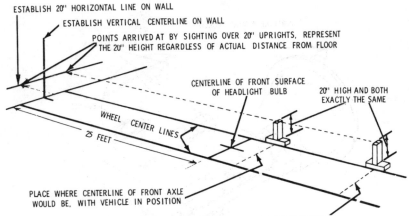

ESTABLISH 20" HORIZONTAL LINE ON WALL

ESTABLISH VERTICAL CENTERLINE ON WALL

POINTS ARRIVED AT BY SIGHTING OVER 20' UPRIGHTS, REPRESENT THE 20" HEIGHT REGARDLESS OF ACTUAL DISTANCE FROM FLOOR

CENTERLINE OF FRONT SURFACE OF HEADLIGHT BULB

20" HIGH AND BOTH EXACTLY THE SAME

WHEEL CENTER LINES

25 FEET

PLACE WHERE CENTERLINE OF FRONT AXLE WOULD BE, WITH VEHICLE IN POSITION

PLACE WHERE CENTERLINE OF REAR AXLE WOULD BE, WITH VEHICLE IN POSITION

Fig. 9. Floor and wall layout for visual aiming of headlights.

and back windows of the vehicle with tape and sight past these to mark the center line of the vehicle on the wall. Measure the distance between the headlight centers (dimension "A" in Fig. 10A) and mark the center lines of the left and right headlights on the wall. Again, the inboard (No. 1) lights are to be adjusted first.

Turn the headlights on bright (high beam) and cover the outboard or No. 2 lights. Adjust the No. 1 lights horizontally and vertically until the light patterns on the wall are positioned as in Fig. 10A.

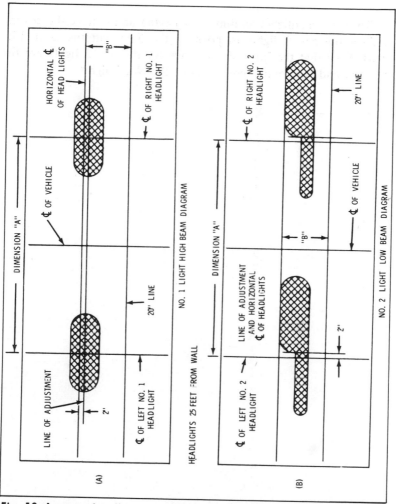

Fig. 10. Layout of wall or screen; (A) No. 1 or inboard lights; (B) No. 2 or outboard lights on low beam.

Turn the headlights on dim (low beam) and remove the covers. Adjust the No. 2 lights to position the light patterns as in Fig. 10B. Note that the lines of reference for the No. 2 lights are the vertical and horizontal centerlines of the No. 2 lights.

CHAPTER 9

Tire Servicing

Servicing of automobile tires includes not only the repair of punctures, blowouts, and other tire damage, but also includes wheel balancing, tire rotation and, in many cases, wheel alignment. Higher driving speeds, increased engine horsepower, and heavier loads make tire servicing more exacting than in the past. Tire manufacturers have kept pace with the changes in driving habits and automotive design by constantly improving and changing their product. Thus, the methods of tire repair and service have also changed.

TIRE MAINTENANCE

Inflation

The weight of an automobile is supported by the air in the tires. Proper inflation is one of the most important facts in insuring satisfactory and long tire life. Fig. 1 shows the appearance of a tire in different stages of inflation on an automobile.

Too little air pressure allows an abnormal distortion of the tire body and causes the tread in the shoulder area to wipe and scuff on the road. Extra strain is placed on the cords in the tire which increases the chances for fabric injury and separation. Excessive flexing of the tire causes internal temperatures to increase which softens the rubber tread resulting in rapid wear.

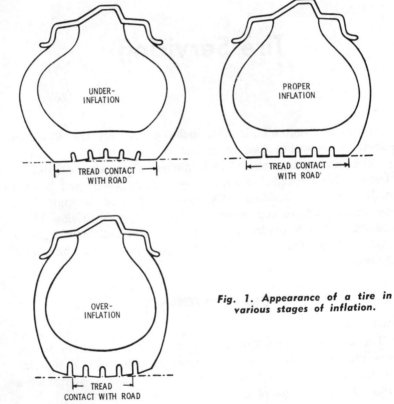

Fig. 1. Appearance of a tire in various stages of inflation.

Too much air pressure is equally bad. Over inflation reduces the tire distortion from normal and causes the tread to wear faster in the center portion than on the outside portion. Overinflated tires are also much more susceptible to fabric breaks.

The following rules will be helpful in preventing tire failure due to improper inflation.

Fig. 2. Abnormal tread wear due to underinflation.

1. Inflate tires to the pressure recommended by the manufacturer for the load and driving conditions to be encountered. Check the tire pressure at regular intervals and inflate only when the tire is cool.
2. Keep the valve caps screwed on finger-tight.
3. Inspect and replace any damaged or worn valve cores.
4. Check for slow leaks if air must be added at frequent and regular intervals.

Repair these slow leaks promptly to prevent permanent tire damage that will result from under inflation.

5. Check air pressure only while tire is cool. Do not bleed the tire (reduce the air pressure) when it is found the tire has a few pounds of extra pressure after being run. Bleeding will

Fig. 3. Abnormal tread wear due to overinflation.

cause excessive flexing of the sidewalls resulting in abnormally high internal tire temperatures. Besides, the tires will be badly underinflated when they cool off.

Abnormal tire wear resulting from underinflation is shown in Fig. 2. Overinflation also causes uneven tread wear such as that shown in Fig. 3. Other types of abnormal tire wear will sometimes be encountered and each will point to some factor which should be corrected promptly before the tire is ruined. For example,

Fig. 4. Tire wear due to fast driving on curves and around corners.

Fig. 5. A single worn spot or a series of cuppings around the tire may be caused by underinflation and/or mechanical irregularities.

excessive speed on curves and around corners will cause the condition illustrated in Fig. 4. A combination of underinflation and unbalance may cause a tire to wear similar to the one in Fig. 5. Incorrect wheel camber can cause the condition shown in Fig. 6, while misalignment resulted in the peculiar tread wear illustrated in Fig. 7.

Fig. 6. Tire wear as the result of incorrect camber.

Rotation

The tires on an automobile all wear differently, even under normal driving conditions, because each does a different kind of work. This is especially true of the front and rear tires. For example, the front tires: (1) withstand the forces exerted in steering the car; (2) hold the car straight on rough roads; (3) absorb bad driving habits and braking wear; and (4) are subject to misalignment and other mechanical irregularities. The rear wheels: (1) propel the car; (2) absorb "jack-rabbit" starts and stops;

(3) help hold the car on curves; (4) absorb the normal driving and stopping forces; (5) absorb spinning and slippage during starting and on curves; and (6) are subject to reverse camber and other mechanical irregularities.

Fig. 7. Feathered edges on the tread of this tire are caused by wheel misalignment.

To equalize the wear on all tires (including the spare) they should be rotated and run on different wheels at regular intervals as specified by the manufacturer. When tires wear unevenly (especially front tires) and are not rotated to different wheel positions, the uneven wear becomes worse and will cause such disturbances as shimmy, vibration, noise, thumps, bumps, and/or rough riding. Periodic rotation of the tires according to the diagram in Fig. 8 will materially lengthen tire life and contribute to greater driving comfort and safety.

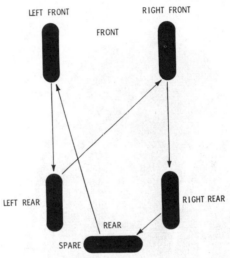

LEFT FRONT   RIGHT FRONT

FRONT

LEFT REAR   RIGHT REAR

REAR

SPARE

Fig. 8. Suggested rotation pattern to equalize tire wear.

TIRE REPAIR

Tube-Type Tires

Nearly everyone is familiar with the methods used to repair the tube-type tire. No trouble should be encountered with this type if the procedure outlined by the manufacturer of the repair material is faithfully followed. A few hints and precautions, however, may simplify the repair of tube-type tires and prevent costly and time consuming mistakes. After the repair has been made, make sure the tube is correctly mounted in the tire by following this procedure.

1. Insert the tube in the tire casing and inflate until nearly rounded out.
2. Apply approved rubber lubricant to the areas indicated in gray in Fig. 9.
3. Deflate the tube and mount the tire on the rim by following the usual standard procedure. Be careful not to pinch the tube, especially if hand tire tools are used instead of a tire-changing machine.

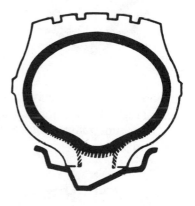

Fig. 9. Rubber lubricant applied to these areas before mounting will aid in positioning the tube correctly within the tire casing.

4. Center the valve and pull it through the hole in the rim. (A valve-fishing tool will be a great help in doing this.) After the valve is pulled through the hole, hold it firmly while inflating until the tire beads are properly seated around the entire circumference of the rim.
5. Completely deflate the tube by removing the valve core.
6. Reinflate to the proper pressure.

If this procedure is followed, the tube will be properly positioned in the tire-bead and rim area, as shown in Fig. 10. Improper lubri-

Fig. 10. The tube should be evenly distributed within the tire casing to prevent premature failure.

cation and mounting may cause the tube to be stretched thin in this area (Fig. 11), causing premature failure.

Other tube failures and their causes are shown in Figs. 12, 13, 14, and 15.

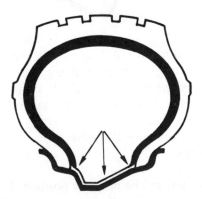

Fig. 11. A tube that has not been positioned properly may be stretched thin in the areas indicated by the arrows. This will almost certainly shorten the life of the tube.

Tubeless Tires

The repair of tubeless tires requires methods and techniques that differ somewhat from those used for tube-type tires. The following procedure should be followed.

1. Locate the leak by inflating the tire to its normal pressure and dip it into a water tank.

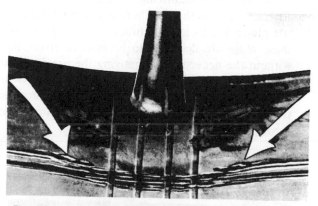

Fig. 12. A tube chafed by the tire beads. Inflating, deflating, and reinflating according to the approved procedure would have prevented this damage.

2. Mark the location of the leak with chalk or crayon. If no tank is available, or if the tire is still on the vehicle, the leak can usually be located by applying soapy water to the suspected areas of the tire.
3. If the leak appears at the valve stem, or around the rim, mark both the tire and rim. The tire will have to be removed from the rim if this type of leak is present, and the procedure listed under Demounting and Mounting followed.

4. If the leak is found to be caused by a cut or puncture, one of the following methods of repair are recommended:

  (a) *Hot-Patch Method*—In using this method it is necessary to thoroughly clean and remove all foreign matter from the hole left by the puncturing object without enlarging the injury. The manufacturer's instructions should then be followed in vulcanizing the patch.

  (b) *Rubber-Plug Method*—There are several types of rubber-plugs available for tubeless-tire repair. Some of these plugs are designed to be inserted from the inside without the necessity of removing the tire from the rim.

  When using this method, make sure to clean and lubricate the hole with the repair cement furnished for this purpose. Follow the instructions included with the repair kit you use.

Fig. 13. A broken valve stem caused by improper mounting or running the tire while underinflated or flat.

(c) *Cold-Patch Method*—This type of repair uses a self-vulcanizing patch. Thoroughly clean and remove all foreign matter from the hole left by the puncturing object without enlarging the hole. Buff an area around

Fig. 14. A tube pinched by tire irons while mounting the tire on the rim.

the hole on the inside of the tire large enough for the patch. Follow the manufacturer's instructions for application of the special cement and the self-vulcanizing cold patch.

(d) *Other Methods*—There are other methods to repair tubeless tires. Consult your tire-repair supplier for information on their availability.

Demounting and Mounting

Most wheels on the modern automobile now have reduced rim-well width and depth dimensions. This reduction was made necessary to provide for new safety features and new brake-drum clearances. These new wheel construction features have made necessary some changes in standard demounting and mounting procedures. (Some tire-changing machines may need adapters to handle tires on the newer-type rims.) These new tire-changing methods may be used for older-type rims as well as for tube-type tires (except for insertion of the tube).

Fig. 15. A crease or fold in a tube can be caused by the tube being larger than the inside of the tire. A wrong size or a stretched tube was used in a new tire.

IMPORTANT: In both mounting and demounting, always start with the narrow bead ledge.

Demounting—Use this method for removing the tire from the rim.

1. Place the tire and rim on the tire changer or on the floor with the narrow bead ledge up, as shown in Figs. 16 and 17.
2. Brush on a liberal amount of approved rubber lubricant on the tire beads.

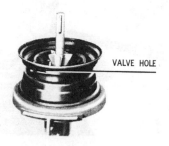

Fig. 16. Proper position of the rim is with the narrow ledge up. In this type, the valve is on the narrow ledge side.

3. Actual removal of the tire must be done carefully. Do not attempt to force the bead into the drop-center portion of the rim at only one spot. Instead, "inch" the bead into the

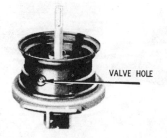

Fig. 17. Proper position of a rim in which the valve hole is in the wide ledge side. Note that the narrow ledge of the rim is up.

Fig. 18. Dents in the rim flanges should be removed with a hammer.

drop center a little at a time, working progressively around the tire to prevent damage to the bead area.

Rim Preparation—After the tire is removed, the rim should be thoroughly examined and corrective measures taken, as necessary.

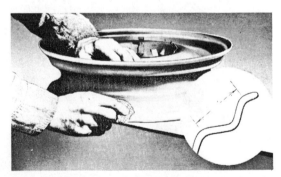

Fig. 19. The rim flange and bead seats must be clean. Steel wool or emery cloth is used in the area shown in the circle.

Fig. 20. Butt-weld grooves or high spots must be removed in the bead area to prevent air leaks.

1. Examine the rim flanges for sharp dents. Remove any dents with a hammer (Fig. 18), after which the hammer dents must be smoothed out with a file. If it is impossible to straighten the rim in this manner, have a rim-and-wheel service dealer do the job.

2. Clean the rim flange and bead seats with emery cloth or coarse steel wool (Fig. 19) to remove all foreign matter. Use a wire brush to remove any rust. Pitted areas may be smoothed with a file.

Fig. 21. The area around the valve hole must be cleaned both inside and outside the rim before installing the valve.

3. Inspect the butt-weld for any grooves or high spots in the bead area. Grooves or high spots may be removed with a file (Fig. 20).

Valve Installation—After the rim has been prepared, the valve is installed as follows.

1. Clean the area around the valve hole, both inside and outside the rim, with steel wool (Fig. 21). Remove any burrs or rough metal with a file.
2. Install the valve. There are two types of tubeless-tire valves available—the metal clamp-in type and the rubber snap-in type.

   (a) To install the metal clamp-in type (Fig. 22), place the larger rubber washer (oval or round, depending on the shape of the hole in the rim) over the valve base and insert the valve in the hole. Slip the smaller rubber washer over the valve stem, followed by the metal washer with the raised center facing up. Screw on the metal nut and tighten it until the small rubber washer is flush with the edge of the metal washer.

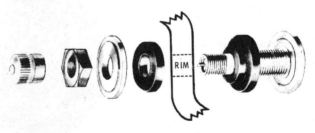

Fig. 22. A clamp-in metal valve assembly.

(b) To install the rubber snap-in type of valve (Fig. 23), first lubricate the valve with rubber lubricant. Insert the valve through the valve hole in the rim. Apply pressure to the base of the valve with a valve inserting tool until the valve snaps into place and is firmly seated against the rim surface. If an inserting tool is not available, the valve can be inserted by using a valve-fishing tool to pull the valve into position.

NOTE: **Rubber snap-in valves should not be used in oval-shaped holes. Metal clamp-in valves should be used instead.**

Fig. 23. A rubber snap-in type valve.

Mounting—After the rim is prepared and the proper valve is in place, the following procedure is recommended to mount the tire on the rim.

1. Lubricate the tire beads, rim flanges, and bead-ledge areas with a liberal amount of rubber lubricant. Properly lubricated beads will seat themselves quickly and easily with a minimum of air pressure.

2. Start the mounting procedure with the narrow ledge of the rim up. Ford, Mercury, and Chevrolet wheels require mounting the white wall or outer side of the tire first.

3. Inflate the tire to *no more than 40 lbs. pressure.* Use an extension slip-on chuck, as shown in Fig. 24, for safety. If 40 lbs. pressure will not seat the beads properly, deflate the tire, relubricating the beads, center the tire on the rim, and reinflate. After the beads have seated, deflate the tire to the recommended operating pressure.

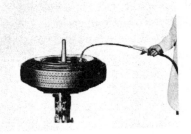

Fig. 24. Correct inflation practice. The operator is standing clear of the tire, using an extension gauge and clip-on chuck.

CAUTION: If a tire is not centered properly on the rim, inflation beyond 40 lbs. of pressure may break a bead with an explosive force, resulting in serious injury or death. DO NOT STAND OVER THE TIRE WHILE INFLATING IT. Lock the wheel down when using a tire-changing machine. Check the pressure frequently to be absolutely sure the 40-lb. limit is never exceeded.

Tire-Mounting Band—The use of a tire-mounting band (bead expander) is helpful when inflating tubeless tires. This device, shown in Fig. 25, constricts the tread center-line of the tire, which helps to force the beads onto the bead seats of the rim.

Fig. 25. A bead expander being used to help force the tire beads into their proper position.

The following procedure is recommended in using a bead expander.

1. Inflate the tire only enough (10 lbs. or less) to move the tire beads out to make contact with the bead seats on the rim. Remove the expander for safety.

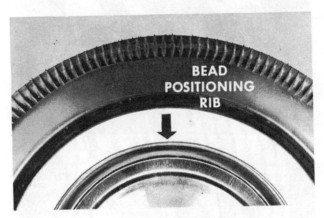

Fig. 26. When the beads are properly seated, the bead-positioning rib on the tire will be visible and evenly spaced around the entire rim.

2. Increase the air pressure as needed (up to 40 lbs.) to fully seat the tire beads on the rim (Fig. 26).

   NOTE: On a safety or hump-type rims, make sure the tire beads have snapped over the hump and are fully seated.

3. Check for leakage and, if none, reduce the air pressure to the recommended level.

WHEEL BALANCING

Modern suspension systems and higher driving speeds have made it necessary that the wheel and tire assembly be in balance if maximum driving and riding comfort, maximum safety, and maximum tire life are to be realized. Front wheels are more sensitive to an unbalanced condition than the rear wheels, but all four should be balanced to prolong tire life.

A wheel and tire assembly can be unbalanced in two ways— statically and dynamically. Static unbalance is indicated by an up-and-down hopping or pounding action, often called "wheel tramp. Dynamic unbalance will cause the wheel to wobble or shimmy. Either type of unbalance can exist without the other, although both types are usually present at the same time.

Wheel balance should be checked at regular intervals, and always after a tire has been repaired, retreaded, or recapped. Wheels which have not been balanced should be placed on the rear axle where an unbalanced condition does not affect the performance of the automobile as much as when they are placed on the front. Any unbalanced condition may be destructive and dangerous, reducing not only the life of the tires, but also the life of other vital parts of the automobile. Wheel balance is the equal distribution of the weight of the wheel, tire (and tube, if used), brake drum, and hub around the axis of rotation. The complete wheel assembly should be balanced both statically and dynamically.

Static Balance

A wheel assembly may be considered to be in static balance when it will remain at rest in any position to which it is revolved on its axis. A wheel that is not statically balanced (Fig. 27) causes the tire to bounce at each revolution. The effect of static unbalance increases with the speed of the automobile.

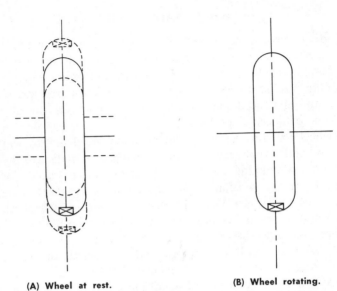

(A) Wheel at rest.   (B) Wheel rotating.

Fig. 27. A wheel assembly with an uneven distribution of weight at right angles to the axis of rotation is statically unbalanced. When the wheel is rotated, the heavy side causes the assembly to move up and down, producing "wheel tramp."

Dynamic Balance

Perfect static balance does not mean that the wheel assembly is in perfect balance. It must still be dynamically balanced.

A wheel that is dynamically out of balance does not have its weight distributed evenly in a plane perpendicular to its axis of rotation. This type of unbalance causes the wheels to vibrate rapidly from side to side as they rotate. The reason for this vibration, or wobble, is the attempt the wheel is making to align the heavy spots in a plane that is at right angles to the axis of rotation (Fig. 28). As the speed of the automobile increases, the wobble increases, and steering becomes more difficult. This causes excessive wear of the tires, wheel bearings, king pins, ball joints, steering connections, etc.

Wheel Run-Out and Eccentricity

A wheel should always be checked for *run-out* (wobble) and *eccentricity* (roundness) before balancing the wheel and tire

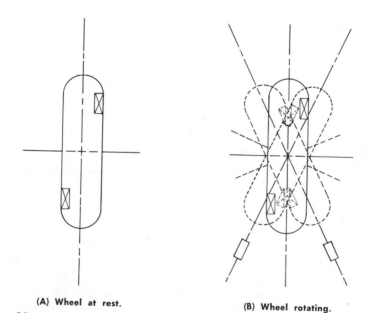

(A) Wheel at rest.   (B) Wheel rotating.

Fig. 28. A wheel assembly that is dynamically unbalanced will wobble when rotated.

assembly. The run-out should not exceed 1/16″ as measured on the side of the rim at the base of the tire.

Excessive run-out can be caused by a bent wheel, an improperly mounted wheel, and worn knuckle bearings or steering connections.

These parts should always be checked and corrected whenever excessive run-out is encountered.

The wheel should also run concentric within 1/16″ as measured on the tire-bead seat of the rim with the tire removed. This is a check of the roundness of the wheel. Any wheel that is out-of-round by more than the specified amount should be replaced with a good unit.

Balancing Methods

Static balancing can be carried out on a locally-made balancing fixture, if necessary. However, dynamic balancing requires special equipment to determine the amount and location of weights to correct the condition without disturbing the static balance. Several types of wheel balancers are available for both static and dynamic balancing. One such model is shown in Fig. 29. The specific instructions provided by the manufacturer of the particular balancer being used should always be carefully followed.

Static Balance—If a special wheel balancer is not available, static balance can be corrected as follows:

1. Remove the wheel and hub from the spindle as a unit.
2. Clean all grease from the wheel bearings and races.
3. Clamp a clean spindle in a bench vise, or clean the spindle on the car carefully.
4. Mount the wheel on the spindle and adjust the bearings loosely so the wheel is just held in position and is practically frictionless.
5. Make sure the tire is inflated to the correct pressure.
6. Spin the wheel by hand and allow it to stop by itself. The wheel will stop with the heavy side at the bottom.
7. Mark the heaviest point and also the lightest point, which will be diametrically opposite.

Courtesy Bear Manufacturing Co.

Fig. 29. A wheel balancer for performing static and dynamic balancing of an automobile wheel assembly.

8. Install two wheel weights, one on the inside and one on the outside of the rim, and both opposite the heavy point on the wheel.

9. Move these two weights equally in opposite directions toward the heavy side until the wheel is in balance.

10. Repack the wheel bearings, and reinstall the wheel according to the manufacturer's specifications.

Static unbalance can be corrected by the use of special balancing equipment. Some of this equipment requires that the wheel be removed from the car. Other makes of wheel balancers, however, allow correcting unbalance without the necessity of removing the wheel from the automobile. Fig. 30 shows a balancer being used to balance the wheel on the automobile.

Dynamic Balance—Special balancing equipment is necessary to balance a wheel dynamically. The instructions of the equipment manufacturer should be carefully followed. The general procedure is as follows:

Courtesy Hunter Engineering Co.

Fig. 30. An on-the-car wheel balancer. The wheel-balancer unit is secured to the wheel, and the wheel is rotated at high speed by means of a spinner unit.

1. Attach the wheel to the balancer, or the balancer to the wheel, depending on which type of unit is being used. In either case the wheel assembly should be clean, with no accumulation of mud or grease.
2. Spin the wheel at high speed.
3. Determine the size of weights needed.
4. Determine the points on both sides of the rim where the weights must be attached and attach them.
5. Recheck the static balance to see that it hasn't been disturbed.

An unbalance of up to one ounce can usually be tolerated without affecting the driving and riding qualities of the automobile.

CHAPTER 10

Brakes

No other part of an automobile contributes more to safe operation than the brakes. Brakes must not only be able to stop a moving automobile, but they must stop it in the shortest possible distance.

Because the brakes are expected to decelerate an automobile at a faster rate than the engine can accelerate it, the brakes must be able to control a greater amount of power than that developed by the engine. For this reason, the brakes on a modern high-powered automobile must be well designed and kept in top-notch operating condition by regular inspection, adjustment, and repair.

Hydraulic brakes are now used on all domestic passenger cars. Power brakes (covered in Chapter 11) are becoming more popular and are available as optional equipment on most cars. Self-adjusting brakes have appeared on all cars manufactured in recent years.

Nearly all cars use essentially the same general type of brake assembly, known as the internal-expanding type. An example of this type of brake is shown in Fig. 1. Notice the hydraulic cylinder which furnishes the power to move the brake shoes outward until they contact the brake drum. The assembly shown in Fig. 1 is not self-adjusting, but must be adjusted manually as the brake linings wear.

Self-Adjusting Brakes

A self-adjusting brake assembly is pictured in Fig. 2. As the brake linings wear, the brake shoes must travel a greater distance to come in contact with the brake drum. When this distance ex-

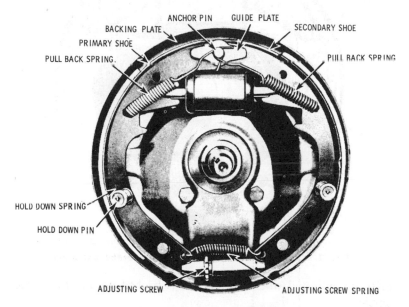

Fig. 1. A typical brake assembly of the internal-expanding type.

ceeds a predetermined amount, and the car is driven in reverse and the brakes applied, the automatic adjusting lever engages the star wheel and turns it as the brakes are released. This action tightens the brakes and will continue each time the car travels in reverse, until the adjusting lever no longer moves far enough to engage the next tooth on the star wheel. Thus, the brakes are auto-

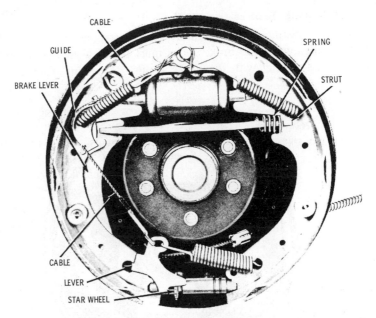

CABLE

GUIDE

BRAKE LEVER

SPRING

STRUT

CABLE

LEVER

STAR WHEEL

Courtesy Dodge Div., Chrysler Motors Corp.

Fig. 2. An example of a self-adjusting brake assembly.

matically adjusted whenever the car is backed up and the brakes applied.

The Hydraulic System

Automobile brakes are controlled by a hydraulic system similar to the one shown in diagram form in Fig. 3. When the brakes are applied, the force from the brake pedal operates the piston in the master cylinder. This action forces the hydraulic fluid out of the master cylinder and into each wheel cylinder through the connecting hoses and metal tubing. The fluid entering the wheel cylinders

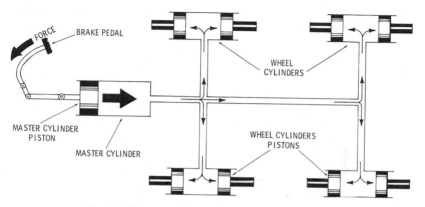

Fig. 3. Diagram of a hydraulic brake system.

forces the opposed pistons farther apart, thus moving the brake shoes outward against the brake drums. As the pressure applied to the brake pedal is increased, greater hydraulic pressure is built up inside the wheel cylinders, and they exert a greater pressure to the brake shoes. When the brake pedal is released, springs on the brake shoes return the pistons in the wheel cylinders to their normal position, forcing the hydraulic brake fluid back into the master cylinder.

Parking Brakes

Parking or emergency brakes on all cars are mechanical and are independent of the hydraulic system. The parking brakes on most cars utilize the brake shoes in the rear brake assembly, actuating them by means of a cable connected to the parking-brake lever through a mechanical linkage. On some Chrysler-built cars, however, a completely independent parking-brake system attached to the rear of the transmission will be found. With this type of parking brake, if the car has an automatic transmission, the brake assembly will be of the internal-expanding type, while with a manual transmission, an external-contracting type is used.

Brake Shoes

Brake shoes may be made of malleable iron, cast steel, drop-forged steel, pressed steel, or cast aluminum. Most passenger automobiles have brake shoes made of steel because of ease and cost of manufacture. In addition, steel shoes expand at about the same rate as the brake drums when heat is generated by braking action, thus maintaining the proper clearance between the brake drum and brake shoe.

A friction lining is riveted or bonded to the face of the brake shoe, and is used to make contact with the brake drum to provide braking action. Bonded linings are secured to the shoe with a special cement and then baked to set the cement.

Brake Drums

Brake drums are usually made of pressed steel, cast iron, or a combination of the two. Cast-iron drums dissipate the heat generated by braking action more rapidly than steel, and offer greater friction to the brake lining. However, cast-iron drums having sufficient strength are much heavier than steel. For this reason, many automobiles have brake drums that are a combination of the two types of metal. Brake drums that are a combination of cast iron and cast aluminum are sometimes used.

Some automobiles, especially the newer models having higher-horsepower engines, have cooling ribs or fins around the brake drum. These ribs or fins offer a greater surface area to the surrounding air, thus allowing the heat generated by braking action to be dissipated more rapidly. Some cars even have slots cut in the wheel covers in such a way as to force air over the surface of the brake drums to increase the cooling effect.

MAINTENANCE AND ADJUSTMENTS

When servicing any brake system, it is very important that absolute cleanliness be observed. Any foreign matter that enters the hydraulic system may clog the lines, ruin the rubber cups in the master and wheel cylinders, cause inefficient operation, or even cause complete failure of the braking system. Dirt or grease on a brake lining may cause that brake to grab when the brakes are first applied, and then fade as heavier brake application is made.

Hydraulic System

Each make and model of automobile may require certain specific procedures for the maintenance and adjustment of the hydraulic system. When such adjustment or maintenance is necessary, the manufacturer's service manual should be referred to for the proper procedure. The following instructions, however, will be adequate in the majority of cases.

Hydraulic Brake Fluid—Only an approved brake fluid should be used when necessary to add fluid or to bleed the brakes. An approved fluid will give satisfactory performance at any atmospheric temperature that will be encountered. In addition, it will have a high boiling point to prevent evaporation and vapor lock, and will remain fluid at the lowest temperature at which the car will be driven. Its chemical composition will be such that it will not deteriorate the rubber gaskets, pistons, valves, and lines in the braking system.

To determine if the brake fluid is contaminated with mineral oil, the following tests can be made.

1. Drain a small amount of the suspected brake fluid into a small glass jar. If the fluid separates into two distinct layers, mineral oil is present.

2. Add 1 part of water to 2 parts of the contents and shake. If the contents turn milky, oil may be present. If the contents remain clear, no oil is present. Discard any fluid drained or bled from the system. Do not reuse, as such fluid may contain particles of dirt or other contamination that might be harmful to the brake system.

In the event that improper fluid has been added to the system, the following procedure will be necessary.

1. Drain the entire system and flush with 180-proof alcohol or a suitable brake-system cleaning fluid.
2. Replace all rubber parts of the system, including brake hoses.
3. Refill the brake system with an approved hydraulic brake fluid.
4. Bleed the system according to the manufacturer's instructions, or the instructions listed next.

Bleeding the Hydraulic System—The hydraulic brake system of an automobile must be bled whenever a pipe line or any part of the system has been disconnected, whenever a leak has allowed air to enter the system or whenever the fluid level in the master cylinder has become too low. The system must be absolutely free of air at all times.

The hydraulic system can be bled manually, or by using pressure bleeding equipment. To bleed the system, proceed as follows:

1. To bleed the brakes manually, check the fluid level in the master-cylinder reservoir and, if necessary, add approved fluid. KEEP THE RESERVOIR AT LEAST HALF FULL DURING THE BLEEDING OPERATION.
2. To bleed the brakes with pressure equipment, connect the

pressure tank to the master-cylinder reservoir and increase the pressure to the point recommended by the manufacturer of the brake-bleeding equipment. This is usually 20 to 30 psi.

3. Attach a bleeder tube to the bleeder valve of the wheel to be bled (Fig. 4). The bleeder tube must be kept submerged in a clean container partially filled with approved brake fluid throughout the entire bleeding operation.

NOTE: Most car manufacturers specify the order in which the wheel cylinders should be bled. Check the service manual for the correct order. Usually, the wheel farthest from the master cylinder is checked first.

4. Unscrew the bleeder valve approximately three-quarters of a turn with a suitable wrench. If pressure equipment is used, watch the flow of liquid from the bleeder tube. When air bubbles stop appearing, close the bleeder valve.

If the brakes are being bled manually, the brake pedal must be pumped during this operation to force the fluid from the bleeder hose. To do this, open the bleeder valve, fully depress the brake pedal, and then close the valve. Slowly release the pedal until it has returned to its normal position. Continue operating the pedal and opening and closing the bleeder valve until all air bubbles stop emerging from the bleeder tube. (This operation, of course, calls for the services of two men, one to operate the brake pedal on signal, and the other to open and close the bleeder valve.)

5. Close the bleeder valve and remove the bleeder tube.

6. Repeat the preceding steps on the remaining wheel cylinders, making sure the fluid in the master cylinder is maintained at the proper level at all times.

7. After the bleeding operation is complete, check the fluid level in the master cylinder and replenish if necessary.

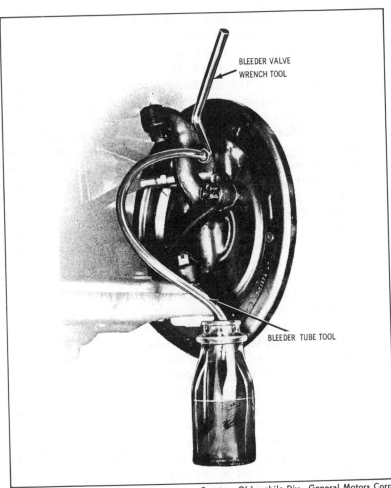

BLEEDER VALVE
WRENCH TOOL

BLEEDER TUBE TOOL

Courtesy Oldsmobile Div., General Motors Corp.

Fig. 4. Bleeder tube connected to the bleeder valve on an automobile wheel. The tube must be kept submerged in brake fluid during the entire operation.

8. Discard all brake fluid removed from the system by the bleeding operation. **Do not reuse.**

Master Cylinder—The operating principles of most master cylinders are very similar. Construction features and appearances may differ, however, depending on the make and model of the automobile. Fig. 5 shows a typical example of a master cylinder used in a late-model car having standard brakes.

An incorrectly adjusted brake pedal can keep the master cylinder piston from fully returning to its released position, which may cause brake drag or lock up. Brake drag may also be caused by improper adjustment of the brake shoes during shoe adjustment. Therefore, always check the free-pedal movement before making brake shoe adjustments.

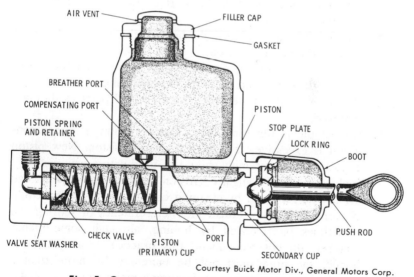

Courtesy Buick Motor Div., General Motors Corp.

Fig. 5. Cross-section of a typical master cylinder.

Misadjustment, binding, or lack of lubrication of the master cylinder push rod can also cause brake drag or lock up, and should be checked before making brake shoe adjustment. The push rod on some automobiles cannot be adjusted, so binding or lack of lubrication will be the only thing that will prevent the foot pedal (and master-cylinder piston) from returning to its normal position.

If it is necessary to remove the master cylinder for repair or overhaul, proceed as follows:

1. Remove the clevis pin from the push rod.
2. Disconnect the push rod.
3. Remove the brake line from the master cylinder. Cover the open end of the line with tape or other suitable material to prevent dirt from entering the system.
4. Disconnect the stop-light leads if a stop-light switch is an integral part of the unit.
5. Remove the nuts and/or bolts holding the master cylinder in place and slide the unit out.
6. Thoroughly clean the outside of the master cylinder, then remove the cover and drain all the brake fluid.
7. Disassemble the master unit, inspecting all parts as they are removed.
8. Inspect the piston for scoring and corrosion. If either condition is excessive, replace with a new piston. New piston cups and valve assembly should be used with a new piston.
9. Light scratches or slight corrosion on the cylinder walls can usually be removed by cleaning carefully with crocus cloth. **Never use emery cloth.** Heavier scratches or scoring can sometimes be removed by honing, although some manufacturers do not recommend this practice. If a cylinder is honed, the bore must not be increased by more than a specified amount (see manufacturer's maintenance manual).

Honing will often cause rapid wear of the piston and rubber cups, and an increased pedal pressure necessary to apply the brakes.

10. Use extreme care in cleaning the master cylinder after reconditioning. Remove all dirt, dust, and grit by flushing with alcohol. (**CAUTION: Do not use antifreeze-type alcohol, gasoline, kerosene, or any other cleaning fluid that might contain even a trace of oil.**) Wipe dry with a clean lintless cloth and reflush with alcohol. Dry the assembly with compressed air, and flush with clean, approved brake fluid. (Make sure the compensator port in the master cylinder is open.)

11. Immerse the piston, cups, and valve assembly in approved brake fluid before assembly.

12. Reassemble the master cylinder and install it. Make sure all connections are tight and the push rod (if adjustable) is adjusted properly.

13. Fill the master-cylinder reservoir to the required level with approved brake fluid.

14. Bleed the brake system to remove all air.

15. Recheck fluid level in master cylinder.

Wheel Cylinders—A wheel cylinder may not function properly due to natural wear, contamination of the brake fluid causing deterioration of the rubber cups, broken or weak spring, scored or corroded piston or cylinder bore, etc. Any of the above troubles will make necessary the removal of the wheel cylinder for inspection, repair or replacement. The operating principle and general construction of nearly all wheel cylinders are similar. An example of a typical wheel cylinder is shown in Fig. 6. The wheel cylinders for the front and rear wheels are usually different and cannot be interchanged.

The procedure for removing the wheel cylinders will vary for different makes and models of cars, and for front and rear wheels. If doubt exists as to the proper method, the service manual for the particular car in question should be consulted.

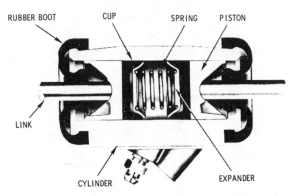

Courtesy Oldsmobile Div., General Motors Corp.

Fig. 6. Cross-section of a typical wheel cylinder.

The general procedure for inspection and repair of wheel cylinders is as follows.

1. Remove the brake drum.
2. Remove the brake shoe pull-back spring. (On some cars, it is also necessary to remove the brake shoes. Consult the service manual for specific instructions.)
3. Disconnect the brake line or hose from the wheel cylinder. Tape the end of the line to prevent entrance of dirt.
4. Remove the wheel-cylinder retaining bolts and lift the wheel cylinder free.
5. Remove the links and rubber boots from the cylinder.
6. Remove the pistons, cups, expanders, and spring.

7. Wash all metal parts in alcohol or brake flushing fluid and blow out all passages with compressed air.

8. Inspect the cups for swelling or distortion. If the cups are swollen, contamination of the brake fluid should be suspected, and the entire hydraulic system should be flushed, all rubber parts in the system should be inspected, including the flexible brake hose. Replace any damaged parts.

9. Inspect the wheel cylinder bore for scratches, scoring, rust, pits, or etches. Any such condition should be corrected if possible. Light scratches, scoring, or corrosion can sometimes be removed by using crocus cloth or by honing. (**NOTE: Some manufacturers recommend replacement instead of any attempt to polish or hone the cylinder bore.**) If honing is performed, the cylinder bore should not be increased beyond the limits specified by the manufacturer (usually .002-.003 inch). If the diameter should be increased beyond the specified limit, the entire wheel-cylinder assembly should be replaced.

10. Check the fit of the pistons in the cylinder bore (Fig. 7). The clearance should be within the manufacturers specified limits (usually .002-.005 inch). Replace the cylinder if the clearance is not within the specified limits.

11. Shake the excess cleaning fluid from the wheel cylinder and lubricate the bore with approved brake fluid. (**NOTE: Some manufacturers recommend assembling the wheel cylinder without lubricating any of the parts with brake fluid. Consult the service manual to determine if this is true for the car being serviced.**)

12. Install the spring, expanders, cups, and pistons in the cylinder bore.

13. Install the boots and links.

14. Install the assembly on the wheel.

15. After the installation is complete, bleed the system to remove any air.

Brake Lines and Hoses—Brake lines and hoses are made of special material to withstand the high pressure that exists when the brakes are applied. Only approved line and hose should be used for replacement. **Do not use copper tubing as a replacement.**

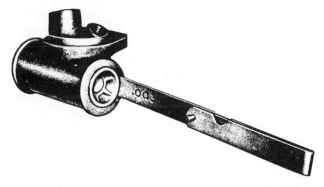

Fig. 7. Checking the piston clearance in a wheel cylinder.

When replacing metal brake tubing, it is important to use the proper flaring tool to flare the ends of the tubing to fit the compression couplings. The tubing should be double flared with a suitable flaring tool, such as the one shown in Fig. 8. This type of tool produces a double-lap flare on the end of the tube that is necessary for a strong and leakproof joint.

Proper bending tools should be used to bend the tubing to fit the underbody or rear axle contours. If an attempt is made to bend the tubing without tools (especially short-radius bends), there is danger of the tubing kinking and collapsing. New tubing should be cleaned and flushed with alcohol before final installation.

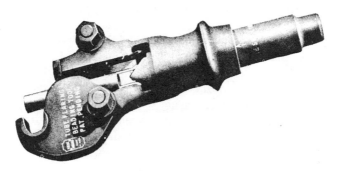

Fig. 8. A double-flaring tool used to flare the ends of hydraulic brake lines.

The new tubing should be routed carefully to prevent interference with any moving part of the vehicle, such as springs, shock absorbers, exhaust pipes, etc. Contact with any of these parts will result in abrasion of the tubing and eventual failure.

Brake hoses should be inspected whenever any brake service is performed. They should be checked for cracks, scuffing, worn spots, interference with chassis parts, and faulty installation that causes twisting, pulling, and contact with wheels, tires, or chassis parts.

Always use approved replacement hose, and check mating surfaces for nicks and burrs. Position the new hose to avoid contact with chassis parts, especially the exhaust pipe and shock absorbers. Check the clearance of the front brake hoses throughout the entire steering range with the normal weight of the car on the wheels.

Bleed all brakes if any connection has been opened for inspection, repair, or replacement.

Brake Drums—Whenever brake drums are removed, they should be inspected for cracks, deep grooves, scoring, and out-of-round. Any of these conditions should be corrected to restore full braking efficiency and to prevent premature failure of other brake parts.

Cracked brake drums should be replaced. Slight scoring can usually be eliminated by rubbing with fine emery cloth. Deep grooves and/or an out-of-round condition can only be corrected by reboring. A brake drum can be checked for an out-of-round condition by measuring the inside diameter at two points at right angles to each other with an inside micrometer fitted with extension rods. The amount of variation between the two readings will depend on the size of the brake drum. Consult the car's service manual for the correct specifications.

Brake drums may be rebored either by turning on a lathe or by grinding. The best brake performance is usually obtained by turning, using a very fine lathe feed. The braking surface must be smooth and free of tool or chatter marks. Drums that are to be used with standard size brake linings should have only a small amount of metal removed. If this is not sufficient to correct the condition, then the drum must be rebored to accommodate oversize linings. Check the specifications to determine the new diameter to which the drum should be rebored. Most car manufacturers specify .06 inch as the maximum amount over the standard diameter. Drums rebored to more than this specified amount will not dissipate the heat properly and will be subject to distortion.

When new drums are to be installed, they must be cleaned with a nongreasy cleaning fluid to remove any rustproofing oil from the braking surface. **Do not use gasoline or kerosene.**

Brake Shoes—Brake shoes should be checked for cracks, distortion, and lining wear whenever trouble is suspected in that area. Cracked or bent shoes should be replaced. The brake linings should be replaced if they are worn to within 1/32 inch of the rivets, or have been saturated with oil or grease. The brake linings on the opposite wheel should also be replaced at the same time. The brake drum must be measured to determine if standard size or oversize brake shoe assemblies are required.

New linings may be riveted or molded on. In either case, the new linings should be ground down on a machine having a cylindrical grinding wheel. The maximum amount they should be ground is specified in the manufacturer's service manual, but usually is from .010 to .025 inch under the diameter of the brake drum. Some replacement linings are preground and, of course, do not require this operation.

A preliminary adjustment should be made whenever new linings have been installed. This is done by using a gauge that is set to the diameter of the brake drum (Fig. 9). The gauge is then turned over and the other side is fitted to the brake shoes by turning the star-wheel brake adjustment until the gauge just slides over the lining (Fig. 10). The gauge is then rotated around the brake shoe surface to assure that proper clearance is present.

NOTE: Whenever it is necessary to back off the brake shoe adjustment on self-adjusting brakes, the adjusting lever must be held away from the sprocket (star wheel).

Care must be taken during any operation in which the brake linings are exposed that grease, oil, or dirt does not come in contact with the braking surfaces of the brake drum and brake shoes.

Brake Adjustment

Specific procedures for adjusting the brakes are given in the service manual for each make and model of car. The following general procedure, however, will be satisfactory for adjusting the brakes on most cars manufactured by American Motors, General Motors, and Ford Motor Company. Some late-model Chrysler-made cars also use this procedure.

1. Raise the car until the wheels are off the floor. If a frame-contact hoist is used, disconnect the parking-brake cables to

Fig. 9. Checking the brake drum diameter with a brake-shoe clearance gauge.

prevent the rear-wheel sag from partially applying the rear brakes.

2. Remove the adjusting hole cover in the brake flange plate. (NOTE: Some General Motors cars have the adjusting hole in the brake drum, as shown in Fig. 11. This type requires

the brake-adjusting tool to be moved in a direction opposite that when the access hole is in the brake flange plate.)

3. Expand the brake shoes (tighten the brakes) by inserting a brake-adjusting tool through the adjusting hole (Fig. 12) and turning the star wheel until a light uniform drag is felt on

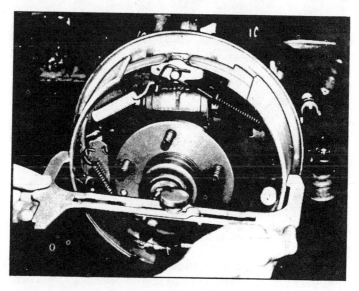

Fig. 10. Checking the brake shoe diameter for proper clearance.

the brake drum. This is accomplished on most cars by moving the end of the adjusting tool downward while it is engaged with the star wheel. (The end of the tool is moved upward when the adjusting hole is in the brake drum.)

4. Turn the adjusting screw back 10 notches, or more if drag is still felt on the brake drums. Always back the adjusting screw off the same number of notches on all four wheels.

Fig. 11. Some makes and models of General Motors cars have the brake-adjusting hole in the brake-drum assembly.

CAUTION: On self-adjusting brakes, it is absolutely necessary to hold the adjuster lever away from the star wheel while backing off the adjusting screw (Fig. 13). Failure to do so will damage the adjusting mechanism.

5. Repeat operations 3 and 4 at each wheel and replace the hole covers.
6. Reconnect the parking-brake cables and adjust the parking brakes if necessary.
7. Road test the brakes.

Fig. 12. Adjusting the service brakes.

The following procedure should be used to adjust the brakes on Chrysler-made cars that have cam-adjusted brakes similar to the one shown in Fig. 14. (Whenever the brake shoes have been replaced or reinstalled for any reason, always apply pedal pressure before making a brake adjustment. This is necessary to center the brake shoes in the brake drum to permit proper adjustment.)

1. Raise the car until the wheels are off the floor.

Front-Brake Adjustment

2. Turn one of the adjusting cams in the direction of forward wheel rotation until the brake drum is solid against the brake drum and the wheel is locked. Refer to Fig. 15.
3. Turn the adjusting cam slowly in the opposite direction until no drag is felt.

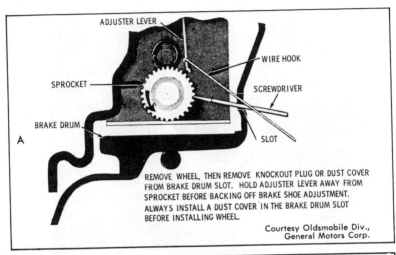

A

REMOVE WHEEL, THEN REMOVE KNOCKOUT PLUG OR DUST COVER
FROM BRAKE DRUM SLOT. HOLD ADJUSTER LEVER AWAY FROM
SPROCKET BEFORE BACKING OFF BRAKE SHOE ADJUSTMENT.
ALWAYS INSTALL A DUST COVER IN THE BRAKE DRUM SLOT
BEFORE INSTALLING WHEEL.

Courtesy Oldsmobile Div.,
General Motors Corp.

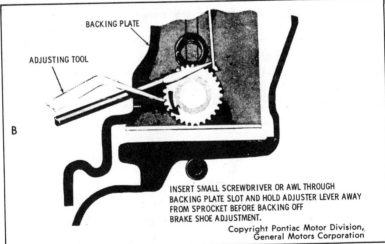

B

INSERT SMALL SCREWDRIVER OR AWL THROUGH
BACKING PLATE SLOT AND HOLD ADJUSTER LEVER AWAY
FROM SPROCKET BEFORE BACKING OFF
BRAKE SHOE ADJUSTMENT.

Copyright Pontiac Motor Division,
General Motors Corporation

Fig. 13. Holding the adjuster lever away from the star wheel to back off the brake adjustment; (A) Adjusting hole in brake drum; (B) Adusting hole in the brake flange plate.

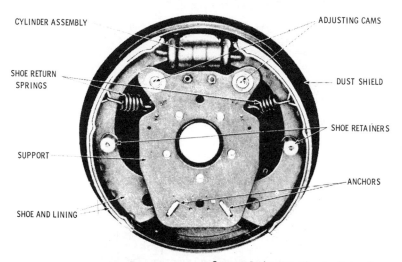

CYLINDER ASSEMBLY

SHOE RETURN
SPRINGS

SUPPORT

SHOE AND LINING

ADJUSTING CAMS

DUST SHIELD

SHOE RETAINERS

ANCHORS

Courtesy Dodge Div., Chrysler Motors Corp.

Fig. 14. Some Chrysler-made cars use brakes that have adjusting cams instead of a star-wheel adjustment.

4. Repeat the operation on the other cam.
5. Repeat steps 2, 3, and 4 on the opposite front wheel.

Rear-Brake Adjustment

6. Turn the forward adjusting cam in the direction of forward wheel rotation (See Fig. 15) until the wheel is locked.
7. Turn the adjusting cam slowly in the opposite direction until no drag is felt.
8. Turn the rearward adjusting cam in the direction opposite to forward wheel rotation until the wheel is locked.
9. Turn the adjusting cam slowly in the opposite direction until no drag is felt.
10. Repeat steps 6, 7, 8, and 9 on the opposite rear wheel.
11. Road test the brakes.

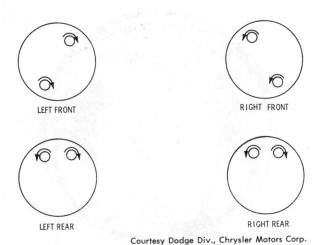

LEFT FRONT   RIGHT FRONT

LEFT REAR   RIGHT REAR

Courtesy Dodge Div., Chrysler Motors Corp.

Fig. 15. Brake adjusting diagram for cam-adjusted brakes used on some Chrysler-made cars.

BRAKE-SYSTEM TROUBLES AND REMEDIES

Symptom and Possible Causes   *Possible Remedy*

Pedal Goes to the Floor (or nearly so)

(a) Fluid low in master cylinder.	(a) Fill and bleed the master cylinder.
(b) Excessively worn brake linings.	(b) Reline and adjust brakes.
(c) Improperly adjusted brake shoes.	(c) Adjust brakes.
(d) Leaking wheel cylinders.	(d) Recondition or replace wheel cylinders and replace linings.
(e) Loose or broken brake line.	(e) Tighten all brake fittings or replace broken line.

Symptom and Possible Causes	*Possible Remedy*
(f) Air in hydraulic system.	(f) Bleed and fill hydraulic system.
(g) Leaking or worn master cylinder.	(g) Recondition or replace master cylinder and bleed the hydraulic system.
(h) Self-adjusters not working.	(h) Clean and free-up all threaded areas of adjuster mechanism. Replace the thrust washer if necessary.

Pedal Spongy

(a) Air in hydraulic system.	(a) Bleed hydraulic system and fill master cylinder.
(b) Improper brake fluid (low boiling point).	(b) Drain, flush, and refill with approved brake fluid.
(c) Excessively worn or cracked brake drums.	(c) Replace defective drums.

All Brakes Drag

(a) Incorrect brake adjustment.	(a) Adjust brakes and check fluid.
(b) Parking brakes engaged.	(b) Release or adjust parking brakes.
(c) Wheel cylinder sticking.	(c) Recondition wheel cylinder.
(d) Weak or broken brake shoe return spring.	(d) Replace return spring.
(e) Brake pedal binding.	(e) Free-up and lubricate pedal and linkage.

Symptom and Possible Causes	Possible Remedy
(f) Master-cylinder cup sticking.	(f) Recondition master cylinder.
(g) Incorrect master-cylinder push-rod adjustment.	(g) Adjust push rod.
(h) Mineral oil in system.	(h) Flush entire brake system, replace all rubber parts, and refill with approved brake fluid.
(i) Compensating port in master cylinder restricted.	(i) Overhaul master cylinder.

One Brake Drags

(a) Loose or damaged wheel bearings.	(a) Adjust or replace wheel bearings.
(b) Weak, broken, or unhooked brake shoe return spring.	(b) Replace return spring.
(c) Brake shoes adjusted too close to brake drum.	(c) Adjust brakes correctly.
(d) Brake shoe bent and binding on backing plate.	(d) Replace shoes.
(e) Brake drum out of round.	(e) Turn brake drum down.

Pedal Applies Brakes but Slowly Goes to Floor

(a) External leaks.	(a) Check master cylinder, wheel cylinder, and all lines for leaks. Repair as necessary.

Symptom and Possible Causes	*Possible Remedy*

Uneven Braking

(a) Grease on linings.

(b) Tires improperly inflated.

(c) Incorrect brake adjustment.

(d) Brake drums out of round.

(e) Bent brake shoes.

(f) Restricted brake hose or line.

(g) Unmatched brake lining.

(h) Front end out of alignment.

(i) Broken rear spring.

(j) Brake drum scored.

(a) Remove drums and clean and dry linings, or replace if necessary.

(b) Inflate tires to the recommended pressure.

(c) Adjust brakes correctly.

(d) Grind or replace brake drums.

(e) Replace defective shoes.

(f) Replace plugged hose or line.

(g) Match lining on all wheels.

(h) Align front end.

(i) Replace spring.

(j) Grind or replace defective drum.

Hard Pedal

(a) Incorrect brake lining.

(b) Incorrect brake adjustment.

(c) Frozen brake-pedal linkage.

(d) Restricted brake hose or line.

(a) Install matched and approved linings.

(b) Adjust brakes correctly.

(c) Free-up and lubricate linkage.

(d) Replace defective hose or line.

Symptom and Possible Causes

(e) Grease, brake fluid, mud, or water on brake linings.

(f) Full surface of linings not contacting brake drum.

(g) Scored brake drums.

Possible Remedy

(e) Clean, dry, or replace linings. Correct cause of grease or fluid.

(f) Free-up shoe linkage, grind linings, or replace shoes.

(g) Turn or grind drums and replace linings.

Wheel Locks

(a) Loose or torn brake lining.

(b) Incorrect wheel-bearing adjustment.

(c) Wheel-cylinder cups sticking.

(d) Loose backing plate.

(a) Replace brake lining.

(b) Clean, pack, and adjust wheel bearings.

(c) Recondition or replace wheel cylinder.

(d) Tighten backing plate.

Brakes Grab

(a) Grease or brake fluid on lining.

(b) Scored drums.

(c) Loose backing plate.

(d) Drums out of round.

(a) Clean or replace linings. Find and correct grease or fluid leak.

(b) Grind or replace drums.

(c) Tighten or replace backing plate.

(d) Grind or replace drums.

Brakes Chatter

(a) Rough or scored brake drum.

(b) Loose backing plate or shoe support.

(a) Grind or replace brake drum.

(b) Tighten the backing plate.

Symptom and Possible Causes

(c) Bent support plate.
(d) Bent brake shoe.
(e) Machine grooves in contact face of brake drum.
(f) Saturated brake lining.
(g) Loose front-suspension system.
(h) Poor lining-to-drum contact.

Brakes Do Not Self-Adjust

(a) Adjuster screw frozen.

(b) Adjuster screw corroded at the thrust washer.
(c) Automatic-adjuster mechanism broken or bent.

Possible Remedy

(c) Replace support plate.
(d) Replace brake shoe.
(e) Grind or replace brake drum.
(f) Replace linings.
(g) Overhaul front-suspension system.
(h) Grind lining to correct contour, replace lining, or replace brake shoe.

(a) Clean and free-up all thread areas.
(b) Clean the threads and replace thrust washer.
(c) Repair automatic-adjuster mechanism as necessary.

CHAPTER 11

Power Brakes

Power brakes are now available for all domestic cars produced in the last few years. They are factory installed as optional equipment, but can be added to existing cars having standard brakes.

The wheel-brake assemblies are the same on cars having power brakes as on cars with standard brakes. The power-brake unit merely provides a lighter pedal pressure with a reduced pedal travel making possible a break-pedal height near that of the accelerator pedal.

The power to operate the power brakes is obtained from the vacuum produced in the intake manifold. This means, of course, the engine must be running in order to provide the vacuum. A vacuum reserve, however, is maintained either in the unit itself or in a separate vacuum tank which permits power assist for three to ten normal power-brake applications after the engine stops running.

The brakes can always be applied manually even though the power unit is malfunctioning. This requires extra pedal effort, but is a necessary safety feature.

GENERAL CONSTRUCTION

The operating principles of all power brake units are similar. The wheel-brake units are energized through the regular hydraulic system with power supplied by the difference in pressure between the engine vacuum and atmospheric pressure. A cross-section of a typical power-brake unit is shown in Fig. 1. This type is mounted on the engine side of the dash panel and contains, as an integral part, the master cylinder for the hydraulic brake system. The oper-

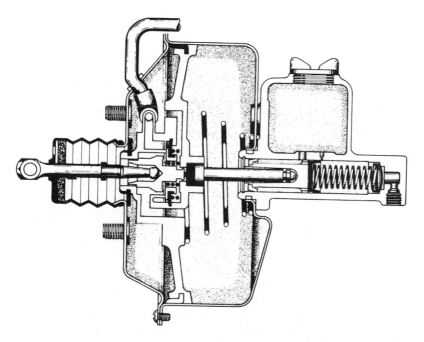

Courtesy Oldsmobile Div., General Motors Corp.

Fig. 1. Cross-section of a Bendix power-brake unit.

ating rod extends through the dash panel and is coupled to the brake pedal.

Another type of power-brake unit is shown in Fig. 2. This type of unit is also mounted on the engine side of the dash panel but differs from the unit in Fig. 1 in that the master cylinder is not

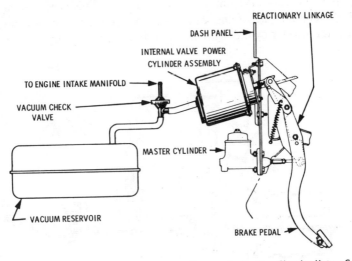

Courtesy Dodge Div., Chrysler Motors Corp.

Fig. 2. A power-brake assembly in which the master cylinder is not an integral part of the power unit.

an integral part of the power unit. In addition, a vacuum reservoir tank is required. The power assist, in this case, is applied to the brake-pedal lever which, in turn, actually moves the piston in the master cylinder in the same manner as with conventional brakes. When used with a power unit, the master cylinder is usually of slightly different design, since the pedal travel is not as great as with standard brakes.

Some makes of automobiles have the power-brake unit mounted on the passenger side of the dash panel and to the left of the brake pedal. With this type, the brake-pedal lever is connected directly to the master cylinder, the power unit being connected to the pedal lever with no connection to the master cylinder.

OPERATING PRINCIPLE

The operating principle may differ slightly between different makes and models of power brakes. The operation of a typical unit, however, will aid in understanding the general operation of all power units.

Fig. 3 shows the position of the internal parts in the power-brake unit used on some Mercury models. With the engine running, and the brakes released, vacuum is admitted to the unit but cannot enter the power-piston chamber because the vacuum port is closed. The atmospheric port is open, however, so the atmosphere is free to enter through the port and on into the chamber ahead of the piston. Thus, atmospheric pressure is present on both sides of the piston and it is suspended in the position shown. Under these conditions, the push rod is exerting no pressure on the master-cylinder piston, so the brakes are not energized.

As the brake pedal starts to move when the brakes are applied, the operating rod moves forward, slightly compressing the valve return spring, and brings the seat of the atmospheric valve in contact with the poppet valve, closing the atmospheric valve. As the operating rod continues to move forward as the brake pedal is further depressed, the poppet valve is moved away from the vacuum-valve seat and the vacuum port is opened. Thus, vacuum enters the chamber ahead of the power piston (Fig. 4).

With vacuum ahead of the piston and atmosphere behind it, a force is developed which moves the power piston, the hydraulic push rod, and the hydraulic piston forward. This forces hydraulic fluid into the wheel cylinders. As the hydraulic pressure starts to increase, however, a counter force is exerted against the push rod, attempting to move it back to its original position. This counter

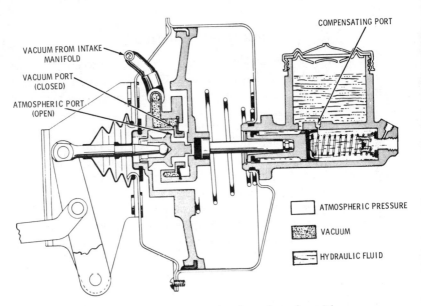

Fig. 3. Power-brake unit in the released position.

force is transmitted to a rubber reaction disc at the rear of the push rod and causes the disc to distribute the force between the power piston and the valve plunger in proportion to their respective contact areas. This action tends to move the valve plunger backward a slight amount with respect to the power piston to close off the vacuum port (Fig. 5). A part of this rearward force reacts through the valve plunger and operating rod against the driver's foot,

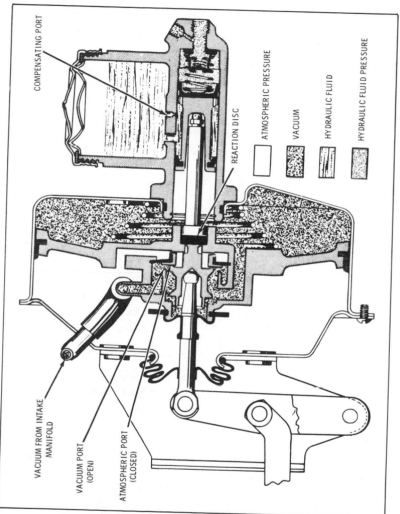

COMPENSATING PORT

REACTION DISC

ATMOSPHERIC PRESSURE

VACUUM

HYDRAULIC FLUID

HYDRAULIC FLUID PRESSURE

VACUUM FROM INTAKE MANIFOLD

VACUUM PORT (OPEN)

ATMOSPHERIC PORT (CLOSED)

Fig. 4. Power-brake unit in the applied position.

providing a certain amount of braking effort "feel." The amount of this reaction force increases in direct proportion to the amount of hydraulic pressure developed in the brake system.

With both vacuum and atmospheric ports closed, a partial vacuum exists in the chamber ahead of the power piston and the unit will hold the brakes at the degree of brake application present at that moment, provided the brake pedal is not moved. When the pedal pressure is increased, the vacuum port will open and move the power piston forward until the reaction disc closes the vacuum port. When the pedal pressure is decreased, the atmospheric port is opened, reducing the vacuum in the chamber ahead of the power piston and causing the power piston to move backward until the reaction valve again closes the port.

If the brake pedal is depressed to its fully applied position, the valve plunger will hold the valve poppet away from the vacuum-valve seat, admitting full manifold vacuum to the chamber ahead of the power piston. This causes the maximum power of the unit to be developed and applied to the brake system. Any additional hydraulic pressure beyond this point must be supplied entirely by the physical effort of the driver. Wheel slide will usually occur below the point of maximum power application by the power unit, however.

In the case of engine failure and consequent loss of engine vacuum, the vacuum in the separate reservoir is sufficient for several power-brake applications. If vacuum is lost completely, the brakes can still be applied in the conventional manner, except that more effort is required.

It must be remembered that all power brakes do not use the same principle of operation. For example, in some units, vacuum exists on both sides of the power piston when the brakes are released. When the brakes are applied, atmospheric pressure is permitted to enter the chamber behind the piston, forcing it for-

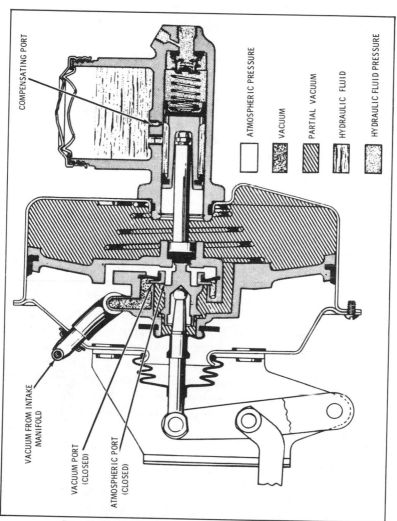

COMPENSATING PORT

ATMOSPHERIC PRESSURE

VACUUM

PARTIAL VACUUM

HYDRAULIC FLUID

HYDRAULIC FLUID PRESSURE

VACUUM FROM INTAKE MANIFOLD

VACUUM PORT (CLOSED)

ATMOSPHERIC PORT (CLOSED)

Fig. 5. Power-brake unit in the holding position.

ward. Also, many units are designed to operate without a separate vacuum reservoir tank. Therefore, for the exact operating principle of a particular make and model power-brake assembly, the shop manual should be consulted.

POWER-BRAKE TESTING PROCEDURE

The following tests are applicable to all power-brake systems and are useful in determining which part of the system is causing trouble.

1. Road test the brakes by applying the brakes while moving about 20 mph to determine if the automobile stops evenly and quickly. If the pedal feels spongy, air may be present in the hydraulic system. Bleed the system to remove the air.
2. With engine stopped and transmission in neutral, apply the brakes several times until all vacuum in the system is depleted. Depress the foot pedal and hold it with a light foot pressure. Start the engine. If the vacuum system is operating, the pedal will tend to fall away, and less foot pressure will be required to hold the pedal in a given position. If no action is felt, the vacuum is not functioning.
3. Stop the engine and again apply the brakes until all vacuum is depleted. Depress the foot pedal and hold with considerable pressure. If the pedal gradually falls away, the hydraulic system is leaking.
4. Start the engine. With the brakes off, run the engine up to medium speed and turn off the ignition, releasing the accelerator immediately. This builds up vacuum. Wait several minutes (the system should hold vacuum for an extended period of up to 12 hours) before trying brake action. If vacuum assist is not present for several slow brake applica-

tions, the vacuum system is leaking. Always check for an external leak before blaming the power unit itself.

CLEANING, INSPECTION, AND OVERHAUL

If trouble is indicated in the power-brake unit, it should be disassembled according to the procedure listed in the manufacturer's service manual. After disassembly, follow these steps:

1. Wipe the fluid from all rubber parts and inspect them for nicks, cuts, or other damage. If any are found defective, discard all the rubber parts.
2. Thoroughly clean the remaining parts of the power unit in diacetone alcohol or clean brake fluid.

   CAUTION: Do not use antifreeze-type alcohol, gasoline, kerosene, or any other cleaning fluid that might contain even a trace of mineral oil. To do so may cause serious damage to the rubber parts.

3. Examine the cleaned parts for nicks, burrs, stripped threads, damage, or excessive wear. Replace any parts or housings that are damaged or show signs of excessive wear. If the inside of the vacuum power chamber is rusted or corroded, polish with fine steel wool or fine emery cloth. Replace the chamber if it is scored.
4. Make certain the small compensating port in the master cylinder (if part of the power unit) is clear.
5. If the outer surface of the air valve shows abrasion, polish out light scores with crocus cloth, then wash and dry thoroughly.
6. Inspect the master cylinder (if part of the power unit) and correct any defects in the manner prescribed in Chapter 10 for the master cylinder used with standard brakes.

7. If any parts indicate that heavy corrosion or abrasive action has caused the brake fluid to be contaminated, replace the damaged parts and thoroughly flush the hydraulic system.

8. Repair kits are available for the overhaul of most power-brake units, and contain all the necessary replacement parts. Use all the new parts contained in the kit, even though the old parts appear satisfactory. In addition, replace any other parts which appear to be unfit for use.

9. Reassemble the power unit according to the procedure outlined in the manufacturer's service manual.

BRAKE-SYSTEM TROUBLES AND REMEDIES

Many brake-system troubles that occur with power brakes are the same as those that occur with standard brakes. Therefore, before checking the power-brake system for the source of trouble, refer to Chapter 10 for the troubles and remedies on standard brakes. After these possible causes have been eliminated, check for power-brake troubles as outlined in the following list.

Some of the troubles and remedies listed are not applicable to all power-brake units. Instead, the list includes the troubles and remedies for power-brake units in general. For specific instructions, the manufacturer's service manual should be consulted for the particular type of unit being serviced.

Symptom and Possible Causes	*Possible Remedy*
Hard Pedal	
(a) Faulty vacuum check valve.	(a) Replace valve.
(b) Collapsed or leaking vacuum hose to manifold or reserve tank.	(b) Replace hose.

Symptom and Possible Causes

(c) Plugged vacuum fittings.

(d) Leaking vacuum reservoir tank.

(e) Vacuum check valve stuck closed.

(f) Internal vacuum hose loose or restricted.

(g) Jammed vacuum-cylinder piston.

(h) Loose piston-plate screws.

(i) Faulty vacuum-cylinder piston seal.

(j) Restricted air-filter element.

(k) Faulty rubber stop in reaction diaphragm.

(l) Tight pedal linkage.

Possible Remedy

(c) Clean or replace fittings.

(d) Replace tank.

(e) Free-up or replace. **Do not oil.**

(f) Tighten, clear, or replace as necessary.

(g) Free-up or replace and correct cause of jam.

(h) Tighten screws.

(i) Replace piston. Check cylinder for scoring.

(j) Replace element.

(k) Replace faulty part.

(l) Adjust linkage.

Brakes Fail to Release

(a) Blocked passage in power piston.

(b) Air valve stuck closed.

(c) Broken air-valve spring.

(d) Tight pedal linkage.

(e) Restricted air-filter element.

(f) Restricted air passage.

(a) Clear passage and replace defective parts if necessary.

(b) Free-up or replace. **Do not oil.**

(c) Replace spring.

(d) Adjust and lubricate as necessary.

(e) Replace element.

(f) Clear passages and replace parts if needed.

Symptom and Possible Causes	*Possible Remedy*
(g) Sticking vacuum valve.	(g) Free-up or replace. **Do not oil.**
(h) Incorrect push-rod adjustment.	(h) Adjust push rod.
(i) Leak in rear housing of power unit.	(i) Locate and correct leak.
(j) Diaphragm out of location in housing.	(j) Reposition the diaphragm.
(k) Sticking or unseated actuating valve assembly.	(k) Free-up and seat properly.

Grunting Noise in Power Unit

(a) Air in hydraulic system.	(a) Bleed brakes.
(b) Valve plunger dry.	(b) Lubricate valve plunger.
(c) Fluid low in master cylinder.	(c) Add brake fluid.

CHAPTER 12

Front Suspension

Correct operation of the front suspension and steering is of the utmost importance in an automobile. Riding comfort, road-holding ability, ease of steering, and longer tire life all depend on the proper adjustment of these two systems. A regular schedule of maintenance, inspection, and adjustment should be followed to keep these important parts of the car in first-class condition. They are too often neglected by the average car owner.

STANDARD SUSPENSION

Passenger cars presently being manufactured in the United States have independent front-wheel suspension similar to that shown in Fig. 1. It should be noted, however, that Chrysler-made cars use a torsion bar instead of the coil spring shown.

Some older-model cars and certain makes of light trucks have a solid-type front axle, somewhat like the one shown in Fig. 2. One of the main disadvantages of the solid axle, as compared to independent suspension, is that the up-and-down motion of one front wheel will affect the camber of the opposite wheel. In other

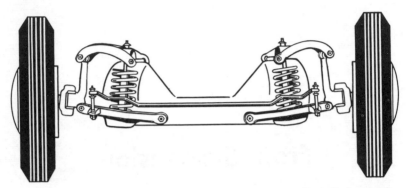

Courtesy Hunter Engineering Co.

Fig. 1. Independent front suspension as used on most domestic automobiles.

words, as one wheel raises in going over a bump, for example, the opposite wheel is tilted outward, tending to cause the vehicle to turn in the direction of the tilt. Independent wheel suspension removes this tendency, because the vertical movement of one wheel is not transferred to the opposite wheel. Thus, steering stability is improved.

Courtesy Hunter Engineering Co.

Fig. 2. Solid-axle type of front suspension.

322

Ball Joints

All automobiles manufactured in recent years have some form of ball-joint suspension instead of the individual kingpin shown in Fig. 1. The use of ball joints reduces the transmission of road

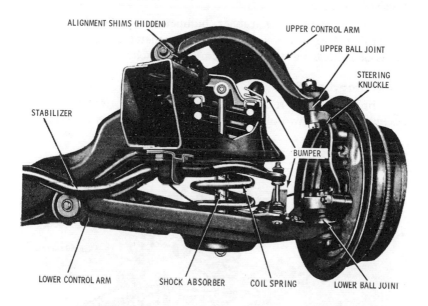

ALIGNMENT SHIMS (HIDDEN)   UPPER CONTROL ARM

UPPER BALL JOINT

STEERING
KNUCKLE

STABILIZER

BUMPER

LOWER CONTROL ARM   SHOCK ABSORBER   COIL SPRING   LOWER BALL JOINT

Courtesy Oldsmobile Div., General Motors Corp.

Fig. 3. Front suspension system of a 1963 Oldsmobile.

shock to the steering wheel and improves the steering stability. A typical front-wheel suspension employing the ball-joint principal is shown in Fig. 3. It will be found that most cars, regardless of make, have this type of suspension, with only minor differences in construction features.

Stabilizer (Sway) Bar

Notice in Fig. 3 that a stabilizer bar is fastened to the lower control arm by means of a rubber-mounted fixture. This bar reduces the tendency for the car to roll and sway.

Rubber Bumpers

An upper and lower rubber bumper is positioned on each suspension assembly to prevent metal-to-metal contact when the limits of vertical travel of the assembly is reached.

Brake Reaction Rods

A brake reaction rod will be found on some front-suspension assemblies. As shown in Fig. 4, this rod is positioned between the

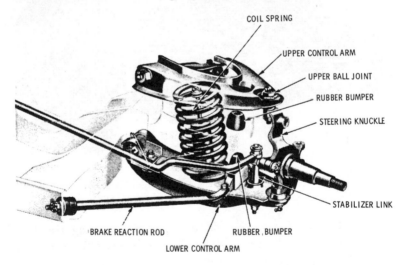

Courtesy Buick Motor Div., General Motors Corp.

Fig. 4. Front suspension system of a 1965 Buick.

lower control arm and the front of the frame side rails. The forward end of the rod is rubber mounted to the frame bracket and held secure by a castellated nut and cotter pin. This reaction rod maintains the position of the lower control arm and helps to resist torsional roll characteristics.

Shock Absorbers

A shock absorber is part of each front-suspension assembly. The upper stem of the shock is secured to the frame by rubber grommets and retainers held in place by a nut. The lower stem of the shock is fastened to the lower control arm and is also insulated with rubber bushings to prevent metal-to-metal contact. The shock absorber is usually positioned inside the coil spring except on those cars equipped with torsion bars.

Coil Springs

Most cars have a large coil spring positioned between the front cross member of the frame and the lower control arm. This type of spring is shown in Figs. 3 and 4.

Torsion Bars

Some Chrysler-made automobiles, especially the later models, have a torsion bar instead of a coil spring in the suspension assembly. One end of this bar is anchored to the frame some distance back from the front wheels. The other end of the bar is connected to the lower control arm. The torsion bar is twisted as the control arm moves upward, and offers a resistance that attempts to return the arm to its normal position in the same manner as a coil-spring arrangement. Torsion bars are designed to be twisted in one direction only, so care must be taken when one is replaced to make sure the correct bar is used. The general location of the torsion bars on an automobile is shown in Fig. 5.

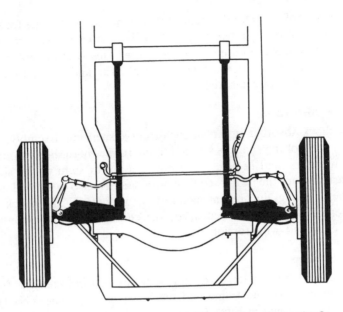

Courtesy Hunter Engineering Co.

Fig. 5. Location of the torsion bars on a typical domestic automobile.

SERVICE PROCEDURES

It is impractical to list the service procedures for all makes and models of automobiles, since each will be slightly different. Instead, typical examples are given. Where specific information is desired, the service manual for the particular make and model of car involved should be consulted.

IMPORTANT: Whenever any part of the front suspension has been removed and installed, front wheel alignment must be checked.

Servicing Ball Joints

The upper and lower ball joints shown in Fig. 6 are typical of those used on most cars. It should be noted, however, that some

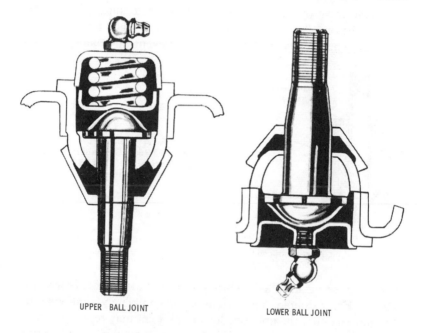

UPPER BALL JOINT   LOWER BALL JOINT

Courtesy Buick Motor Div., General Motors Corp.

Fig. 6. Upper and lower ball joints used on 1965 Buicks.

ball joints have a plug instead of a grease fitting (Fig. 7). This type is sealed and requires lubrication only at widely-spaced intervals of 25,000 to 35,000 miles, or as specified by the manufacturer.

The ball joints should be checked periodically for wear. This can be done on most cars by raising the front end until the wheels are hanging free and shaking each wheel by grasping it at the top and bottom. Any ball joint showing excessive wear should be replaced, following the procedure outlined in the manufacturer's service manual.

Replacement of the ball joints on most cars require special tools, such as the one shown in Fig. 8 for a 1963 Dodge 880. Care must be taken when replacing ball joints to prevent any damage to the

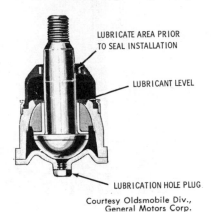

LUBRICATE AREA PRIOR
TO SEAL INSTALLATION

LUBRICANT LEVEL

LUBRICATION HOLE PLUG

Courtesy Oldsmobile Div.,
General Motors Corp.

Fig. 7. A sealed ball joint used on a 1963 Oldsmobile requires lubrication only at 30,000 mile intervals.

new parts being installed. Always follow the manufacturer's procedure. For example, on certain cars, completely removing the stud nut on either the upper or lower ball joint may result in serious injury due to the sudden release of the compressed coil spring. **Follow the correct procedure.**

Stabilizer-Bar Servicing

When replacing the stabilizer bar or support bushings, no oil or grease must be used. Either install the bushings on the bar dry, or use water to make their installation easier. Grease or oil will cause these parts to deteriorate rapidly.

Coil-Spring Replacement

The coil springs must be replaced if they become weak or if they are broken. This operation usually requires disconnecting the lower control arm at the lower ball joint and swinging the control arm

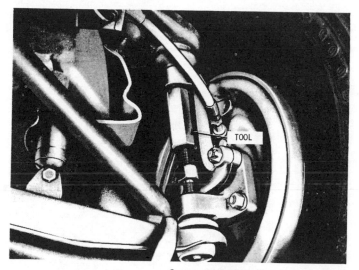

Courtesy Dodge Div., Chrysler Motors Corp.

Fig. 8. A special tool used to remove the lower ball joint on a 1963 Dodge 880.

down to free the spring (Fig. 9).**Care must be taken during this operation to prevent the coil spring from suddenly releasing and causing injury to the mechanic.** The manufacturer's procedure should be carefully followed. These procedures generally indicate the use of a special tool to compress the spring during this operation. Such a tool is shown in Fig. 10 being used to compress a 1960 Mercury coil spring.

Torsion-Bar Service

Late-model Chrysler-made cars use torsion bars for the front suspension instead of coil springs. These bars are provided with adjustments which make it possible to raise or lower the suspension

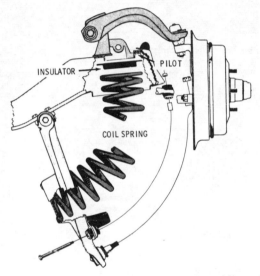

Courtesy Oldsmobile Div., General Motors Corp.

Fig. 9. Coil spring installation.

height of the car. Fig. 11 shows this adjustment feature which is located at the rear end of the torsion bar. Turning the adjusting bolt clockwise increases the suspension height, and turning the bolt counterclockwise decreases the height.

The front-suspension height must be within the specified limits to provide satisfactory tire life. The following procedure can be used to measure this height. The tires must be at the recommended pressures, the gas tank must be full, and the car must have no load in the passenger compartment or trunk.

1. Clean all foreign material from the bottom of the ball-joint assembly on each side of the car. Also clean the bottom of each lower control-arm bushing between the flanges.

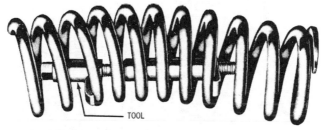

TOOL

Fig. 10. A coil spring compressed for installation.

2. Bounce the car several times, releasing it on the downward motion.
3. Measure the distance from the lowest point on one of the lower control-arm bushing housings to the floor (measurement A in Fig. 12), and from the flat portion on the bottom of the lower ball joint to the floor (measurement B in Fig. 12). The difference between measurement A and B should be within ⅛-inch of the reading specified for the particular model being serviced.
4. Measure the other side in the same manner. The difference between the two sides should not exceed ⅛-inch.
5. Adjust the torsion bars, if necessary, until the readings for each side of the car are within the specifications and within ⅛-inch of one another.

6. Bounce the car after each adjustment before rechecking the measurements. Both sides should be measured, even though only one side has been adjusted.

It will be necessary to install a new torsion bar if it is impossible to bring the suspension to the correct height by the torsion-bar adjustment or if the torsion bar is broken. The torsion bars are

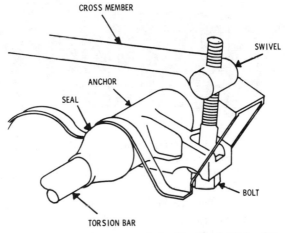

Courtesy Dodge Div., Chrysler Motors Corp.

Fig. 11. Torsion-bar adjustment assembly.

not interchangeable side for side. They are marked either right or left by an "R" or an "L" stamped on one end of the bar.

To remove a torsion bar, proceed as follows:

1. Raise the car in such a manner that the front suspension is completely unloaded.
2. Release the load on the torsion bar by turning the anchor

332

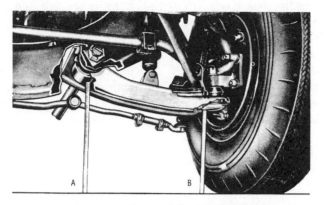

Courtesy Dodge Div., Chrysler Motors Corp.

*Fig. 12. Checking front suspension on a Chrysler-
made car.*

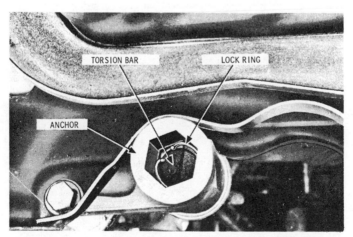

Courtesy Dodge Div., Chrysler Motors Corp.

Fig. 13. View of the torsion-bar anchor assembly.

adjusting bolt counterclockwise. Remove the bolt and swivel, and discard if damaged.

3. Remove the plastic seal from the rear end of the torsion-bar anchor and remove the lock ring. See Figs. 13 and 14.

4. Slide the torsion bar to the rear until the forward end is disengaged from the lower control arm. Slip the rear-anchor balloon seal off the anchor and forward along the torsion bar, being careful not to damage the seal.

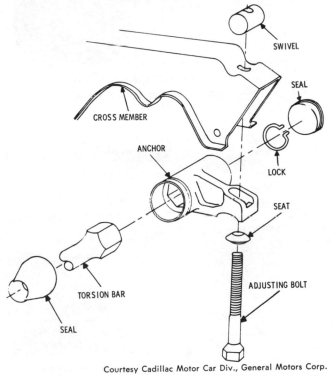

Fig. 14. Exploded view of the torsion-bar anchor assembly.

5. Remove the torsion bar either by sliding it forward and down until it is clear of the rear anchor, or by sliding it out through the rear of the rear anchor.

To install the torsion bar, proceed as follows:

1. Inspect the balloon seal for damage and replace if necessary.
2. Inspect the torsion bar for scores and nicks. Dress down all scores and nicks to remove the sharp edges, then paint the repaired area with rust preventive.
3. Slide the balloon seal over the torsion bar with the cupped side toward the rear anchor.
4. Apply a thick coating of chassis lubricant around each end of the torsion bar.
5. Slide the rear of the torsion bar into the rear-support assembly and turn until the adjusting lug is positioned approximately 120° down from the frame.
6. Engage the front end of the bar in the hex opening of the lower control arm. If the adjusting lug on the rear anchor is not in the position described in step 5, it will be impossible to adjust the front suspension to the correct height.
7. Center the bar so that the full contact is obtained at both the rear anchor and the control arm.
8. Install the lock ring, making sure it is seated firmly in its groove.
9. Pack the opening in the forward end of the rear anchor full of multi-purpose lubricant. Position the lip of the balloon seal in the groove in the anchor hub. Install the plastic seal into the rear end of the torsion-bar anchor.
10. Position the adjusting-bolt swivel and install the adjusting bolt and seat. Tighten the adjusting bolt until approximately 1 inch of threads is showing out of the swivel. This is an ap-

proximate setting used as a starting point to adjust for the correct suspension height. This setting also places a load on the torsion bar before lowering the vehicle to the floor.

11. Lower the vehicle to the floor, and measure and adjust the suspension height as required.

AIR SUSPENSION

An air-suspension system that replaces the coil springs is used on some automobiles. This system incorporates leveling valves to control the riding qualities and maintain the car at a constant height regardless of the amount of load it is carrying. Most air-suspension systems, while differing somewhat in overall design according to the make and model of car, generally consist of the following units:

1. Air-spring (bellows) units.
2. Height-control (leveling) valves.
3. Air compressor.
4. Air storage tank (accumulator).
5. Manual control valve.

A diagram of a typical air-suspension system is shown in Fig. 15.

Air-Spring Units—Air springs are located in the same general position as the coil springs on cars with standard suspension. Each air-spring unit (Fig. 16) consists generally of a barrel- or dome-shaped air chamber into which a rubber diaphragm or bellows is positioned. This diaphragm is compressed by a specially-shaped plunger, the lower end of which is fastened to the axle or lower control arm. The air chamber is fastened to the frame of the car. Thus, the plunger pushes against the diaphragm, attempting to collapse it into the air chamber.

The normal air pressure in the chamber is 100 lbs. or more per square inch. If the car load weight is increased, however, the leveling valve causes more air to enter the chamber, increasing the pressure. Thus, the trim height is adjusted to maintain a constant level. A reverse action takes place when the load weight of the car is decreased.

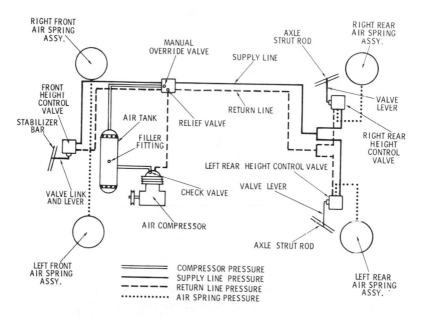

Fig. 15. *A diagram of a typical air suspension system showing the air-line connections between the various units.*

Normal bumps and road vibrations cause no leveling-valve action to take place. Therefore, the air-spring units function very much like conventional coil springs during normal driving.

Height-Control Valves—Most cars equipped with air suspension have three height-control valves, one at the front and two at the rear. Through the use of these three valves, a constant relationship is maintained in the distance between the spring weight (frame and body) and the ground, regardless of any variations in car loading.

The function of these leveling valves is to control the flow of air to and from the air-spring units at each of the four wheels as required to maintain the level of the body parallel to and at a fixed distance from the ground. The leveling-valve assemblies are secured to some portion of the car frame, and each actually consists of two valves in one unit. One valve allows air to enter the air domes, and the other valve allows air to escape to the lift valve and then to the atmosphere.

The front leveling-valve assembly is mechanically actuated by a link connected to the stabilizer bar. Each of the rear leveling-valve assemblies is mechanically actuated by a link connected to some point on the rear-axle assembly.

A dashpot is included in each of the leveling valves to delay the valve action for approximately one second. This prevents the leveling valves from operating as the wheels move rapidly up and down over rough roads. Thus, the leveling system is essentially inactive under most conditions when the car is in motion.

Air Compressor—An air compressor driven by a belt from the crankshaft pulley furnishes the compressed air to operate the air-suspension system. A pressure of approximately 250 lbs. per square inch is maintained in the air storage tank by this compressor. When the pressure of the air in the storage tank equals the capacity of the compressor, the inlet and exhaust valves in the compressor cannot operate and no additional air is supplied.

The compressor unit is usually lubricated by the oil from the car engine and, therefore, needs no manual lubrication when this method is employed. Clean air is drawn into the compressor either through a filter furnished as part of the equipment, or through the carburetor air cleaner.

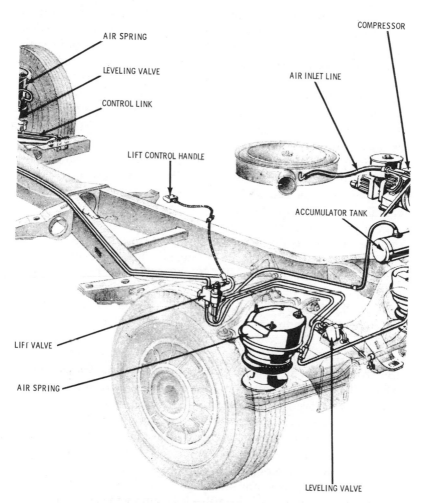

AIR SPRING

LEVELING VALVE

CONTROL LINK

LIFT CONTROL HANDLE

COMPRESSOR

AIR INLET LINE

ACCUMULATOR TANK

LIFT VALVE

AIR SPRING

LEVELING VALVE

Fig. 16. A front air-spring unit.

Air Storage Tank—Compressed air for the system is stored in an air storage tank, sometimes called an accumulator. Its function is to store enough high-pressure air to re-level the car from its curb weight to a normal passenger load without the need for additional air from the compressor. In addition to storing air, the accumulator traps any dirt, oil, or water that might enter the system through the compressor. A drain valve is usually provided in the bottom of the tank to permit draining any accumulated dirt or water. This should be done at regular intervals, such as each time the car is lubricated.

A tire-type valve, located on top of the tank, is also usually provided to introduce air from a service-station hose in case the air supply is exhausted while working on the system. Air pressure can also be checked at this valve.

A high-pressure relief or blow-off valve is also located on the tank or at some point in the high-pressure line leading from the tank. This valve is spring loaded to open if the air pressure should exceed a specified limit, usually 300 to 400 p.s.i. This valve will close automatically after the pressure falls below the specified limit.

A check valve to prevent leakback of air from the accumulator tank when the compressor is not running is located at the port of the tank.

Manual Control Valve—A manual control or lift valve is usually located in an accessible position in the engine compartment. This valve normally contains two major units—a pressure-regulator valve, and an override valve.

The pressure-regulator valve controls the amount of air pressure from the air storage tank through the leveling valves to the air-spring units. The maximum pressure that is allowed to reach the leveling valves and air-spring units is predetermined by a factory adjustment of the regulator screw.

The purpose of the override valve is to supply the air springs with regulated air pressure if conditions require that the car body be raised above its normal standing height. The valve is actuated manually at the unit or, in some cases, by means of a cable-connected handle located on the dash panel. Pulling the control handle out shifts the air pressure into the return air lines from the leveling valves and, at the same time, blocks the exhaust port to the atmosphere. Since the regulated air pressure is greater than the exhaust pressure, the air flow from the air springs through the return lines is reversed, and air enters the air springs, raising the car up to the rebound bumpers. The car will remain at this height until the control handle is pushed back in.

NOTE: Some air suspension systems do not contain a manual control valve as previously described. Instead a manual shutoff valve is included which, when closed, prevents the complete exhaust of air from the system. This valve is used when the car is to be hoisted by other than drive-on ramp-type hoists, or when the frame will be disturbed in relation to the wheel position, such as jacking up one side of the frame, etc.

SUSPENSION-SYSTEM TROUBLES AND REMEDIES
STANDARD SYSTEM

Symptom and Possible Causes   *Possible Remedy*

Hard Steering

(a) Low tire pressure.

(b) Lack of lubrication.

(c) Improper wheel alignment.
(d) Sagging front or rear spring.

(a) Inflate tires to recommended pressure.
(b) Lubricate according to instructions.
(c) Align front end.
(d) Replace springs as required.

Front Suspension

Symptom and Possible Causes	*Possible Remedy*
(e) Bent wheel or spindle.	(e) Straighten or replace wheel, or replace spindle.
(f) Defective wheel bearings.	(f) Replace wheel bearings as required.
(g) Tight ball joints.	(g) Lubricate or replace as required.
(h) Upper or lower control arms bent.	(h) Replace control arms as required.

Front Wheel Shimmy

(a) Underinflated tires.	(a) Inflate tires to recommended pressure.
(b) Broken or loose wheel bearings.	(b) Replace or adjust wheel bearings.
(c) Worn ball joints.	(c) Replace ball joints.
(d) Improper wheel alignment.	(d) Align front end.
(e) Loose wheel lugs.	(e) Tighten lugs.
(f) Bent wheel.	(f) Straighten or replace wheel.
(g) Wheels out of balance.	(g) Balance wheels.

Excessive Play in Steering System

(a) Worn ball joints.	(a) Replace ball joints.
(b) Front wheel bearings worn or loose.	(b) Replace or adjust wheel bearings as required.
(c) Front stabilizer-bar link loose or bushings worn.	(c) Tighten link or replace bushings as required.

AIR-SUSPENSION SYSTEM

Symptom and Possible Causes   *Possible Remedy*

System Will Not Hold Air

(a) Leaks in system.

(a) Check all lines, fittings, valves, reservoir, and air-spring bellows for leaks, and repair or replace as required.

(b) Compressor output low.

(b) Check efficiency of compressor as per manufacturer's instructions.

(c) Safety valve leaking.

(c) Repair or replace safety valve.

(d) Drain cock leaking or open.

(d) Replace or close drain cock.

(e) Lift-valve control handle in middle position.

(e) Place handle either all the way in or all the way out.

Air-Spring Unit Not Functioning Properly

(a) Broken, bent, or worn leveling valve.

(a) Repair or replace leveling valve.

(b) Pinched or plugged air line to leveling valve.

(b) Replace line.

(c) Ruptured bellows on air-spring unit.

(c) Replace bellows.

(d) Leak in air dome.

(d) Test air dome and fittings for leaks. Install new O-ring seal and tighten fitting.

Symptom and Possible Causes　　　*Possible Remedy*

System Loses All Air When Car is Hoisted

(a) Manual shutoff valve open.

(a) Close manual shutoff valve before hoisting.

Car Raises to Full-Rebound Position

(a) Manual shutoff valve closed with compressor running.

(a) Open manual shutoff valve.

(b) Lift-control handle pulled out.

(b) Push lift-control handle in.

(c) Lift-control valve defective.

(c) Repair or replace lift-control valve.

Car Will Not Rise to Design Height With Compressor Operating

(a) Compressor discharge line not connected or broken.

(a) Connect or replace discharge line.

(b) Accumulator drain cock open.

(b) Close drain cock.

(c) Excessive number of leaks in system.

(c) Check entire system for leaks and repair as required.

Hard Riding

(a) Incorrect standing height.

(a) Check and adjust front and rear standing height.

(b) Insufficient air pressure in system.

(b) Replenish air supply and check for leaks.

344

Symptom and Possible Causes   *Possible Remedy*

Air System Too Sensitive—Excessive Leveling Action

(a) Leveling-valve dashpot does not delay valve action.

(a) Replace dashpot.

Frequent Operation of Accumulator Blow-Off (Safety) Valve

(a) Pressure too high because of carbon deposits in compressor cylinder.

(a) Remove compressor cylinder heads and remove carbon.

(b) Defective blow-off valve.

(b) Replace blow-off valve.

CHAPTER 13

Steering Systems

Many different types of steering systems have been used on automobiles in the past. Constant improvement and new design made necessary to meet the demands of higher driving speeds and changed suspension, however, have resulted in one general type of system being used on nearly all cars manufactured at the present time.

CONTROL LINKAGE

The proper design and correct adjustment of the steering control linkage is of the utmost importance if satisfactory tire wear and good car-handling characteristics are to be obtained. The linkage mechanism shown in Fig. 1 is typical of that found on most cars in use today, and is the result of careful design after years of research.

Turning Angles

The steering geometry designed into the steering system causes all wheels to pivot around the same center as the car is turned. When this happens, a different turning angle exists for each front

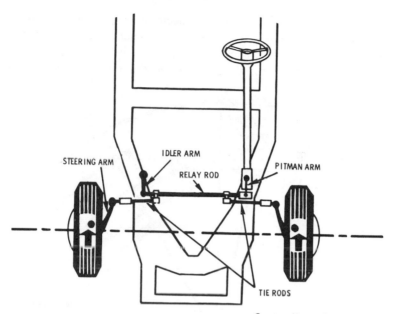

STEERING ARM

IDLER ARM

RELAY ROD

PITMAN ARM

TIE RODS

Fig. 1. Steering control linkage of a typical automobile.

wheel, as shown in Fig. 2. Notice that the front wheels are actually toed-out under this condition. The amount of this toe-out increases as the turn is shortened. In order to provide the correct toe-out when turning, the steering arms are positioned at an angle with the wheels. The angle the steering arms should make with the wheels is determined by extending an imaginary line through the plane of each arm and having the two lines intersect at the center of the rear axle (Fig. 3).

If the steering arms were placed parallel to the front wheels, as in Fig. 4, the wheels would remain parallel on a turn and all tires would scuff. In addition, turning effort would be increased.

The turning angle of the front wheels of an automobile can be checked on special wheel-alignment equipment. If, for example, one of the front wheels is turned in 20°, as in Fig. 5, this wheel simulates the wheel on the outside of the curve of a turning

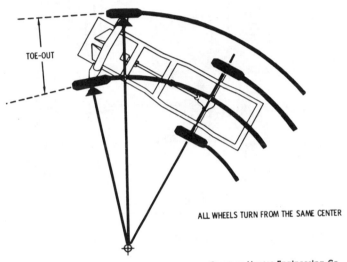

TOE-OUT

ALL WHEELS TURN FROM THE SAME CENTER

Courtesy Hunter Engineering Co.

Fig. 2. All wheels of an automobile should pivot around the same center when a turn is made.

vehicle. The opposite, or inside, wheel should then be at a turned angle of more than 20°. The correct angles for the two wheels are listed in the specifications of the car manufacturer or in the charts supplied with the wheel-alignment equipment. Some car manufacturers specify the turning angle of the wheel on the outside of the curve when the inside wheel is turned out 20°. In this case, the specified angle of the outside wheel will be less than 20° (Fig. 6).

348

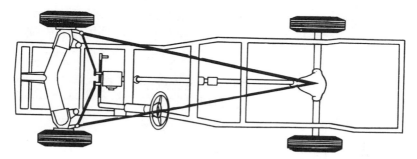

Fig. 3. The manner in which the angle that the steering arms make with the wheels is determined.

If the turning angle readings are different than those specified, one or both steering arms have been bent and must be replaced. Do not attempt to straighten a bent arm, either cold or hot, for to

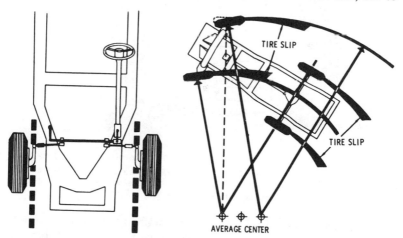

Courtesy Hunter Engineering Co.

Fig. 4. Steering arms that are parallel to the wheels cause each front wheel to pivot around a different center. This causes all tires to slip.

do so may cause the arm to break while the car is being driven. Therefore, always replace a bent steering arm with a new unit.

Toe-In

All four wheels of an automobile should be parallel with one another when the car is traveling in a straight line. If the wheels are

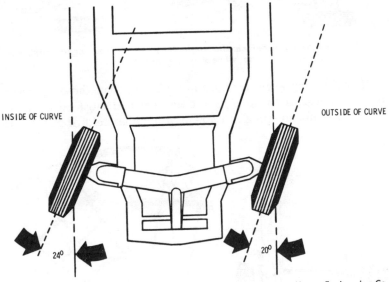

INSIDE OF CURVE

OUTSIDE OF CURVE

24°

20°

Courtesy Hunter Engineering Co.

Fig. 5. A check of the turning angle in which the wheel on the outside of the curve is turned to 20°. The inside wheel then should be at some specified angle greater than 20°.

not parallel, tire scuff will result. To obtain this parallel condition for average driving, it is usually necessary to set a small amount of toe-in to the front wheels when the car is stationary. As shown in Fig. 7, toe-in is the amount that the front wheels are closer together at the extreme front of the tires than they are at the extreme rear. This amount is measured in fractions of an inch.

Toe-in compensates for small deflections caused by rolling resistance and braking, which tends to spread the front of the

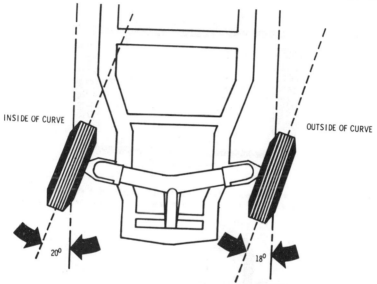

INSIDE OF CURVE

OUTSIDE OF CURVE

20°

18°

Courtesy Hunter Engineering Co.

Fig. 6. Some manufacturers specify the angle at which the outside wheel should be when the opposite wheel is turned out 20°.

wheels outward. The steering linkage on most cars is symmetrical, and is designed so that the path of the ball stud on the end of the tie rod is nearly the same as the path of the suspension-system geometry. This is shown in Fig. 8. Thus, the change in the amount of toe changes very little as the car is loaded. Nevertheless, a small change does take place, and accounts for another reason for a toe-in of the wheels while the car is standing unloaded.

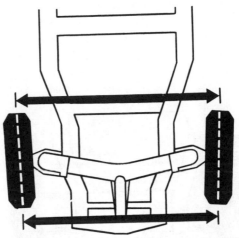

Fig. 7. Toe-in is the amount that the front wheels are closer together at the extreme front of the tires than they are at the extreme rear.

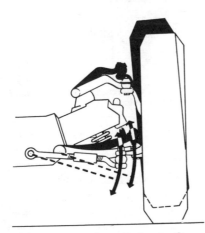

Fig. 8. The steering linkage on most cars is symmetrical and designed so the path of the tie-rod ball is nearly identical to the path of suspension system geometry.

A small amount of running toe-out will cause no more tire wear than the same amount of toe-in. Why, then, is it necessary to have toe-in? The answer to this is that even a small amount of toe-out will tend to cause the car to wander.

Any wear or looseness in the steering linkage will have an unfavorable effect on the toe conditions, causing a running toe-out even though the proper toe-in setting is made while the car is stationary.

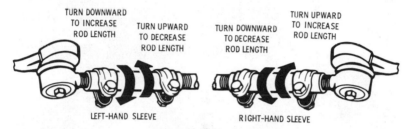

Fig. 9. The sleeve on the end of each tie rod is turned to change the length of the tie rod.

Toe-in adjustment is made by turning the sleeves located on the end of each tie rod. These sleeves are secured by clamps which must be loosened before adjustment can be made. As shown in Fig. 9, the left-hand sleeve is turned in the direction of tire rotation when driving to *decrease* toe-in. The right-hand sleeve must be turned in the opposite direction to decrease toe-in. Whether the sleeves are turned to decrease or increase toe-in, both should be turned exactly the same amount. If one sleeve is turned more than the other, the steering wheel will not be in its normal center position, even though the correct toe-in may exist.

A commercial toe-in gauge being used to measure the distance between the extreme front of the front wheels is shown in Fig. 10. A similar measurement made at the extreme rear of the front wheels is necessary before the amount of toe-in existing can be determined.

Center-Point Steering

Center-point steering means that condition when the steering wheel is in its normal (level or straight-ahead) position, the worm

Courtesy AMMCO Tools, Inc.

Fig. 10. A toe-in gauge being used in aligning the front wheels.

gear is in the center of the steering worm, the pitman and idler arms are in a centered position, and each of the front wheels is at the same angle with an imaginary line drawn down through the center of the vehicle (Fig. 11). On new cars this condition can be expected to exist. Therefore, by leveling the steering wheel, the

354

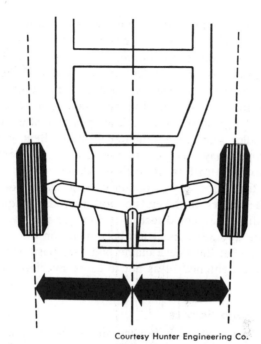

Courtesy Hunter Engineering Co.

Fig. 11. The front wheels of an automobile, when in a straight-ahead position, are not necessarily parallel. When correctly aligned, each front wheel is at the same angle with an imaginary line drawn through the center of the car.

front wheels should then be in the straight-ahead position necessary for measuring and correcting toe-in.

On older vehicles, or those that might have been damaged, it is recommended that the complete steering assembly be checked for center-point steering. With the car stopped (after being driven straight ahead for a short distance), turn the steering wheel completely to the right. Now turn the wheel completely to the left, counting the exact number of revolutions plus any fractions of a revolution (for example, three and one-half turns). Turn the steering wheel back to the right exactly half of this number of revolutions (one and three-quarter revolutions, in this case). Check the position of the pitman and idler arms. If they are not centered, it means the steering worm gear is not centered on the steering arm. In this case it may be necessary to remove the steering wheel and reposition it in a level position after setting the pitman and idler arms in a centered position. Bent parts of the steering linkage may also cause this condition. Replace such parts—**do not attempt to straighten them.**

It is sometimes possible to obtain correct center-point steering by turning the sleeves on the ends of both tie rods an equal amount in the same direction. The direction to turn the sleeves is shown in Fig. 12. When any adjustment has been made on the tie-rod ends, it is important that the sleeve clamp bolts are positioned correctly before they are tightened so as not to cause interference with any part of the car.

Steering-Linkage Service

All parts of the steering linkage should be examined periodically or whenever steering troubles are encountered. Any part that has been bent should be replaced with a new unit. **Do not attempt to straighten any part of the steering linkage.** To do so may cause failure of that part while the automobile is being driven.

Ball Studs

Ball studs are used on most steering linkages to provide ease of movement and to minimize wear. It is necessary to lubricate these joints on most older cars at regular intervals, such as the 1000-mile schedule recommended for other parts of the chassis. On newer models, however, the joints have been redesigned to be permanently lubricated as long as the seals remain undamaged. Some manufacturers provide a plug in the ball stud that can be removed and a regular grease fitting substituted. Thus, if a squeak develops in a ball stud on a high-mileage car, it can be lubricated

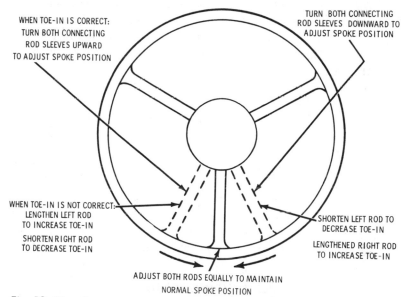

Fig. 12. Direction to turn the sleeves on the ends of the tie rods to correct toe-in or to adjust the position of the steering wheel.

through this fitting. If a plug is not provided, either the ball stud must be replaced with a new unit, or the old unit must be rebuilt and packed with lubricant.

Any ball stud showing excessive looseness should be replaced as no adjustment is provided on most cars to correct this condition. Care must be taken when tightening the nut on a ball stud that it is tightened to the torque specified by the manufacturer. **Make**

357

sure the cotter pin is installed through the castellated nut and through the bolt to prevent the nut from working loose.

Tie-Rod Ends

When new tie-rod ends are installed, make sure both ends are threaded into the tie rods an equal amount. Usually, from ¼" to ⅜" of thread should be exposed between the tie-rod end and the sleeve. This amount of exposed threads is necessary to allow adjustment for toe-in and center-point steering.

Pitman and Idler Arms

Any time either the pitman or idler arms are removed, the steering linkage should be placed in the straight-ahead position and kept there until the arm or arms have been replaced. The steering wheel should be secured in some way to prevent it turning. In addition, before removing the pitman arm, a mark should be inscribed on both the arm and pitman shaft to insure that the arm will be positioned correctly on the splined shaft when reinstalled.

Make sure the idler-arm support bracket is adjusted according to specifications, if it is the adjustable type.

STEERING GEAR

The steering gear, mounted on the end of the steering column, operates the pitman arm which moves the steering linkage. The number of revolutions the steering wheel must make to turn the front wheels from hard left to hard right is determined by the ratio of the steering sector gear to the worm gear. The ratio is different for different makes and models, and whether they have manual or power steering. An average ratio for manual steering is around 24:1, while for power steering the ratio is somewhat lower, usually around 18:1. The higher the ratio, the more revolutions the steering wheel must make to turn the front wheels from hard left to hard right, or vice versa. Generally, older-model cars will have a lower gear ratio than new cars.

Recirculating Ball Worm and Nut

The steering gear assembly in all General Motors and Ford-made cars manufactured in recent years are very much alike, using the recirculating ball worm and nut design. Fig. 13 shows a typical steering gear used on a modern car. Two sets of 25 balls each are used in the steering gear shown, with each set operating independently of the other. The worm on the lower end of the steering shaft, and the ball nut which is mounted on the worm have mating spiral grooves in which the steel balls circulate to provide a low-friction drive between the worm and unt.

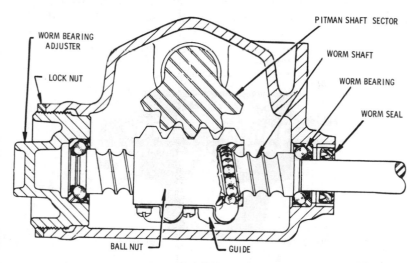

Courtesy Buick Motor Div., General Motors Corp.

Fig. 13. Cross-sectional view of a 1965 Buick steering gear.

A cutaway view of a similar steering gear is shown in Fig. 14. The only appreciable difference between this unit and the one shown in Fig. 13 is the number of steel balls used. There are 27 balls, instead of 25, in each set in the gear shown in Fig. 14.

The circuit through which each set of balls circulate includes the grooves in the worm and ball nut, and a ball-return guide attached to the outside of the nut. When the steering shaft turns to the left, the ball nut is forced toward the lower end of the worm by the balls which roll between the worm and ball nut. As the balls reach the outer surface of the nut, they enter the return guides which direct them across and down into the other side of the ball nut, where they enter the circuit again. When a right turn is made, the ball nut is forced toward the upper end of the worm, and the balls circulate in the reverse direction.

Teeth on the side of the ball nut mesh with the teeth of a sector gear forged on the end of the pitman shaft. The teeth on

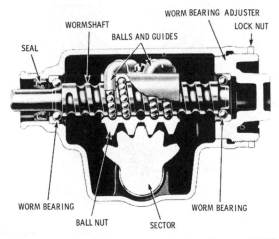

Fig. 14. Cut-away view of the steering gear used on a 1958 Chevrolet.

the ball nut are made so that a tighter fit exists between them and the teeth on the sector gear when the front wheels are in the straight-ahead position. In addition, the teeth of the sector gear and ball nut are slightly tapered so that the proper lash between the two can be obtained by moving the pitman shaft endways by means of an adjusting screw which extends through the side cover of the gear housing. The taper on the teeth of the ball nut and the proper installation of the ball nut on the worm are shown in Fig. 15.

End play of the worm and the proper preloading of the upper and lower worm bearings is taken care of by an adjustment nut at either the upper or lower worm bearing. This adjustment is at the lower worm bearing on General Motors cars, and at the upper worm bearing on Ford-made cars.

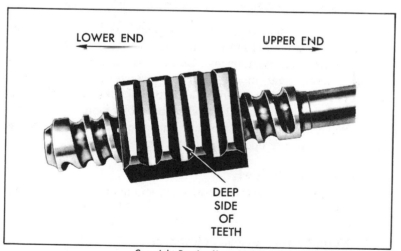

Fig. 15. Proper installation of the ball nut on the worm of a 1964 Tempest steering gear.

Worm and Roller

Late-model American Motors and Chrysler-made cars use a worm-and-roller type manual steering gear similar to the one shown in Fig. 16. In this type of steering gear, a roller in the cross (pitman) shaft meshes with the worm on the lower end of the steering shaft. As the worm rotates, the roller actually turns, instead of sliding as with a normal worm and sector gear. This greatly reduces friction and the effort necessary to steer the automobile.

End play of the worm is adjusted by adding or removing shims between the worm-bearing cover and the steering housing. Proper mesh between the roller and worm is obtained by an adjusting screw at the roller end of the cross shaft.

STEERING-GEAR SERVICE AND ADJUSTMENT

Correct adjustment of the steering gear is extremely important for maximum driving comfort and safety, and to prevent damage to the steering gear components. Before any adjustments are made to the steering gear in an effort to correct conditions such as shimmy, hard or loose steering, and road shocks, a check should be made to determine that shock absorbers, ball joints, tie-rod ends, wheel balance, front-end alignment, and tire pressure are adjusted correctly and/or are operating satisfactorily.

Recirculating-Ball Type

There are two adjustments on the recirculating-ball type steering gear:

1. Worm bearing preload adjustment.
2. Sector and ball-nut backlash adjustment.

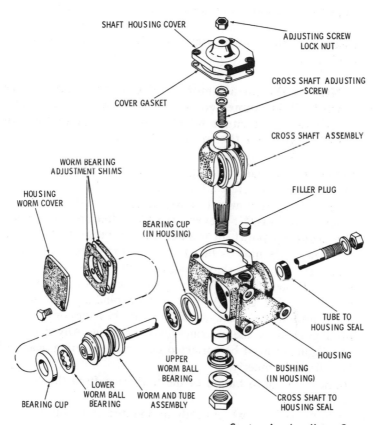

SHAFT HOUSING COVER

ADJUSTING SCREW
LOCK NUT

CROSS SHAFT ADJUSTING
SCREW

COVER GASKET

CROSS SHAFT ASSEMBLY

WORM BEARING
ADJUSTMENT SHIMS

FILLER PLUG

HOUSING
WORM COVER

BEARING CUP
(IN HOUSING)

TUBE TO
HOUSING SEAL

HOUSING

UPPER
WORM BALL
BEARING

BUSHING
(IN HOUSING)

LOWER
WORM BALL
BEARING

WORM AND TUBE
ASSEMBLY

CROSS SHAFT TO
HOUSING SEAL

BEARING CUP

Courtesy American Motors Corp.

Fig. 16. Exploded view of a worm-and-roller type manual steering gear used on a 1964 Rambler.

CAUTION: It is very important that the adjustments on the steering gear be made in the foregoing sequence. Failure to do so may result in damage to the steering gear.

To adjust the worm-bearing preload, proceed as follows:

1. Disconnect the pitman arm from the steering linkage assembly.

   NOTE: Do not attempt to adjust the steering gear while it is connected to the steering linkage. The steering gear must be free of all outside load in order to make the proper adjustments.

2. Loosen the pitman-shaft adjusting screw lock nut and back off the adjusting screw a few turns (Fig. 17).
3. Turn the steering wheel slowly from one extreme to the other. **(CAUTION: Never turn the wheel hard against the stopping point on the gear, as damage to the ball-nut assembly may result.)** The steering wheel should turn freely and smoothly throughout its entire range. Any roughness indicates faulty internal parts, requiring disassembly of the steering gear. A hard pull or binding indicates an excessively tight adjustment of the worm bearings or excessive misalignment of the steering shaft coupling. Any excessive misalignment must be corrected before the steering gear can be adjusted properly.
4. Remove the horn button or the horn ring from the steering wheel.
5. Turn the steering wheel gently in one direction until it stops. This positions the gear away from the "high-point" load that exists in the straight-ahead position.
6. Attach a lb.-in. torque wrench to the steering wheel retaining nut and check the torque required to turn the steering shaft in the range where lash exists between the ball nut and pitman sector gear.

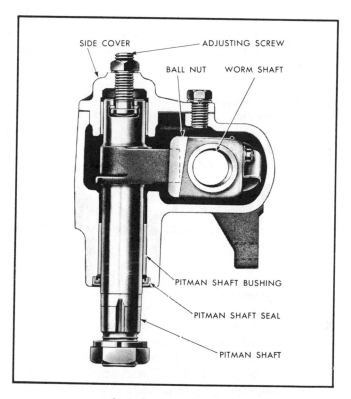

Fig. 17. Cross-sectional view of a steering gear showing the pitman shaft and adjusting screw.

NOTE: Take a reading while pulling the torque wrench in one direction, and then take a reading pulling the wrench in the other direction. Total both readings and take one-half of the total as the average torque.

The torque required should be within the specifications listed by the car manufacturer (usually from 5 to 10 lb.-in. Check the service manual of the car being serviced for exact figures).

7. To correct the worm preload torque, loosen the worm-bearing adjuster lock nut with a brass drift punch and turn the adjuster to bring the torque within the limits specified by the manufacturer.
8. Retighten the lock nut when the torque is correct, and re-check as in Step 6.

To adjust the sector and ball-nut backlash (sometimes called pitman-shaft over-center preload), proceed according to the following steps:

1. After the worm-bearing preload has been adjusted correctly, turn the pitman-shaft adjusting screw clockwise until a pull of 5 to 11 lb.-in. higher than the worm-bearing preload is required to turn the steering shaft through the center (straight-ahead) position. The total torque required to turn the steering shaft through the center position should not exceed 18 lb.-in. (NOTE: These figures are only typical and will differ for different makes and models of automobiles. Always consult the manufacturer's specifications for exact limits.)
2. Tighten the pitman-shaft adjusting screw locknut and re-check the torque limits.
3. Reassemble the pitman arm to the steering linkage, with the steering wheel in the straight-ahead position. If the front wheels are not straight ahead, adjust the tie-rod ends to bring the wheels to the correct position.

Worm-and-Roller Type

There are two adjustments on the worm-and-roller type steering gear:

1. Worm bearing adjustment.
2. Roller-and-worm mesh adjustment.

To adjust the worm-bearing end play, proceed as follows:

1. Rotate the steering wheel one turn from the straight-ahead position and secure the wheel to prevent any movement.
2. Shake one of the front wheels sideways and note any end movement between the steering wheel hub and the steering jacket tube.
   CAUTION: **Make sure any movement present is not caused by looseness in the steering jacket tube bearing.**
3. If end play is present, adjust the worm bearing by loosening the four cover cap screws about one-eighth inch. Separate the top shim with a knife and remove. Do not damage the remaining shims. Tighten the cover cap screws and inspect for worm-bearing end play. Remove only one shim at a time to prevent adjusting the worm bearings too tight, which will cause hard steering and possible damage to the bearings.

To adjust the mesh between the roller and worm, proceed as follows:

1. Disconnect the pitman arm from the steering linkage, and turn the steering wheel to the mid-position of its turning limits.

2. Shake the pitman arm sideways and check for movement. A movement of the pitman arm in excess of 1/32-inch indicates an adjustment of the mesh between the roller and worm should be made.
3. Adjust the mesh by loosening the lock nut on the adjusting screw and turning the screw clockwise. Do not overtighten. Check for proper mesh after adjusting by shaking the pitman arm.
4. Tighten the adjusting screw lock nut while holding the adjusting screw to keep it from turning. Recheck for correct mesh.
5. Reconnect the pitman arm to the steering linkage.
   NOTE: A spring scale attached to the rim of the steering wheel to measure the amount of force necessary to turn the wheel can also be used to check for proper worm-bearing and worm-and-roller mesh adjustment. Consult the car manufacturer's specifications for the correct scale readings.

POWER STEERING

Two general types of power steering are in use today. One type (Fig. 18) uses a separate hydraulic power cylinder controlled by a valve assembly coupled to the pitman arm to assist in steering the automobile. The second general type has the power cylinder and control valve as an integral part of the steering assembly, as shown in Fig. 19.

Both types of power-steering systems require an oil pump to furnish oil under pressure to operate the hydraulic cylinder when the steering wheel is turned. This oil pump is driven by a belt coupled to the crankshaft vibration damper.

The steering ratio on a car having power steering is usually less than in one having manual steering. The steering effort re-

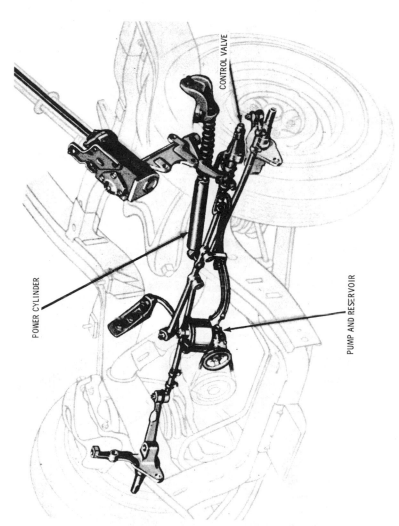

CONTROL VALVE

POWER CYLINDER

PUMP AND RESERVOIR

Fig. 18. 1964 Ford power-steering system.

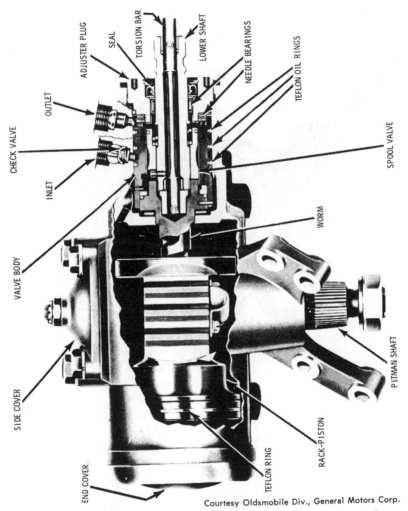

Courtesy Oldsmobile Div., General Motors Corp.

Fig. 19. A typical power-steering system in which the power unit is an integral part of the steering gear.

quired with manual steering is reduced by increasing the steering ratio. With power steering, this ratio can be reduced because the extra effort needed is supplied by the power unit.

Both types of power steering incorporate a "fail-safe" design which permits manual steering even though hydraulic pressure is lost due to some malfunction. More effort is required to steer the car under this condition than is required to steer the same make car with standard steering.

Linkage-Type

This type of steering system includes a fluid reservoir and pump, a control valve, a power cylinder, connecting fluid lines, and the necessary steering linkage. The hydraulic pump is belt driven from the engine crankshaft, and provides fluid pressure for the system. A pressure-relief valve is incorporated in the pump, and is used to govern the pressures within the system according to the varying conditions of operation. The fluid in the system returns to the reservoir after it has passed from the pump to the control valve and power cylinder.

The control valve is operated by the movement of the steering wheel, and serves to direct the path and amount of the oil to the proper place in the system, and at the correct pressure necessary for the oil to perform its required task. For example, when the front wheels are in the straight-ahead position and no force is applied to the steering wheel, the control-valve spool is held in the center (neutral) position by its centering spring, as shown in Fig. 20A. Fluid flows around the valve lands and returns to the reservoir.

When a force of 4 to 7 pounds (depending on the make and model of car) is exerted at the rim of the steering wheel for a left turn, the valve spool overcomes the force of the centering spring and moves toward the right-hand end of the valve. This

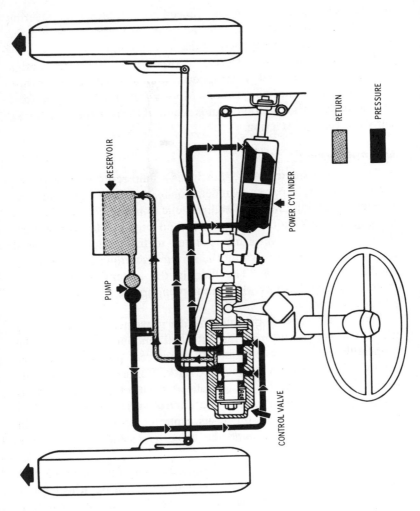

Fig. 20. Flow of hydraulic fluid in a

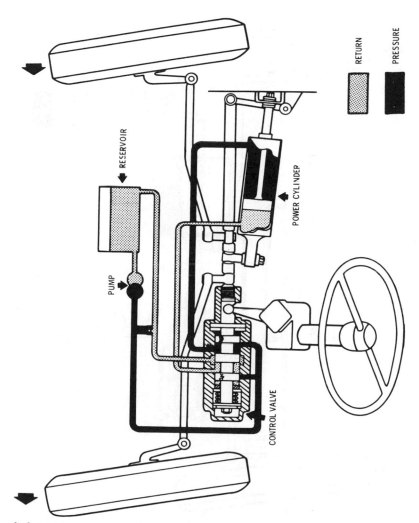

RETURN

PRESSURE

RESERVOIR

POWER CYLINDER

PUMP

CONTROL VALVE

linkage-type power-steering system; (A) Straight-ahead position;

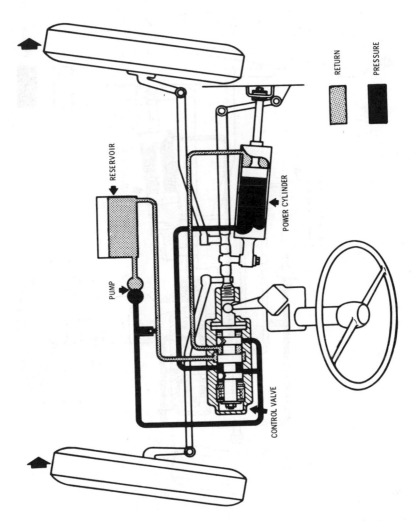

RETURN

PRESSURE

RESERVOIR

POWER CYLINDER

PUMP

CONTROL VALVE

(B) Left-turn position; (C) Right-turn position.

causes pressure to be exerted on the right side of the power-cylinder piston, and causes the fluid in the left side to be returned to the reservoir. This condition is shown in Fig. 20B.

When the force on the steering wheel falls below the design force of 4 to 7 pounds, the valve-spool centering spring forces the spool back to the center position, causing the pressure on both sides of the power-cylinder piston to become equal. With the absence of operative pressure within the power cylinder, the front wheels will tend to return to the straight-ahead position. This is a normal effect of the front-wheel alignment.

When a right turn is made, the directional forces explained for a left turn are reversed. The fluid flow for a right turn is shown in Fig. 20C.

If, for any reason, the pump fails to deliver fluid pressure, the car can still be steered, but with a considerable increase in manual effort.

Road shock in this type of system causes movement of the control valve in relation to the valve spool. This movement sets up a counteracting pressure momentarily to the power cylinder, which absorbs the shock.

Integral-Type

This type of power-steering system includes a fluid reservoir and a pump driven by the engine crankshaft. The pump is connected by flexible hydraulic lines to a power piston that, along with a control valve, is an integral part of the steering gear.

With the engine running, steering is manual as long as the steering effort at the rim of the steering wheel is less than one pound. (Note: This is an approximate figure and may vary slightly depending on the make and model of car.) When a greater effort is required, the power mechanism operates to assist in turning the front wheels. The effort required increases to a maximum of from

3 to 4 pounds, above which the power assist furnishes any extra effort needed to steer the automobile. This condition will exist on normal turns and when parking. The variable feature just described gives the driver a "feel" of steering and removes the objection many drivers had to earlier types of power steering, which gave the feeling of "driving on ice."

When the steering wheel is released to recover from a turn, the front wheels return to the straight-ahead position (in the same manner as with manual steering) without assistance or interference from the power mechanism.

When the engine is stopped, or if any part of the power mechanism is inoperative, the steering gear will operate manually. This gives the driver full control of the car at all times.

The control valve in this system is a rotary type and is located in the upper section of the gear housing. It consists of a stub shaft, a torsion bar, a valve body, a valve spool, and a valve-body cap. These parts are shown in the sectional view in Fig. 21.

Basically, the valve assembly is divided into two separate sections which are fastened together by the torsion bar. One section is connected to the steering wheel and consists of the stub shaft, valve spool, and upper end of the torsion bar. A pin on the outside diameter of the stub shaft secures the valve spool to it, and a pin at the upper end of the stub shaft fastens the upper end of the torsion bar and stub shaft together.

The other section of the valve assembly is connected to the front wheels of the car through the steering linkage, the pitman shaft, sector gear, ball-nut and piston, and the worm. This section consists of the worm, valve body, valve-body cap, and lower end of the torsion bar. The worm is attached to the valve body by a pin at the upper end of the worm. A pin on the inside diameter of the valve body fastens the valve-body cap to the valve body. To complete the assembly, a pin attaches the valve body cap to the lower

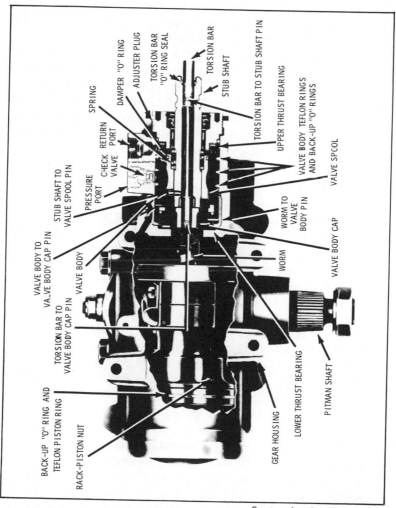

DAMPER "O" RING

ADJUSTER PLUG

TORSION BAR
"O" RING SEAL

TORSION BAR

STUB SHAFT

TORSION BAR TO STUB SHAFT PIN

UPPER THRUST BEARING

VALVE BODY TEFLON RINGS
AND BACK-UP "O" RINGS

VALVE SPOOL

VALVE BODY CAP

WORM TO
VALVE
BODY PIN

WORM

PITMAN SHAFT

LOWER THRUST BEARING

GEAR HOUSING

SPRING

CHECK RETURN
VALVE   PORT

PRESSURE
PORT

STUB SHAFT TO
VALVE SPOOL PIN

VALVE BODY TO
VALVE BODY CAP PIN

VALVE BODY

TORSION BAR TO
VALVE BODY CAP PIN

RACK-PISTON NUT

BACK-UP "O" RING AND
TEFLON PISTON RING

Courtesy American Motors Corp.

Fig. 21. A sectional view of a typical power-steering gear.

end of the torsion bar. Thus, the steering wheel is coupled to the steering gear only through the torsion bar.

When the steering wheel is turned, the torsion bar will twist and cause the stub shaft and valve spool to rotate with the steering wheel. Thus, the relationship between the valve spool and valve body is changed, and the flow of oil is directed by slots on the valve spool through holes in the valve body to the proper side of the power piston to assist the turning action. The torsion bar can only be twisted a predetermined amount. If this limit is exceeded, as in the case of power mechanism failure, two slots in the end of the stub shaft will contact two tangs on the upper end of the worm, and steering will be manual.

The worm shaft turns in the ball nut, using the steel balls as a rolling thread. The ball groove is made shallower in the center of the worm so that a slight worm-to-ball nut preload exists in the straight-ahead position.

The straight-ahead position of the control-valve assembly is shown in Figs. 22 and 23. Oil flows from the pump into the pressure port, through the open center of the valve spool, and out the return port. There is no flow of oil to either side of the power piston, but each side is full of oil at all times. In the straight-ahead position, the pressure on both sides of the piston is equal, so it does not move. The oil acts as a cushion to absorb shocks so they are not transferred to the steering wheel. In addition, the oil serves to lubricate all internal parts of the steering gear.

When the steering wheel is turned to the right, the torsion bar is twisted, changing the relationship between the slots in the valve spool and the slots in the valve body. As shown in Fig. 24, the oil now flows into the lower chamber of the power piston, forcing it upward. At the same time, the oil in the upper chamber of the power piston is forced out through the valve and back to the reservoir. The greater the turning effort applied to the steering

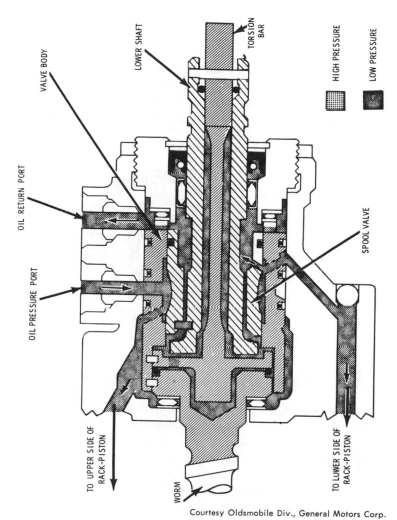

Courtesy Oldsmobile Div., General Motors Corp.

Fig. 22. Cross-sectional view of the control valve in the neutral or straight-ahead position.

wheel, the more the torsion bar is twisted, and the greater will be the change in the relationship between the valve spool and body. This condition causes a greater oil pressure to be applied to the lower side of the power piston. Thus, the proper amount of power assist is supplied for variable turning conditions. Fig. 25 shows an end view of the rotary valve during a right turn.

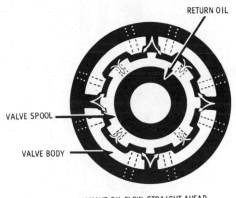

RETURN OIL

VALVE SPOOL

VALVE BODY

VALVE OIL FLOW-STRAIGHT AHEAD

Courtesy American Motors Corp.

Fig. 23. End view of the control valve in the neutral position.

The instant that turning effort is removed from the steering wheel, the torsion bar untwists, returning the valve spool to a straight-ahead position with relation to the valve body. When this happens the oil pressure again becomes equal on both sides of the power piston, and no further power assist is present. The front wheels will now return to the straight-ahead position due to the steering geometry and wheel alignment.

The reverse procedure takes place when the steering wheel is turned to the left. Oil pressure is routed to the upper chamber of the

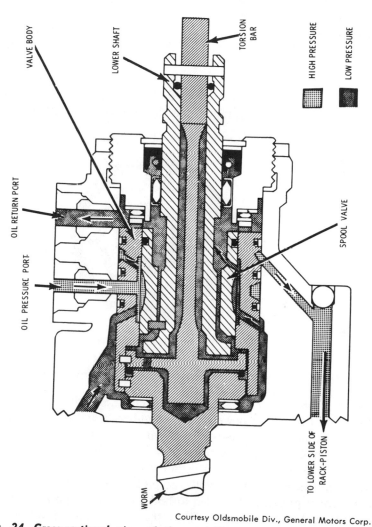

VALVE BODY

LOWER SHAFT

TORSION BAR

HIGH PRESSURE

LOW PRESSURE

OIL RETURN PORT

OIL PRESSURE PORT

SPOOL VALVE

TO LOWER SIDE OF RACK-PISTON

WORM

Courtesy Oldsmobile Div., General Motors Corp.

Fig. 24. Cross-sectional view of the control valve during a right turn.

power piston, forcing it downward. Fig. 26 shows the valve and oil flow under this condition. Fig. 27 shows an end view of the valve assembly during a left turn.

The power steering used on some Chrysler-made cars differ somewhat from the system just described. The power-piston assembly is similar in operation, but the control valve differs. In-

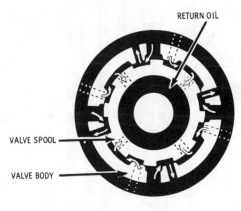

VALVE OIL FLOW RIGHT TURN

Courtesy American Motors Corp.

Fig. 25. End view of the control valve during a right turn.

stead of a torsion bar to "sense" turning effort and control the flow of oil into the proper power-piston chamber, reaction springs are used. Turning effort causes the worm to be displaced slightly, tilting a pivot lever to control the flow of oil. The reaction springs maintain the pivot lever in a center position until turning effort overcomes their resistance. With the pivot lever in the center position, equal pressure is applied to both ends of the power piston, so it does not attempt to move. Thus, the reaction springs introduce a power assist that is proportional to the amount of turning effort

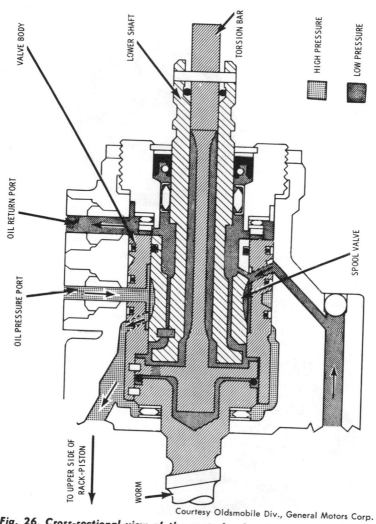

VALVE BODY

LOWER SHAFT

TORSION BAR

HIGH PRESSURE

LOW PRESSURE

OIL RETURN PORT

OIL PRESSURE PORT

SPOOL VALVE

TO UPPER SIDE OF
RACK-PISTON

WORM

Courtesy Oldsmobile Div., General Motors Corp.

Fig. 26. Cross-sectional view of the control valve during a left turn.

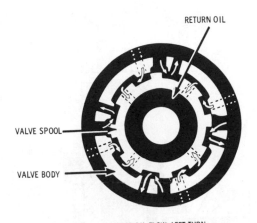

VALVE OIL FLOW LEFT TURN

Courtesy American Motors Corp.

Fig. 27. End view of the control valve during a left turn.

being applied. This provides the driver with the driving "feel" necessary for safe steering. Manual steering, with increased effort, is possible if any part of the power system should fail.

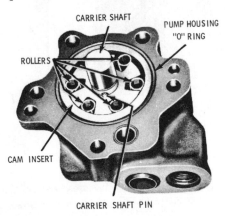

Fig. 28. A roller-type power-steering pump.

POWER-STEERING PUMPS

There are three general types of pumps used in power steering systems. Ford-made cars use a roller-type, General Motors cars use a vane-type, and American Motors and Chrysler-made cars use a slipper-type. All three types of pumps are driven by a belt from the engine crankshaft.

The roller-type pump is shown in Fig. 28. A rotor having slots in which rollers ride is positioned off center in a circular chamber. As the rotor rotates, the rollers are forced outward by centrifugal force and thus follow the inside surface of the circular chamber. The oil is picked up between the rollers and, as they move around

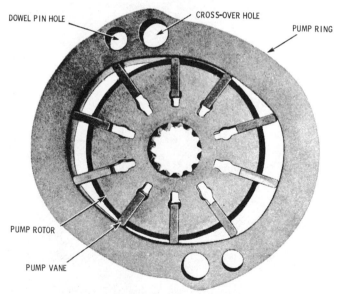

DOWEL PIN HOLE   CROSS-OVER HOLE   PUMP RING

PUMP ROTOR

PUMP VANE

Fig. 29. A vane-type power-steering pump.

the chamber, the space for the oil becomes smaller causing the oil to be forced through an opening.

An input and output opening are provided and the oil is thus circulated around the system under pressure. If the engine speed increases, the oil pressure will also increase. A safety valve is therefore included. When the pressure exceeds a specified amount, the safety valve opens and by-passes the oil, preventing an excessive load on the pump.

The vane-type pump operates on the same principle as the roller-type, except that vanes instead of rollers are held in the

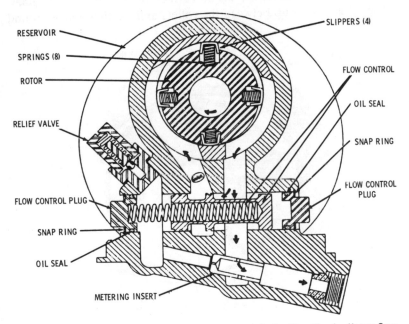

Courtesy Dodge Div., Chrysler Motors Corp.

Fig. 30. A slipper-type power-steering pump.

rotor slots. Another difference is the shape of the chamber in which the rotor rotates. As shown in Fig. 29, the rotor is elliptical. This provides double pumping action for each revolution of the rotor.

The slipper-type pump is shown in Fig. 30. The operation of this pump is very similar to the roller- and vane-types, but uses spring-loaded "slippers" instead of rollers or vanes.

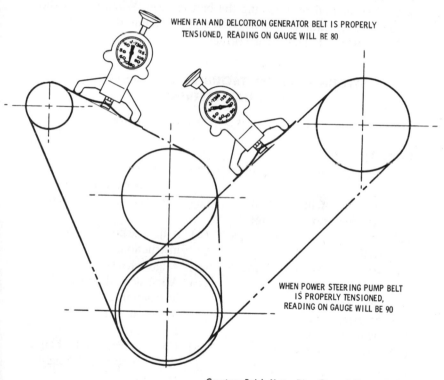

WHEN FAN AND DELCOTRON GENERATOR BELT IS PROPERLY TENSIONED, READING ON GAUGE WILL BE 80

WHEN POWER STEERING PUMP BELT IS PROPERLY TENSIONED, READING ON GAUGE WILL BE 90

Courtesy Buick Motor Div., General Motors Corp.

Fig. 31. Typical application of a belt tension gauge.

Correct belt tension to the pump is very important in any power-steering system. A loose belt may cause hard steering, jerky steering (especially when parking), noise, etc. Some manufacturers recommend the use of a gauge to adjust the belt to the correct tension. Fig. 31 illustrates one type of gauge and the method of application to measure the belt tension on a 1965 Buick with a 300 cu. in. engine. Some other manufacturers list the belt-deflection method of adjusting the belt tension. When this method is used, specifications are listed for the amount the belt can be deflected when its tension is correct.

STEERING-SYSTEM TROUBLES AND REMEDIES
MANUAL STEERING

Symptom and Possible Causes   *Possible Remedy*

Hard Steering

(a) Low or uneven tire pressure.

(a) Inflate tires to recommended pressures.

(b) Insufficient lubricant in steering gear or linkage.

(b) Lubricate as necessary.

(c) Steering gear adjusted too tight.

(c) Adjust according to instructions.

(d) Front wheels out of line.

(d) Align wheels.

(e) Steering column misaligned.

(e) Align according to instructions.

(f) Steering wheel rubbing against gearshift bowl.

(f) Adjust to correct condition.

(g) Front spring sagged.

(g) Check front-end height. Replace spring if height is too low.

(h) Frame bent or broken.

(h) Repair frame as necessary.

388

Symptom and Possible Causes	Possible Remedy
(i) Steering knuckle bent.	(i) Replace knuckle.
(j) Ball joint galled or too tight.	(j) Replace ball joint.
(k) Suspension arms bent or twisted.	(k) Check camber and caster. Replace arms if bent.
(l) Tight over-center adjustment.	(l) Adjust to specifications.
(m) Thrust-bearing adjustment too tight.	(m) Adjust to specifications.

Poor Return of Steering

(a) Steering wheel rubbing against gearshift bowl.	(a) Adjust as necessary.
(b) Front wheels out of alignment.	(b) Align front wheels.
(c) Steering linkage too tight.	(c) Lubricate and check end plugs.
(d) Suspension ball joints too tight.	(d) Lubricate.
(e) Steering adjustment too tight.	(e) Readjust according to instructions.
(f) Nut and worm preload too tight.	(f) Remove gear and replace balls as necessary.

Car Pulls to One Side

(a) Front end misaligned.	(a) Align front end.
(b) Incorrect tire pressure.	(b) Inflate tires to recommended pressures.
(c) Brakes dragging.	(c) Adjust brakes.

Symptom and Possible Causes	*Possible Remedy*
(d) Front and rear wheels not tracking.	(d) Adjust as necessary.
(e) Broken or weak rear springs.	(e) Replace defective springs.
(f) Bent suspension parts.	(f) Replace defective parts.

Excessive Play in Steering Wheel

(a) Lash in steering linkage.	(a) Adjust or replace parts as necessary.
(b) Excessive lash between sector gear and ball nut.	(b) Adjust to specifications.
(c) Ball nut and worm preload incorrect.	(c) Remove gear and change balls to obtain specified preload.
(d) Ball joints loose.	(d) Replace ball joints.
(e) Front-wheel bearings worn or incorrectly adjusted.	(e) Replace or adjust bearings as necessary.
(f) Steering gear housing attaching bolts or nuts loose.	(f) Tighten according to specifications.
(g) Steering arms loose.	(g) Tighten according to specifications.

POWER STEERING

Troubles listed here are in addition to those listed for manual steering.

Symptom and Possible Causes	*Possible Remedy*

Hard Steering

(a) Sticky spool valve.	(a) Remove and clean or replace valve assembly.

Symptom and Possible Causes

Possible Remedy

(b) Sticking flow-control valve in pump.

(b) Remove valve and clean or replace.

(c) Low oil level in pump reservoir.

(c) Fill to proper level with approved liquid.

(d) Pump belt loose.

(d) Tighten pump belt to correct tension.

(e) Faulty pump.

(e) Check pump pressure and correct as necessary. Check for oil leaks in system and correct as necessary.

(f) Restriction in pump hoses.

(f) Clean or replace as necessary.

Car Pulls to One Side

(a) Worn or damaged valve or shaft assembly.

(a) Replace valve and shaft assembly.

(b) Valve body out of adjustment (Chrysler-made cars).

(b) Move steering valve housing up or down on the steering housing according to instructions.

(c) Valve pivot lever damaged (Chrysler-made cars).

(c) Remove steering gear and repair or replace as necessary.

Poor Return of Steering

(a) Sticky valve spool.

(a) Remove and clean or replace valve.

(b) Faulty or damaged valve pivot lever.

(b) Repair or replace as necessary.

Symptom and Possible Causes *Possible Remedy*

Lack of Assist in One Direction

(a) Broken or worn ring on power piston.

(a) Repair as necessary.

(b) Piston end plug loose.

(b) Replace worm and piston assembly.

(c) Reaction seal missing.

(c) Repair as necessary.

Increased Effort to Turn the Wheel Fast

(a) Oil level low.

(a) Add oil to reservoir.

(b) Pump belt slipping.

(b) Tighten belt to specifications.

(c) High internal leakage.

(c) Replace rings and seals on power piston. Replace valve as necessary.

(d) Engine idle speed too slow.

(d) Increase idle speed to specifications.

(e) Air in system.

(e) Turn steering wheel right and left several times to expel air. Add oil to proper level.

Steering Gear Hiss

(a) Normal in some units when parking or when steering wheel is turned to extreme limits.

(a) If objectionable, replace valve and shaft assembly.

(b) Gear loose on frame.

(b) Tighten bolts to specifications.

Symptom and Possible Causes   *Possible Remedy*

Steering Wheel Surges When Turning
(a) Loose pump belt.   (a) Tighten to specifications.

Valve "Squawks" When Turning
(a) Worn or damaged ring on valve spool.   (a) Repair or replace.

(b) Loose or worn valve.   (b) Replace valve and shaft assembly.

No Effort Required to Turn
(a) Broken torsion bar.   (a) Replace valve and shaft assembly.

Pump Noise
(a) Loose belt.   (a) Tighten belt.
(b) Hose touching other parts of the car.   (b) Relocate position of hose.
(c) Oil level low.   (c) Add oil.
(d) Air in oil.   (d) Check oil level.
(e) Excessive back pressure caused by restriction in hose or valve.   (e) Locate restriction and remove.
(f) Scored pressure plate.   (f) Hone light scoring. Replace heavily scored part.
(g) Vanes, rollers, or slippers not properly installed.   (g) Install properly.
(h) Scored rotor in pump.   (h) Hone light scoring. Replace heavily scored part.

CHAPTER 14

Front-Wheel Alignment

The purpose of wheel alignment is to cause the wheels of an automobile to roll without scuffing, dragging, or slipping while traveling in a straight line and around curves. This provides greater driving safety, easier steering, longer tire wear, and less strain on the parts that make up the front end of the automobile.

ALIGNMENT ANGLES

Five simple angles are the basis of wheel alignment. These angles are designed into the automobile by the manufacturer to correctly locate the weight on the moving parts and to make steering easier. The manufacturer specifies a range for each of the angles to permit correct adjustment when necessary. These angles must be maintained within the specified limits if correct steering and riding performance is to be expected.

Camber

Camber is the inward or outward tilt of the wheel at the top from the true vertical position. Camber is a tire-wearing angle and is measured in degrees. Positive camber is when the top of

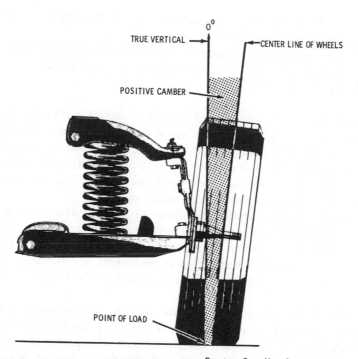

TRUE VERTICAL

0⁰

CENTER LINE OF WHEELS

POSITIVE CAMBER

POINT OF LOAD

Courtesy Bear Manufacturing Co.

Fig. 1. Camber is the amount by which the centerline of the tire is displaced from the true vertical. This illustration shows an example of positive camber and is exaggerated for clarity.

the wheel is tilted outward, as shown in Fig. 1. Negative camber is when the top of the wheel tilts inward. Car manufacturers indicate negative and positive camber in their specifications by the letters (N) and (P). Where a letter is not indicated, the camber is to be regarded as positive.

The reasons for providing camber is as follows:

1. To bring the point at which the tire touches the road more nearly under the load.
2. To cause easier steering by having the weight of the automobile borne by the inner wheel bearing and spindle.
3. To prevent excessive tire wear.

The camber of a wheel will change slightly for different load conditions and with the up-and-down movement of the wheel on rough roads. This slight change in camber is caused by the independent front-suspension design. The front-end design has been constantly improved, however, until the camber on late-model cars has been reduced to zero or nearly so.

The purpose of introducing camber to a wheel when the car is standing still and unloaded is to provide as near an average zero camber as possible when the car is loaded normally and traveling down the road. Zero camber gives maximum tire life since the tire tread contacts the road surface equally on both sides of the tire.

When preferred specifications are listed by a manufacturer, the camber should be adjusted to these specifications. In the case where preferred specifications are not given, both wheels should be adjusted to within ½° of each other. Generally, a zero to positive camber should be maintained.

Fig. 2 shows an exaggerated effect of camber angle on tire contact with the road and helps to explain why positive camber tends to cause the car to pull in the direction the wheel is leaning. Notice from the illustration that the rolling radius is different at different parts of the tire tread. At each separate radius the tire is actually rolling on a different diameter. Thus, a wheel with excessive camber acts like part of a cone which will roll in a circle if rotated. Therefore, the wheel tends also to roll in a circle, accounting for the pulling force of camber. Since the wheel is forced to move in a straight line, the outer or smaller diameter must roll faster than the inner diameter, causing the outer tire tread to be ground off by slipping and scuffing.

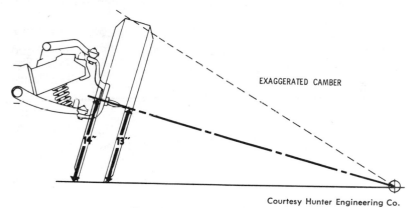

EXAGGERATED CAMBER

Fig. 2. Exaggerated camber.

The harmful effects of incorrect camber are:

1. Excessive ball-joint wear.
2. Excessive wheel-bearing wear.
3. Excessive tire wear (negative camber—inside tread; positive camber—outside tread).
4. Side pull of vehicle if camber is unequal.

Kingpin Inclination

Kingpin inclination is the angle (viewed from the front of the car) between the true vertical and a line drawn through the kingpin or through the axis of the ball joints (Fig. 3). At one time, all cars were built with the kingpin axis vertical. With this arrangement, forces created by the tire hitting a bump tended to turn the wheels and caused a great amount of road shock to be transmitted to the steering wheel. To offset these effects, positive camber was introduced. It was later discovered that inclining the kingpin axis greatly reduced the lever action on bumps and allowed the camber angle to be decreased.

With the present combination of kingpin inclination and camber angle, the line through the kingpin and the line through the center plane of the wheel more nearly intersect at the road surface (Fig. 4) virtually eliminating the lever action previously described. Some specifications list the "included angle" instead of kingpin inclination. The included angle is the sum of the kingpin inclination and the camber angle. For example, with a kingpin inclination of 6° and a camber angle of negative ½°, the included angle is 5½°.

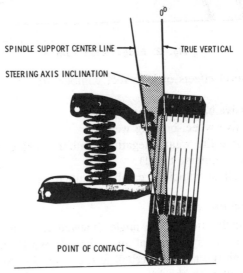

Courtesy Bear Manufacturing Co.

Fig. 3. Kingpin or steering-axis inclination.

Another advantage of kingpin inclination is the automatic steering effect it offers. As the front wheels are turned, the front of the car is actually lifted a small amount. Thus, the weight of the car actually tries to turn the wheels back to the straight-ahead position. Therefore, the wheels tend to straighten themselves after coming out of a curve.

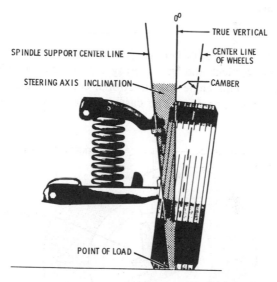

Fig. 4. Camber and kingpin inclination.

The purposes of kingpin inclination are:

1. To reduce the need for excessive camber.
2. To distribute the weight of the car more nearly in the center of the tire tread where it contacts the road.

399

3. To provide a pivot point about which the wheel can turn to produce easy steering.
4. To aid steering stability.

Kingpin inclination is nonadjustable. If the angle is found to be incorrect, it will be because the spindle or spindle support arm has become bent. This condition calls for replacement of the defective part.

Caster

Caster is the angle (when viewed from the side of the car) between true vertical and the steering axis of the kingpin or ball joints (Fig. 5). This angle is a directional control angle and can be either positive or negative. The caster angle is positive when the

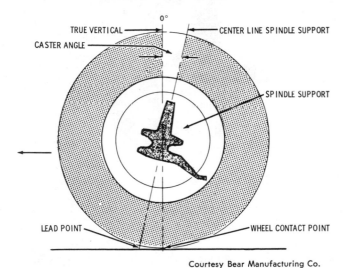

Courtesy Bear Manufacturing Co.

Fig. 5. Caster angle.

spindle support arm is tilted backward, as in Fig. 5, and is negative when the support arm is tilted forward. Manufacturers indicate negative and positive camber by the letters (N) and (P). Where a letter is not indicated, the caster is to be regarded as positive.

The purposes of caster are:

1. To obtain directional control of a car by causing the front wheels to maintain a straight-ahead position or to return to a straight-ahead position out of a turn.
2. To offset road crown.

Tilting the spindle support arm tends to cause the front wheels to maintain a straight-ahead position by projecting the center line of the support arm ahead, and establishing a lead point ahead of the wheel contact point on the road. The same condition exists at the front wheel of a bicycle, as shown in Fig. 6, and accounts for the fact that a bicycle can be ridden and steered without touching the handlebars.

Negative caster has been designed into some recent cars. Wider treads on tires and an increase in steering-axis inclination is responsible for maintaining directional control, even with a negative caster. On older-model cars, especially those with solid-axle construction, negative caster can develop momentarily, and can prove very dangerous. As shown in Fig. 7, a change in wheel height in relation to the vehicle will affect caster. Braking torque on the front wheels of a leaf-spring type solid axle may also develop negative caster (Fig. 8). Either of these conditions is dangerous and can throw the car completely out of control under certain combinations of driving conditions.

It is easy to see that any change in suspension height may seriously affect the steering stability of an automobile. The practice of some owners to use lowering blocks or to raise the front or rear of the car in some manner can actually be dangerous and should be discouraged in the interest of driving safety.

Caster is not a tire-wearing angle. Some manufacturers of alignment equipment, and some manufacturers of cars recommend that the right front wheel be given approximately ½° more positive camber than the left front wheel to offset road crown. This variation must, however, stay within the manufacturer's specifications.

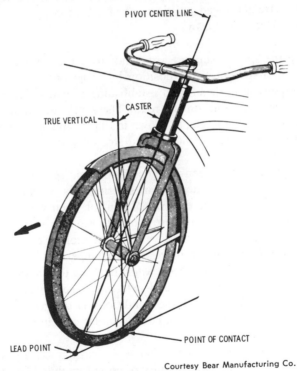

PIVOT CENTER LINE

CASTER

TRUE VERTICAL

LEAD POINT

POINT OF CONTACT

Courtesy Bear Manufacturing Co.

Fig. 6. The caster angle on a bicycle allows it to maintain a straight-ahead position without touching the handlebars.

Courtesy Hunter Engineering Co.

Fig. 7. A change in caster angle can occur with a change in the height between the wheel and frame of the car.

The harmful effects of incorrect caster are:

1. Unequal caster will cause the car to pull toward the side of least positive caster.
2. Too little caster may cause wander and weave.
3. Too little caster may cause instability at high speeds.
4. Too much caster may cause hard steering.
5. Too much caster may cause road shock and shimmy.

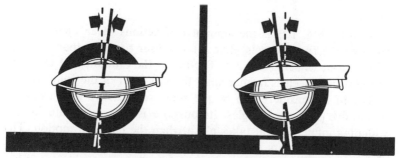

Courtesy Hunter Engineering Co.

Fig. 8. Braking torque on the wheels of a car equipped with front leaf springs may change the caster angle.

403

Turning Radius

The turning radius of a car is the angle of each front wheel when the car is turning. As can be seen in Fig. 9, the inner front wheel turns shorter than the outer front wheel, resulting in a toe-out condition any time the car is turning. The design of the steering arms in relation to the wheelbase of the car provides the proper turning of each wheel.

Turning radius is a tire-wearing angle and is measured in degrees. The car manufacturer usually specifies the amount of toe-out that should exist when the wheels are turned a specific amount. Correct turning radius allows the front tires to roll free on turns. Incorrect turning radius will cause the tires to slip sideways, resulting in excessive tire wear. The turning radius will be correct if all other alignment angles are correct, providing the steering arms are not bent.

The harmful effects of incorrect turning radius are:

1. Excessive tire wear on turns.
2. Squealing tires on turns, even at low speeds.

Toe-in

Toe-in (Fig. 10) is the amount in fractions of an inch that the front of the front wheels (line B) is closer together than the rear of the front wheels (line A). Toe-out is the amount that the front of the front wheels is farther apart than the rear of the front wheels.

Toe-in is considered to be the most serious tire-wearing angle of the five alignment angles. Its purpose is to compensate for the widening influence that takes place when the car is in motion. The tire wear that occurs due to incorrect toe-in appears as a feather-edged scuff across the face of both tires. In some instances it has been found that too much toe-in will cause tire wear on the out-

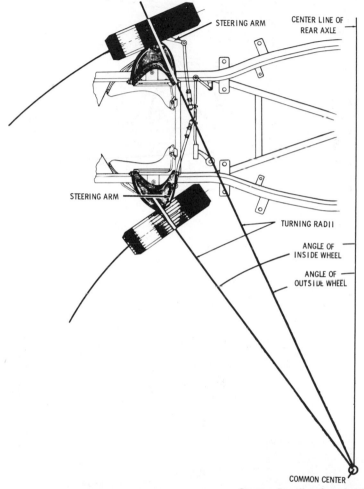

STEERING ARM

CENTER LINE OF
REAR AXLE

STEERING ARM

TURNING RADII

ANGLE OF
INSIDE WHEEL

ANGLE OF
OUTSIDE WHEEL

COMMON CENTER

Courtesy Bear Manufacturing Co.

Fig. 9. The turning radius of a car causes toe-out on a turn, and is determined by the angle at which the steering arms are attached to the wheels.

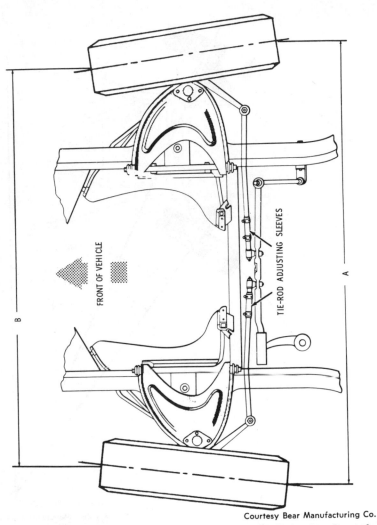

FRONT OF VEHICLE

TIE-ROD ADJUSTING SLEEVES

Courtesy Bear Manufacturing Co.

Fig. 10. Front wheel toe-in. The adjusting sleeves will be found on the outboard end of the tie rods on some makes of automobiles.

side of the right front tire only. Conversely, too much toe-out has been found to cause tire wear on the inside of the left front tire only.

Toe-in is the last alignment to be adjusted in any wheel-alignment procedure. Adjustment is made by turning each adjusting sleeve an equal amount until the correct toe-in, as specified by the car manufacturer, exists.

The harmful effects of incorrect toe-in are:

1. Excessive tire wear due to scuffing and dragging.
2. Tendency of car to wander with toe-out.

ALIGNMENT PROCEDURES

Periodic wheel alignment is necessary to provide maximum driving and riding qualities, and to prevent excessive wear of the tires and suspension components. The procedure involved in checking and correcting the various alignment angles require the use of precision equipment by qualified operators.

There are several makes and types of alignment equipment available ranging from very elaborate to comparatively simple units. Regardless of the complexity or the manufacturer, each equipment has been designed to accurately check the wheel alignment of any make or model of domestic automobile. Generally speaking, the more elaborate the equipment, the less time and labor is involved in making a complete alignment check.

For those shops specializing in wheel alignment, a permanent installation is most often used. Figs. 11 and 12 show such installations in which a light from an assembly fastened to the front wheels is projected on a calibrated screen. The position of this light is determined by the various alignment angles existing on the car under test. Thus, it is possible to determine which of the angles require adjustment, and to determine very accurately when the correct adjustment has been made.

Less elaborate equipment is available for the shop that has only occasional alignment work and does not have the space for a permanent installation. An example of this type of equipment is shown in Fig. 13. These portable alignment stands can be positioned in any free area that might be available. After the stands are leveled, the car is jacked up and the stands placed under the wheels. A combination camber/caster/kingpin-inclination gauge, such as the one in Fig. 14, is then used to check these three alignment angles. These alignment stands can also be used in

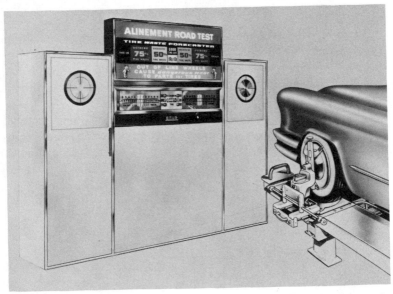

Courtesy Bear Manufacturing Co.

Fig. 11. A Bear wheel-alignment installation.

conjunction with the gauge shown in Fig. 15 to check caster and camber. Toe-in is measured with a separate toe-in gauge, while toe-out on turns (turning radius) can be checked by reading the degree dial on each of the turntables as the front wheels are turned a specified amount.

Courtesy Hunter Engineering Co.

Fig. 12. A Hunter wheel-alignment installation.

Another type of wheel aligner is shown in Fig. 16. According to the manufacturer, this portable unit can be used anywhere on any reasonable level surface. It requires no other auxiliary equipment, and is capable of checking the five major alignment angles already discussed, plus checking center-line steering and rear-wheel track. It features a "sight-sound" system for taking toe readings. The correct toe-in reading is set on the unit and the operator makes the necessary adjustments on the tie-rod ends. When the correct adjustments have been reached, a light flashes and a buzzer is energized to give both a visual and audible indication that the correct setting has been made. This makes it unnecessary for the operator to crawl from under the car and repeatedly check the gauges to see if the setting is correct.

Fig. 13. AMMCO portable wheel-alignment stands.

ADJUSTMENTS

All alignment checks and adjustments should be made with the car level, at curb weight, spare tire in place, normal supply of water, fuel, and oil, but with no passengers or load. All tires should be inflated to the recommended pressures, and the wheel assemblies balanced before alignment. Special care should be taken to check for bent wheels and out-of-round tires. Alignment

Courtesy AMMCO Tools, Inc.

Fig. 14. A combination gauge to measure camber, caster, and kingpin (steering-axis) inclination.

should not be attempted until these conditions are corrected. Neither should alignment be made if the tires are excessively or abnormally worn, if the car frame is bent, or if any part of the suspension and/or steering system is defective.

Preliminary Inspection

Before any alignment adjustments are attempted, a systematic inspection should be made of the suspension, steering, and frame

411

to determine if any parts are loose, broken, worn, or bent. If any of these defects exist, they must be corrected, for if they are not, alignment will be useless if not impossible.

Fig. 15. A gauge used to measure caster and camber angles. This gauge is held in place by magnetic attraction and attached to the face of the wheel hub after the hub cap and dust cover are removed from the wheel.

Courtesy AMMCO Tools, Inc.

A definite step-by-step procedure should be followed for this preliminary inspection to insure that all parts are checked, and to help the operator perform his work easier and faster. An inspection report form, similar to the one shown in Fig. 17, should be filled out to aid in estimating the cost of any needed repairs. These forms are usually available from the alignment equipment manufacturers, or a similar form can be prepared by a local printer.

The following is a suggested procedure to follow in making a preliminary inspection:

Courtesy Hunter Engineering Co.

Fig. 16. A portable wheel aligner called the Tune-A-Line.

1. Check with the owner of the car to determine if he has any complaints that might serve as a clue to possible trouble location. Some of the more common complaints are:

   (a) Excessive tire wear.
   (b) Cupping and dishing of tire tread.
   (c) Front-wheel shimmy.
   (d) Vehicle vibration.
   (e) Car wander.
   (f) Car pulls to one side when braking.
   (g) Car pulls to one side at all times.
   (h) Car steers too hard or too easy.
   (i) Steering has excessive play or looseness.

413

STEERING ALINEMENT INSPECTION REPORT

Name .... 19 ......

Address .... License No.................... Speedometer ....

Phone .... Make.............. Body Type.............. Year and Model..............

Inspection and checks made with Bear Precision Gauges and all corrections are made with Bear Equipment.

	LEFT FRONT		RIGHT FRONT		LEFT REAR		RIGHT REAR	
	OK	NOT OK	OK	NOT OK	OK	NOT OK	OK	NOT OK
Air Pressure in Tires All Around								
Spring Sag All Around								
Spring Shackles (Condition)								
Shock Absorbers (Condition)								
Wheels Bent or Eccentric								
Wheel Balance (All)								

	LEFT		RIGHT			LEFT		RIGHT	
	OK	Not OK	OK	Not OK		OK	Not OK	OK	Not OK
Spindle Bolts and Bushings					Steering Arm (Condition)				
Wheel Bearings (Condition)					Spindle (Limit .005)				
Tie Rod Ends					Axle (Condition)				
Upper Support Arm Pins and Bushings					Torsion Bar Height				
Lower Support Arm Pins and Bushings					Radius Arm (Condition)				
Lower Control Arms and Bushings					Ball Joint, Upper				
Lower Control Arm Shaft (Condition)					Ball Joint, Lower				

	LEFT	RIGHT	FACTORY STANDARD	DIFFERENCE LEFT	RIGHT	REAR HOUSING		
Toe-In						Camber (Right)		
Camber						Camber (Left)		
Caster						Toe-In		
Turning Radius						Toe-Out		
King Pin (Incl.)						Drive Shaft		

	OK	NOT OK		OK	NOT OK
Steering Gear (Condition)			Pitman Arm (Condition)		
Center Control Steering Arm (Condition)			Drag Link (Condition)		
Idler Arm (Condition)			Third Steering Arm (Condition)		
Frame (Condition)	Front End Swayed		Rear End Swayed		
Tracking	Diamond Shape		Sagged in Middle		

REMARKS: ....

....

(All Work Strictly Cash)

Work Performed by.. Checked by ....

W. O. No.................... Reg. No .... Work Authorized by: ....

FORM NO. 104   Furnished by BEAR MANUFACTURING CO., Rock Island, Ill.   PRINTED IN U. S. A.

Courtesy Bear Manufacturing Co.

Fig. 17. An Inspection Report Form should be filled out for each alignment job.

From the facts given by the owner it is often possible to recognize the trouble area before a complete inspection.

2. Check and inflate tires to recommended pressures.
3. Examine tires for unusual or excessive wear.

   (a) Excessive wear on the outside shoulder may indicate too much positive camber.
   (b) Excessive wear on the inside shoulder may indicate too much negative camber.
   (c) Excessive wear on both inner and outer shoulders indicate under-inflation or turning corners at too high a speed.
   (d) Excessive wear on the center portion of the tire indicates overinflation.
   (e) Cupping or dishing indicates an out-of-balance condition.
   (f) Saw-tooth wear on tread indicates improper toe-in condition.

4. Raise the front wheels with jacks placed under the lower control arms and as close to the wheels as possible.
5. Grasp each wheel, in turn, at the top and bottom and wiggle it in and out (Fig. 18). Excessive play indicates loose or worn wheel bearings. These should be tightened or replaced, as the case may be. Worn or damaged bushings should also be replaced.
6. Grasp the wheel at the front and rear, as in Fig. 19, and check for side play. Excessive play indicates worn or loose steering assembly components. Inspect for bushing wear, loose idler arms, loose or worn tie-rod ends, loose or worn ball joints, loose steering gear housing, and loose or worn pitman-arm connections.

Fig. 18. Checking for loose or worn wheel bearings.

Courtesy Hunter Engineering Co.

Courtesy Hunter Engineering Co.

Fig. 19. Checking for loose idler arms, tie-rod ends, ball joints, steering-gear housing, and pitman-arm connections.

416

7. Check for abnormal play in the ball joints by means of a pry bar placed under the tire (Fig. 20).
8. Check the car for accident damage. Correct alignment cannot be made if the frame, steering linkage, or suspension parts have been bent.
9. If accident damage is suspected, check the wheelbase on each side of the car and compare (Fig. 21). The two measurements should be within ¼-inch. To check for a bent frame, diagonal measurements can be made on certain parts of the frame, as shown in Fig. 21. It may be necessary to transfer the measuring points to a level floor in order to measure properly. This

Courtesy Hunter Engineering Co.
Fig. 20. Checking for excessive play in ball joints.

point transfer can be made with a plumb bob. Corresponding measurements should be within ¼-inch of each other. Measurements differing by more than this amount indicate a bent frame, which should be straightened before wheel alignment is attempted.

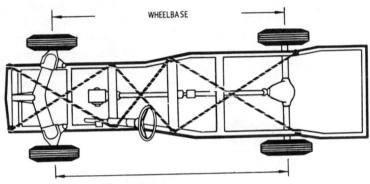

Fig. 21. *Measurements made on the frame to detect incorrect rear-axle alignment or a bent frame.*

10. Check shock absorbers by bouncing the car up and down Fig. 22). If the shocks are too tight, the car may not settle to a normal position. If the shocks are worn, the car will continue to bounce two or three times after the force is removed. Defective shocks should be replaced, and always in pairs (both front shocks and/or both rear shocks).
11. Check the brakes for correct and even adjustment (Fig. 23).
12. Check for sagging springs, both front and rear, or for suspension height on cars with torsion bars. Correct before alignment.
13. Check for rear-axle shift caused by loose axle clamps.

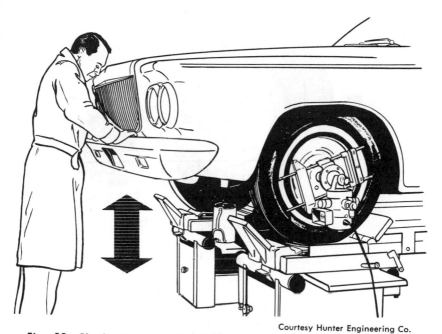

Courtesy Hunter Engineering Co.

Fig. 22. Shock absorbers should be checked before wheel alignment is attempted.

14. Check rear sway bar (Fig. 24) for proper adjustment. If too tight, the rear wheels will not track.
15. Check any other parts of the suspension and steering systems not listed for wear or breakage.

All of the preceding checks should be considered as a routine procedure before proceeding with any alignment adjustments. In addition, the car should be positioned on a level surface, and each time the car is jacked up and lowered, it should be bounced up and down two or three times to settle it in a normal position.

419

Courtesy Hunter Engineering Co.

Fig. 23. A check of the brake adjustments should be made prior to wheel alignment.

Caster and Camber Adjustments

There are only a few basic types of construction found in the different makes and models of cars for adjusting the caster and camber angles. These are:

1. Shims.
2. Eccentric bushing.
3. Eccentric pin.
4. Eccentric bolt and cam.
5. Adjustable strut rod.
6. Bolt holes in control-arm shaft.

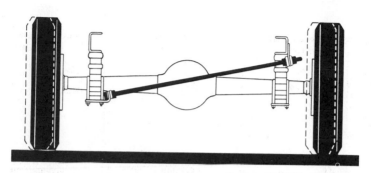

Courtesy Hunter Engineering Co.

Fig. 24. The rear sway bar should be checked for proper adjustment.

The use of shims is the most common type of caster and camber adjustment, and will be found on many Ford and General Motors cars.

Shims at Upper Control Arm and Inside the Frame—The following cars have shims at the upper control arm and inside the frame, as shown in Fig. 25A, to adjust the caster and camber.

Buick 61-65	Dodge 57-58
Cadillac 57-60	Imperial 57-58
Chevrolet 55-64	Mercury 54-56
Chevelle 64-65	Oldsmobile 61-65
Chrysler 57-58	Plymouth 57-58
De Soto 57-58	Pontiac 58-63

Both the caster and camber can be adjusted on these cars by removing or adding shims between the inner shaft of the upper suspension arm and the mounting bracket on the frame in the engine compartment. To increase the caster toward positive, remove shims from the front and/or add shims to the rear. To increase camber toward positive, remove an equal number of shims from both the front and rear.

421

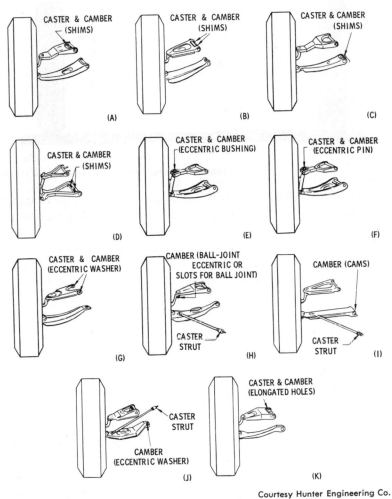

Courtesy Hunter Engineering Co.

Fig. 25. Caster and camber adjustment methods.

Shims at Upper Control Arms and Outside the Frame— The following cars have shims at the upper control arm and outside the frame, as shown in Fig. 25B, to adjust the caster and camber.

Edsel 58-60
Ford 54-64

Mercury 57-58, 61-65
Oldsmobile 57-60

Both the caster and camber can be adjusted on these cars by removing or adding shims between the inner shaft of the upper suspension arm and the mounting bracket on the underbody in the engine compartment. To increase the caster toward positive, add shims to the front and/or remove shims from the rear. To increase camber toward positive, add an equal number of shims to both front and rear.

Shims at Lower Control Arm—The following cars have shims at the lower control arm to adjust the caster and camber.

Buick 57-60 (Fig. 25C)
Rambler American 58-63 (Fig. 25D)

Both the caster and camber can be adjusted on these cars by removing or adding shims between the inner shaft of the lower control arm and the frame. On 57-60 Buick (Fig. 25C) to increase caster toward positive, remove shims from front and/or add shims to rear. On 57-60 Buick, to increase camber toward positive, remove an equal number of shims from both the front and rear. (Note: The preceding procedure is for small adjustments only. If major adjustments are necessary, shimming at the upper control-arm shaft is recommended.)

On 58-63 Rambler American (Fig. 25D) to increase caster toward positive, add shims to the front and/or remove from the rear. To increase camber toward positive, add an equal number of shims to both front and rear.

Eccentric Bushing—The following cars have an eccentric bushing at the outer end of the upper and/or lower control arms to adjust the caster and camber (See Fig. 25E).

Chrysler 41-56	Ford 49-53
De Soto 41-56	Mercury 49-53
Dodge 41-56	Plymouth 41-56

The caster on 41-56 Chryslers, De Sotos, Dodges, and Plymouths is obtained by the correct assembly of the upper and lower control arms and is not adjustable. The camber on these cars is adjusted by turning the eccentric bushing right or left, but no more than ½ revolution. Set camber on left side ½° greater than on right side to offset side pull on crowned roads.

Caster on 49-53 Fords and Mercurys is adjusted by turning the eccentric bushing on the outer end of the lower control arm. If the correct caster can not be obtained, check for bent parts. Camber on these cars is adjusted by turning the bushing on the outer end of the upper control arm either right or left, but no more than ½ revolution. Set camber on left side ½° greater than on right side to offset pull on crowned roads.

Eccentric Pin—The following cars have an eccentric pin at the outer end of the upper control arm (Fig. 25F) to adjust the caster and camber.

Buick 46-56	Oldsmobile 46-56
Cadillac 46-56	Pontiac 46-57
	Studebaker 50-65

Both the caster and camber are affected on these cars when the eccentric pin is turned. Therefore, both angles must be checked simultaneously. It is necessary on some cars to average these two settings to bring each within limits.

To make the caster adjustment, turn the pin (remove lubrication fitting to reach pin) clockwise with an Allen wrench to increase caster toward positive.

To make camber adjustment, turn the pin right or left, but no more than ½ revolution.

Eccentric Bolt and Cam—The following cars have an eccentric bolt and cam (Fig. 25G) at the inner end of the upper control arm to adjust caster and camber.

Chrysler 59-65	Dodge 59-65
De Soto 59-61	Plymouth 59-65
Rambler (10,80 Series) 62-65	

On Chrysler, De Soto, Dodge, and Plymouth, to increase the caster toward positive, turn the front cam out and the rear cam in. On Rambler, to increase caster toward positive, turn the front cam in and the rear cam out.

To increase camber toward positive on Chrysler, De Soto, Dodge, and Plymouth cars, turn front and rear cams out. To increase camber toward positive on Ramblers, turn the front and rear cams in.

Adjustable Strut Rod and Eccentric Ball Joint—The following cars have an adjustable strut rod to set the caster angle and an eccentric ball joint to set the camber. (See Fig. 25H.)

Cadillac 61-65

To increase the caster toward positive, turn the retaining nuts on the forward end of the strut rod to shorten the rod. To change the camber, loosen the ball-joint stud and turn the eccentric to obtain the correct camber angle.

Adjustable Strut Rod and Eccentric Cam—The following cars have an adjustable strut rod to set the caster angle and an eccentric cam to set the camber. (See Fig. 25I.)

Chevrolet 65
Chevy II 62-65

To increase the caster toward positive, shorten the strut rod. To change the camber angle, turn the eccentric cam right or left, but no more than ½ turn.

Adjustable Strut Rod and Eccentric Washer—The following cars have an adjustable strut to change the caster angle and an eccentric washer to adjust the camber. (See Fig. 25J.)

Rambler American 64-65

To increase the caster toward positive, lengthen the strut rod. To change the camber angle, turn the eccentric washer right or left, but no more than ½ turn.

Slotted Cross Member—The following cars have slotted cross members that permit changing the caster and camber angles. (See Fig. 25K.)

| Lincoln Continental 61-65 | Mercury Monterey 59-60 |
| Ford Fairlane 62-65 | Mercury Meteor 62-63 |

To increase the caster toward positive, move the front bolt outboard and the rear bolt inboard. To increase the camber toward positive, move both the front and rear bolts outboard an equal amount.

Toe-In Adjustments

The procedure for adjusting the toe condition is practically the same for all makes and models of automobiles. A typical steering linkage similar to the one found on all cars is shown in Fig. 26. Both tie-rods are adjustable as to length.

To adjust the toe-in, first check the steering wheel for a straight-ahead position. If the steering wheel is not in the correct position with the front wheels straight ahead, adjust by loosening the clamps on the tie-rod ends and shorten one tie-rod and lengthen the other an equal amount until the steering wheel position is correct.

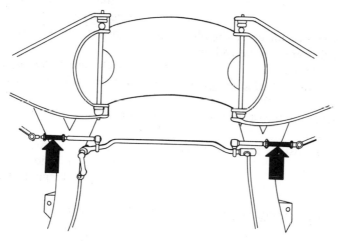

Fig. 26. Location of toe adjustments on a typical car.

To obtain the correct toe-in, turn the tie-rod ends to either lengthen or shorten each tie rod an equal amount until the correct toe is obtained.

WHEEL-ALIGNMENT TROUBLES AND REMEDIES

Symptom and Possible Causes   *Possible Remedy*

Hard Steering

(a) Low or uneven tire pressures.

(a) Inflate tires to recommended pressures.

427

Symptom and Possible Causes	Possible Remedy
(b) Steering gear or connections adjusted too tightly.	(b) Inspect steering system for binding with front wheels off the ground. Adjust as necessary and lubricate.
(c) Dry steering gear, kingpins, ball joints, or tie-rod ends.	(c) Lubricate as necessary.
(d) Excessive caster.	(d) Check caster and adjust.
(e) Steering knuckle or spindle bent.	(e) Replace with new part.
(f) Kingpin thrust bearings worn.	(f) Install new bearings.
(g) Suspension arms bent or twisted.	(g) Install new arms and adjust caster and camber, and check kingpin inclination.
(h) Front springs sagged.	(h) Check car spring height and replace both front springs if one is defective.
(i) Frame out of line or broken.	(i) Check car tracking and frame alignment. Repair frame as necessary.

Excessive Play in Steering System

(a) Worn kingpins and bushings or worn ball joints.	(a) Install new kingpins and bushings or new ball joints.
(b) Worn or incorrectly adjusted front-wheel bearings.	(b) Adjust bearings or replace with new units.
(c) Steering gear adjusted too loosely or worn.	(c) Adjust or install new parts.

Symptom and Possible Causes

(d) Loose steering-gear mounting.

(e) Pitman arm loose on cross shaft.

(f) Drag link loose.

(g) Tie-rod ends worn.

Possible Remedy

(d) Tighten steering-gear mounting bolts.

(e) Replace worn parts or tighten cross-shaft nut.

(f) Adjust or replace with new parts.

(g) Install new tie-rods ends.

Erratic Steering When Brakes are Applied

(a) Low or uneven tire pressures.

(b) Brakes incorrectly adjusted.

(c) Brake linings oil or grease soaked.

(d) Front-wheel bearings worn or incorrectly adjusted.

(e) Front springs and/or shock absorbers weak.

(f) Excessive caster.

(g) Steering knuckle or spindle bent.

(h) Spring U-bolts broken or loose.

(i) Spring center bolt broken.

(a) Inflate tires to recommended pressures.

(b) Adjust brakes.

(c) Replace brake linings and clean brake drum.

(d) Replace or adjust bearings.

(e) Replace with new springs and/or shock absorbers (in pairs).

(f) Check caster and adjust.

(g) Replace with new parts.

(h) Replace or tighten.

(i) Install new center bolt.

Car Pulls to One Side

(a) Low or uneven tire pressures.

(a) Inflate tires to recommended pressures.

Symptom and Possible Causes	Possible Remedy
(b) Brakes incorrectly adjusted.	(b) Adjust brakes.
(c) Brake linings oil or grease soaked.	(c) Replace brake linings and clean brake drums.
(d) Incorrect or uneven caster angles.	(d) Check caster and adjust.
(e) Excessive unequal camber angles.	(e) Adjust camber.
(f) Toe-in or toe-out incorrect.	(f) Adjust tie-rod ends for correct toe-in.
(g) Front tires scuffed.	(g) Rotate tires.
(h) Steering knuckle or spindle bent.	(h) Replace with new knuckle or spindle.
(i) Spindle support arm bent.	(i) Replace with new arm.
(j) Front springs sagged.	(j) Check front spring height. Replace both front springs if one is found sagged.
(k) Rear axle shifted.	(k) Check for loose spring clips or broken center bolt. Measure from the spring anchor bolts to the rear housing. This distance on both sides of the car should be equal.
(l) Frame out of line or broken.	(l) Check tracking and frame alignment. Correct and repair frame.

Symptom and Possible Causes	*Possible Remedy*
Scuffed Tires	
(a) Tires improperly inflated.	(a) Inflate tires to recommended pressures.
(b) Incorrect toe-in.	(b) Adjust tie-rod ends for correct toe-in.
(c) Wheels or tires out of true.	(c) Check wheels and tires for wobble. Correct condition or replace.
(d) Worn kingpin thrust bearings.	(d) Install new bearings.
(e) Incorrect toe-out on turns.	(e) Check caster and adjust. Install new steering arms.
(f) Worn or incorrectly adjusted front-wheel bearings.	(f) Adjust or replace bearings.
(g) Suspension arms bent or twisted.	(g) Install new arms and adjust caster and camber. Check kingpin inclination.
(h) Steering knuckle or spindle bent.	(h) Replace with new unit.
(i) Excessive speeds on turns.	(i) Caution driver.
Cupped Tires	
(a) Tires improperly inflated.	(a) Inflate tires to recommended pressures.
(b) Wheels, tires, and/or brake drums out of balance.	(b) Balance wheel assemblies. Check for eccentric brake drums, wheels, and tires and replace if necessary.

Symptom and Possible Causes	Possible Remedy
(c) Dragging brakes.	(c) Adjust or repair brakes.
(d) Worn or incorrectly adjusted front-wheel bearings.	(d) Adjust or replace bearings.
(e) Improper camber angle.	(e) Adjust camber.
(f) Steering knuckle or spindle bent.	(f) Replace with new knuckle or spindle.
(g) Worn or loose steering linkage and suspension parts.	(g) Replace defective part or parts.

Front-Wheel Shimmy

(a) Low or uneven tire pressures.	(a) Inflate tires to recommended pressures.
(b) Worn or incorrectly adjusted steering connections.	(b) Adjust or install new parts.
(c) Loose steering-gear mounting.	(c) Tighten steering-gear mounting bolts or nuts.
(d) Incorrectly adjusted steering gear.	(d) Adjust steering gear.
(e) Worn or incorrectly adjusted front-wheel bearings.	(e) Adjust or replace bearings.
(f) Out-of-balance wheels, tires, or brake drums.	(f) Balance wheel assemblies. Check for eccentric brake drums, wheels, and tires.
(g) Wheels and/or tires out of true.	(g) Check for wheel and tire wobble. Correct condition or replace with good units.
(h) Incorrect or unequal caster.	(h) Adjust caster.

Symptom and Possible Causes	*Possible Remedy*
(i) Dead or weak shock absorbers.	(i) Replace with correct type. Always replace in pairs.
(j) Worn kingpin thrust bearings.	(j) Install new bearings.
(k) Incorrect toe-in.	(k) Adjust toe-in.
(l) Steering knuckle or spindle bent.	(l) Replace with new knuckle or spindle.

Front- or Rear-Wheel Tramp

(a) Out-of-balance wheels, tires, or brake drums.	(a) Balance wheel assemblies. Check for eccentric brake drums, wheels, or tires and replace if necessary.
(b) Weak front springs.	(b) Replace both front springs if only one is weak.
(c) Dead or weak shock absorbers.	(c) Install new units of the correct type. Always replace in pairs.

Wander

(a) Low or uneven tire pressures.	(a) Inflate tires to recommended pressures.
(b) Loose steering-gear mounting.	(b) Tighten steering-gear mounting bolts or nuts.
(c) Worn or loose steering gear or connections.	(c) Adjust or install new parts.
(d) Tight steering gear or connections.	(d) Inspect steering system with front wheels off ground. Adjust as necessary and lubricate.

433

Symptom and Possible Causes	*Possible Remedy*
(e) Dry steering linkage.	(e) Lubricate with correct lubricant.
(f) Worn kingpin thrust bearings.	(f) Install new bearings.
(g) Incorrect front-wheel toe.	(g) Adjust toe.
(h) Incorrect caster.	(h) Adjust caster.
(i) Steering knuckle or spindle bent.	(i) Replace with new unit.
(j) Rear axle shifted.	(j) Check for loose spring clip or broken center bolt. Measure from the spring anchor bolt to the rear housing. This distance should be the same on both sides of the car. Correct as necessary.
(k) Inoperative stabilizer.	(k) Inspect grommets and links, replacing worn parts.
(l) Tread on rear tires better than on front tires.	(l) Change tires, placing best tread on front.

Road Shocks

(a) Low tire pressure.	(a) Inflate tires to recommended pressures.
(b) Steering gear or connections incorrectly adjusted.	(b) Adjust steering gear and connections.
(c) Excessive caster.	(c) Adjust caster.
(d) Dead or weak shock absorbers.	(d) Replace shocks in pairs.

Symptom and Possible Causes	*Possible Remedy*
(e) Front springs weak or sagged.	(e) Check car spring height. If incorrect, replace springs in pairs.
(f) Wrong type or size of tires used.	(f) Install new tires of correct type and size.
(g) Steering knuckle or spindle bent.	(g) Install new unit.

CHAPTER 15

Chassis, Springs, and Shocks

The chassis of an automobile is the underpart, consisting of the frame with the wheels attached. In simpler terms, it is that portion of the automobile that suports the body and engine.

FRAME

The frame of most automobiles is a base to which the body and other units are fastened. The most important requirement of the frame is stiffness which must be sufficient to withstand unusual twisting under load, to absorb road shocks, and to keep the attached units in correct alignment.

The plan and construction of the frame differ somewhat in various automobiles, but most consist of side rails, cross members, and gussets, riveted or welded into some form of "A", "X", "Y", or "K" in order to gain maximum stiffness with minimum weight. This type of frame is shown in Fig. 1. Most of the stiffness of the frame is obtained from the steel body structure. One manufacturer does not include a separate frame, as such. Instead, the body forms the principal supporting structure to which the wheels and other units are attached. In this type, shown in Fig. 2, the under-body and sills are welded together to form one single unit. The body is then welded to this assembly, which results in the required stiffneses.

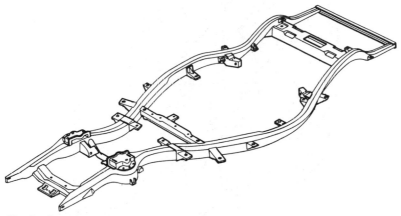

Fig. 1. A typical automobile frame. The body of the car is bolted to this base, the combination forming a rigid unit.

Another manufacturer uses two partial frames, one at the front and one at the rear (Fig. 3), welded to the car underbody.

Checking Frame Alignment

Regardless of the type of construction, any misalignment in the frame structure can affect the front-wheel alignment and cause improper operation and abnormal wear of the chassis parts. Cracked window glass, poor-fitting and hard-to-close doors, trunk lids, and hoods, are often the cause of a bent or twisted frame.

Before checking frame alignment, inspect the frame for damage and loose parts. Inspect all frame members for cracks, twists, and bends. Check all welded connections for cracks. Inspect all rivets,

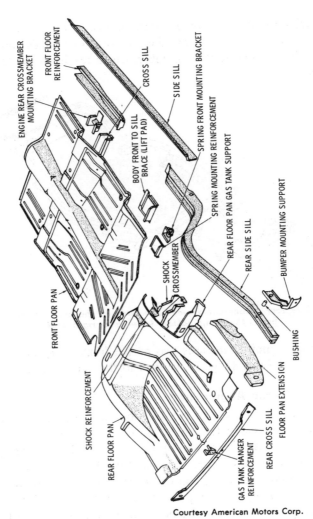

Courtesy American Motors Corp.

Fig. 2. A welded-type construction provides the required stiffness in some automobiles.

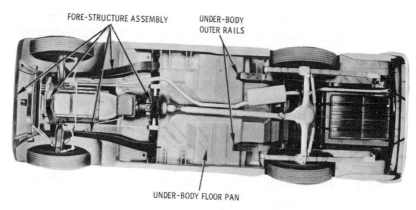

FORE-STRUCTURE ASSEMBLY

UNDER-BODY OUTER RAILS

UNDER-BODY FLOOR PAN

Courtesy Dodge Div., Chrysler Motors Corp.

Fig. 3. Front and rear semi-frames welded to the under-body of the car is used by one automobile manufacturer.

bolts, and body-support brackets for looseness. Make any necessary repairs or replacements.

Several types of commercial frame-alignment equipment are available, with complete instructions for their use. If such equipment is not present, however, an adequate job of alignment can usually be accomplished with portable equipment found in most shops. The following procedure outlines a convenient method of checking the frame alignment.

1. Place the car on a clean level floor and set the parking brake.
2. Select several points along one frame side member (or along one side of the underbody if the car has no frame) and very carefully transfer these points to the floor by means of a plumb bob.
3. Locate the corresponding points along the opposite side of the frame (or underbody) and carefully transfer these points to the floor in the same manner.

4. Move the car away from the marks on the floor, and measure between points, as shown in Fig. 4. The corresponding diagonal measurements should be within ⅛-inch of each other. If the measurements differ by more than ⅛-inch, re-alignment of the frame is indicated.

Frame Repair and Replacement

Misalignment of the frame can be corrected by straightening the defective parts, or by replacing the cross-members, braces, or brackets, if they are badly damaged.

To prevent internal stresses in the metal, frame straightening should be limited to those parts which are not severely bent. If heat is needed to straighten a frame member, keep the temperature below 1200°F. This is the temperature at which the metal will glow a dull red. Excessive heat may weaken the metal and cause permanent damage.

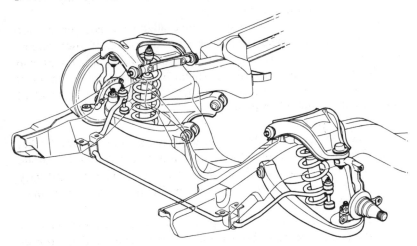

Fig. 4. A typical coil-spring type front suspension.

Electric welding equipment should be used for all frame welding. Heat should be isolated to as small an area as possible to keep the hardness of the metal from being affected. When a reinforcement is to be welded to a frame side member, run the welds lengthwise along the side of the reinforcement.

If a frame member is to be replaced, use the same method of attachment as on the original member. New bolts or rivets, if required for replacement of parts, should be of the same specifications as the original bolts or rivets.

SPRINGS

The front suspension on all cars manufactured in recent years either utilize coil springs, as in Fig. 4, or torsion bars, as in Fig. 5. The maintenance procedure for both of these types of suspension have been discussed previously in another chapter and will not be repeated here.

The rear suspension used on most cars will be found to be one of two general types—the coil-spring type as shown in Fig. 6, or the leaf-spring type in Fig. 7.

CHECKING REAR SUSPENSION

The coil-spring type of rear suspension should be checked at regular intervals to determine the condition of the rubber bushings in the control arms. A sagging or weak spring should be replaced, following the procedure outlined in the service manual for that particular car. If the rear wheels do not track, check for a bent or misadjusted rear stabilizer bar. Some cars have swing-type rear axles, in which case the toe-in of the rear wheels must be checked and adjusted at regular intervals or when abnormal steering indicates the toe-in is incorrect.

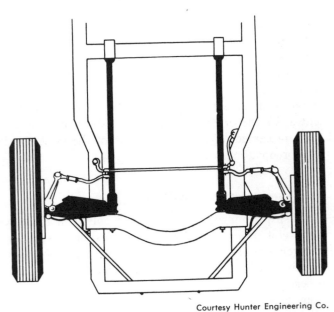

Courtesy Hunter Engineering Co.

Fig. 5. Torsion bars are used in the front suspension system of some cars.

On cars with leaf-type rear springs, the rubber bushings, shackles, and hangers should be inspected periodically for wear and looseness. Any defective parts should be replaced.

Check for broken spring leaves, and for worn or missing anti-squeak inserts between the leaves. Replace any worn, broken, or missing parts. Inspect the rear stabilizer bar (if so equipped) for damage, worn grommets, or misadjustment. Repair or adjust as necessary.

SHOCK ABSORBERS

The shock absorbers for all makes and models of automobiles are very similar in construction and operation. They differ only

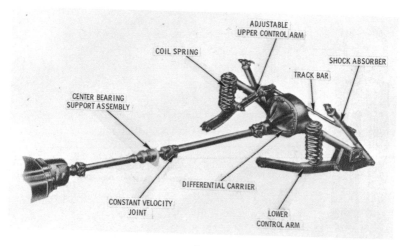

Fig. 6. A typical coil-spring type rear suspension.

in calibration, physical dimensions, and type of attaching bolt or lug. A cross-sectional view of a typical shock absorber is shown in Fig. 8.

All shocks are filled with a calibrated amount of fluid and sealed during construction. It is therefore impossible to refill or service them other than replacement of deteriorated rubber bushings or grommets on the end fittings.

Fig. 7. A leaf-spring type rear suspension.

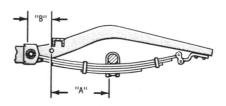

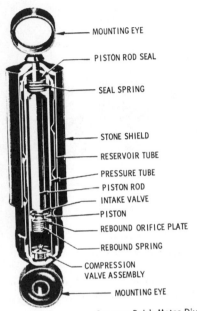

MOUNTING EYE

PISTON ROD SEAL

SEAL SPRING

STONE SHIELD

RESERVOIR TUBE

PRESSURE TUBE

PISTON ROD

INTAKE VALVE

PISTON

REBOUND ORIFICE PLATE

REBOUND SPRING

COMPRESSION
VALVE ASSEMBLY

MOUNTING EYE

Fig. 8. The rear shock absorber for a 1965 Buick is similar to the units used on all automobiles.

Courtesy Buick Motor Div.,
General Motors Corp.

The front shocks are usually mounted on the inside of the coil spring (when the car is so equipped). The upper stem is attached to some part of the frame by means of rubber grommets or bushings to prevent metal-to-metal contact. The lower stem is fastened to the lower control arm, also being insulated from the arm by rubber fittings.

The rear shocks are normally mounted at an angle, with the upper ends in toward the center of the car, to provide greater stability. The upper end is fastened to the frame or body by means of rubber grommets, bushings, or washers. The same method is used to attach the lower end to some part of the rear axle housing.

Front shock absorbers are interchangeable with respect to right or left, as are the rear shocks. However, the front and rear units are not interchangeable with each other on most cars.

Servicing

Defective shock absorbers cannot be repaired, but must be removed and replaced. However, they should only be replaced if they have lost their resistance, are damaged, or if they drip oil. A slight amount of oil moisture on the outside of the shock is not sufficient cause to warrant replacing the unit, however.

To test the shock absorber after it is removed, hold it in an upright position with the dust shield or piston-rod section at the top. Extend the shock to its maximum length and turn it upside down. Now compress the shock absorber. Repeat this procedure until it is certain that all air is removed from the unit. Do not extend the shock while it is upside down or laying on its side, because air will enter the unit.

After the air has been bled from the shock, a steady resistance should be felt as the unit is extended and compressed. If no resistance is felt, replace the shock.

A new shock absorber should be bled of all air, in the manner just described, before it is installed. In addition, compressing it to its shortest length will usually be necessary in order to make the installation.

CHAPTER 16

Fuel Pumps

The fuel pump in an automobile is used to move the gasoline from the tank to the carburetor in sufficient quantity to supply the requirements of the engine under all operating conditions. These conditions vary over wide limits, from idle to full speed and during periods of sustained full acceleration.

OPERATING PRINCIPLES

A diaphragm-type fuel pump, similar to the one in Fig. 1, is almost universally used. Most fuel pumps are actuated mechanically, although electric models are available for use on some cars. The operating principles of all mechanical fuel pumps are practically the same, regardless of their construction features or method of attachment to the engine. (NOTE: A filter unit is shown attached to the fuel pump in Fig. 1. Some pumps have a sediment bowl and filter that snaps on the bottom of the unit. Other pumps may have a sediment bowl and/or filter element on the inlet side.)

The fuel pump is operated by the rotation of an eccentric on the camshaft. A flexible diaphragm in the pump is actuated by a combination of rocker-arm action and calibrated spring tension.

On the intake stroke (Fig. 2A), the camshaft eccentric moves the rocker arm (by means of a push rod or by direct contact), causing the diaphragm to compress the diaphragm spring. This action draws gasoline from the fuel tank, through the intake valve of the pump, and into the fuel chamber. On the output cycle (Fig. 2B), the camshaft continues its rotation, and the force on the rocker arm is removed, allowing the diaphragm spring to try and return the diaphragm to its normal position. This action causes the intake valve to close, with the result that the gasoline in the fuel chamber is forced through the outlet valve by the pressure of the diaphragm and spring, and through the fuel line to the carburetor. The pulsator diaphragm and body dampens the fuel-pump pulsations that otherwise would be felt by the inlet needle valve in the carburetor.

Gasoline is delivered to the carburetor only when the inlet valve of the carburetor is open. This valve is opened and closed by the level of gasoline in the float chamber of the carburetor. When the chamber is full, the valve is closed; gasoline is used by

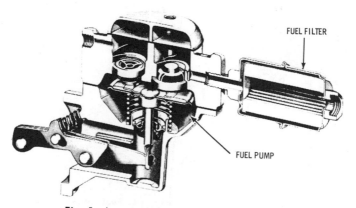

Fig. 1. A typical diaphragm-type fuel pump.

FUEL FILTER

FUEL PUMP

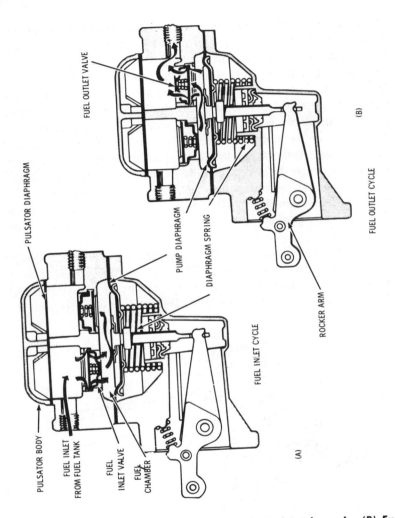

Fig. 2. Operation of a typical fuel pump; (A) Fuel intake cycle; (B) Fuel output cycle.

448

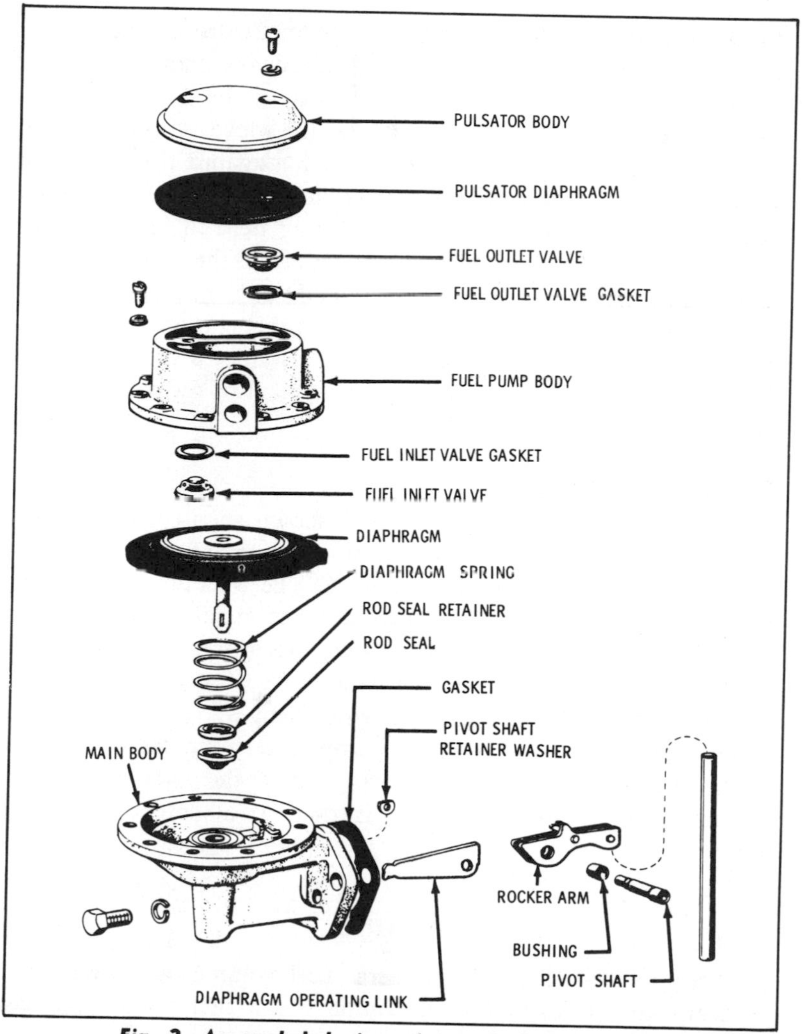
PULSATOR BODY
PULSATOR DIAPHRAGM
FUEL OUTLET VALVE
FUEL OUTLET VALVE GASKET
FUEL PUMP BODY
FUEL INLET VALVE GASKET
FUEL INLET VALVE
DIAPHRAGM
DIAPHRAGM SPRING
ROD SEAL RETAINER
ROD SEAL
GASKET
PIVOT SHAFT
RETAINER WASHER
MAIN BODY
ROCKER ARM
BUSHING
PIVOT SHAFT
DIAPHRAGM OPERATING LINK

Fig. 3. An exploded view of a typical fuel pump.

the engine, the fuel level in the float chamber drops, opening the valve. With the carburetor inlet valve closed, the diaphragm spring in the fuel pump is not strong enough to force the diaphragm back to its normal position. Since the link on the rocker arm is designed to move the diaphragm only in the direction against the diaphragm spring, it exerts no force to move the diaphragm back to its normal position. Thus, with the diaphragm spring held in its fully compressed position by the fuel pressure acting on the diaphragm, the rocker-arm action continues, but no additional gasoline is drawn into the pump. The diaphragm remains in this stationary condition until there is again a demand for more gasoline to the carburetor. The exploded view shown in Fig. 3 is typical of most fuel pumps in use today.

Combination Pumps

A combination fuel pump and vacuum pump will be found on some automobiles. A cross-sectional view of a combination unit of this kind is shown in Fig. 4. The vacuum portion has nothing to do with the fuel system, but has merely been added to the fuel pump because of convenience. Its purpose is to furnish a nearly constant vacuum to the windshield wipers so their speed will not vary as the load on the engine changes.

The operation of the vacuum pump is very similar to the fuel pump except that more valves are used in the vacuum unit. A separate link to the rocker arm is used to actuate the vacuum pump.

TESTING

Three tests—fuel-pump pressure, fuel volume, and fuel-pump vacuum—are necessary to determine if the fuel pump and fuel lines are in satisfactory condition.

If both the fuel-pump pressure and volume (rate of flow) are within specifications, then the pump and fuel lines are satisfactory. However, if the pump volume is within specifications, but the pressure is too high or too low, the fuel-pump vacuum test must be made to isolate the cause of trouble.

If both the pressure and vacuum are correct, but the volume is less than specified, inspect the fuel line for obstruction, crimps, or

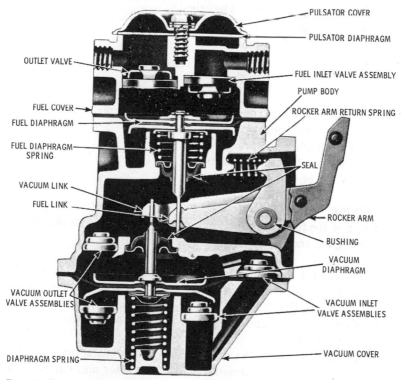

Fig. 4. Cross-sectional view of a combination fuel and vacuum pump.

451

leaks. Replace the fuel filter (if the car is so equipped) and retest the volume.

High fuel-pump pressure and volume can be caused by one or more of the following:

1. Gasoline between the layers of the diaphragm, causing it to bulge.
2. Diaphragm too tight across its surface.
3. Diaphragm too strong (too rigid).
4. Rocker-arm link to diaphragm "frozen".
5. Diaphragm spring too strong.

Low fuel-pump pressure can be caused by one or more of the following:

1. Worn rocker arm, push rod, or rocker-arm pivot pin.
2. Punctured diaphragm.
3. Weak diaphragm spring.
4. Clogged valves in fuel pump.
5. Leaking or restricted fuel line.

Fuel-Pump Pressure Test

A test of the fuel-pump pressure should be made with the pump on the engine, and using the following procedure:

1. Disconnect the fuel line at the carburetor and attach a fuel-pump pressure gauge between the line and the carburetor inlet, as in Fig. 5.
2. Start the engine and run at 500 rpm unless some other speed is specified.
3. Compare the pressure reading with the specifications (usually 3 to 5 psi). If the pressure is low, check for and correct any restrictions in the lines or filter, or any loose fittings that

would allow air to enter the system. After correcting any defects, retest the pressure. If it is still low, repair or replace the fuel pump. If the pump pressure exceeds the specifications, the fuel pump should be repaired or replaced.

Fuel-Pump Volume Test

A test of the fuel-pump volume should be made with the pump on the engine, and only after it has been determined that the pressure is normal. Use the following procedure:

1. Disconnect the fuel line from the carburetor and arrange to catch the discharge from this line (through a hose, if necessary) in a graduated container.
2. Start the engine and operate at idle speed (the engine should continue to run a sufficient length of time on the gasoline in

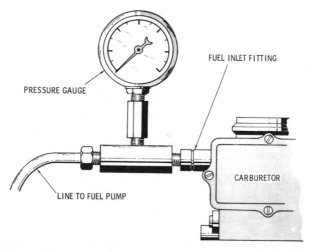

Fig. 5. Setup for checking the pressure of a fuel pump.

the float chamber). Note the time required to pump a specified quantity of gasoline into the container. Compare with the specifications (usually one pint in 15 to 20 seconds). If the quantity pumped is less than the amount specified, and there are no restrictions in the fuel line, it will be necessary to remove the pump for repair or replacement.

Fuel-Pump Vacuum Test

A vacuum test of the fuel pump is made while it is installed on the engine, and using the following procedure:

1. Install a vacuum gauge between the inlet to the fuel pump and the fuel line to the gas tank.
2. Start the engine and run at idle speed.
3. Compare the gauge reading with the specifications (usually not less than 6 inches of mercury).
4. Stop the engine. The gauge should continue to indicate a vacuum for at least 10 seconds.

A reading less than the specified vacuum indicates a defective fuel pump which should be repaired or replaced. If vacuum is lost in less than 10 seconds after the engine is stopped, a defective pump or an air leak in the fuel line or fittings is indicated. The trouble must be isolated and corrected.

Fuel-Line Hose Leak Test

The fuel-line hose should be inspected occasionally for chafing, cracks, brittleness, rotting, and kinks or collapse.

The line can be tested for air leaks and restrictions by using the vacuum pump of a distributor tester.

1. Remove the flexible hose to be checked from the vehicle.
2. Hold your thumb over the end of the vacuum hose from the

distributor tester and adjust the regulator until the vacuum gauge reads 10 inches of mercury.

3. Connect one end of the fuel-line hose to the vacuum hose of the tester. Hold your thumb over the free end of the fuel line hose. If the vacuum gauge reads less than 10 inches of mercury, the fuel-line hose leaks air. Observe the hose for signs of collapsing while making the test. The hose should also be inspected for internal deterioration while it is removed for this test. Any signs of leaks or damage should be cause for replacing the hose with a new one.

Vacuum-Pump Test

The following test is to be made only on the vacuum portion of combination pumps.

1. Fully open the windshield-wiper valve and observe the wiper-blade speed as the engine is alternately idled and accelerated. The blade speed should be faily constant regardless of engine speed or throttle opening. (NOTE: A dry windshield will slow the wiper speed. Take this into account, or spray the windshield with water during the test.)

2. Inspect the hose connections at the pump, wiper motor, and control button, making sure the connections are air tight. Replace the hose if cracked or deteriorated.

3. If the wipers do not operate properly after correcting any leakage, detach both hoses at the vacuum pump and join them with a piece of tubing. Slowly increase the engine speed from idle to 1000 rpm; the wipers should run at full speed, operating on the engine vacuum only. If they do not, either the wiper motor or connecting tubing is defective. The vacuum pump is defective if the wipers operate properly on engine vacuum but not on pump vacuum.

4. A further test of the vacuum pump can be made by attaching a vacuum gauge to the inlet port (the port that normally is connected to the wiper motor) with the outlet hose disconnected. **(CAUTION: Always make sure the outlet port is open before making this test.)**

5. With the engine operating at 750 rpm, the gauge should show from 10 to 12 inches of vacuum. Less than 10 inches indicates a defective vacuum pump.

SERVICING

Most fuel pumps can be dismantled for repair. There are some exceptions, however, in which the pump is a sealed unit and must be replaced if it becomes defective in any way.

Repair kits are available to rebuild defective fuel pumps, and complete instructions are included for their use. Factory-rebuilt pumps are also available for most cars. An allowance is usually given for the old unit, if it is in repairable condition, when the rebuilt pump is purchased.

To repair a defective pump, the instructions given in the service manual should be followed. The procedure varies somewhat for each make and type of fuel pump, making it impractical to include a detailed description here. However, a few basic rules that apply to the repair of most fuel pumps are as follows:

1. Disconnect all lines from the pump unit.
2. Loosen the retaining bolts (usually 2) but do not remove them.
3. Jog the engine until the camshaft eccentric is in a position where the least amount of pressure is exerted on the rocker arm of the fuel pump.
4. Remove the retaining bolts and lift the pump and gasket

free. If a pushrod is used to actuate the pump, it may have to be unhooked or removed before the pump can be lifted free. Discard the gasket, as a new one should be used when the pump is replaced.

5. Plug all openings in the pump assembly and thoroughly wash the exterior with solvent to remove all dirt and grease.

6. Scratch a mark on the cover or covers and the pump body to make sure of proper alignment when the unit is re-assembled.

7. Disassemble the pump according to instructions, taking care not to damage any parts that may have to be used in the re-paired unit.

8. Clean the various parts of the pump with a suitable solvent and blow out all passages in the body, housing, and cover with compressed air.

9. Inspect the pump body, valve housing, and cover for cracks, burrs, or damage. Examine all screw holes for stripped or crossed threads. Replace any defective unit.

10. Inspect the valves for proper action and seating. If any part of the valve assembly is defective, replace the entire unit.

11. Inspect the diaphragm for pin holes, punctures, cracks, etc., and for torn or elongated screw holes around its circumference. Replace if any defect is found.

12. The diaphragm spring and rocker-arm spring should be replaced as they are very apt to be weak, corroded, or distorted.

13. Inspect the rocker-arm, link, and rocker-arm pivot for signs of wear or distortion. Replace if necessary.

14. Reassemble the unit, taking care that the diaphragm is centered correctly. Never use shellac or gasket compound on the diaphragm.

15. Install the fuel pump on the engine, using a new gasket, and connect the fuel lines.

FUEL-PUMP TROUBLES AND REMEDIES

Symptom and Possible Causes   *Possible Remedy*

Fuel Pump Leaks Gasoline

(a) Loose housing screws.
(b) Ruptured or torn diaphragm.
(c) Loose fittings.
(d) Threads stripped on fittings.

(a) Tighten screws.
(b) Install new diaphragm.

(c) Tighten fittings.
(d) Install new fittings.

Fuel Pump Leaks Oil

(a) Hole in diaphragm.
(b) Leak at mounting flange.

(c) Damaged oil seal.

(a) Install new diaphragm.
(b) Install new gasket and tighten mounting bolts to required torque.
(c) Replace oil seal.

Insufficient Fuel Delivery

(a) Loose fuel-line fittings.
(b) Damaged diaphragm.
(c) Cracked or broken fuel line.
(d) Weak or broken diaphragm spring.

(a) Tighten fittings.
(b) Install new diaphragm.
(c) Replace line.

(d) Replace spring.

Fuel Pump Noise

(a) Pump loose at mounting.
(b) Worn rocker arm or push rod.
(c) Broken or weak rocker-arm spring.

(a) Tighten mounting bolt.
(b) Replace worn unit.

(c) Install new spring.

CHAPTER 17

Carburetors

Automobile engines will not run on raw, liquid gasoline. Instead, the gasoline must be broken up into tiny drops, then vaporized to produce a highly combustible air-fuel mixture. This mixture is then introduced into the cylinders under controlled conditions of temperature, pressure, and time.

The device which mixes the gasoline and air is the carburetor. Not only does it mix the fuel and air, but it also automatically varies the proportion. It provides a richer mixture (a greater proportion of gasoline) for starting, idling, and acceleration, and a leaner mixture (a smaller proportion of gasoline) for part-throttle operation. In addition, the carburetor also regulates the engine speed and power by controlling the amount of the fuel-air mixture reaching the cylinders. In order to accomplish all these tasks, a carburetor has a variety of fixed and adjustable passages, jets, ports, and pumps arranged in systems or circuits.

BASIC OPERATING PRINCIPLES

Although a carburetor is relatively complicated, its basic operation depends simply on differences in pressure. An understanding of how these pressure differences are put to work in a carburetor will help in making adjustments and diagnosing carburetor troubles.

A piston moving down on the intake stroke draws air from the cylinder and from the intake manifold. This action creates a vacuum that draws atmospheric air through the only opening into the cylinder at that time—through the carburetor. This flow of air through the carburetor causes fuel to be drawn from the carburetor, through the manifold, through the intake valve, and into the cylinder.

The Venturi Principle

When air is passed rapidly through a tube having a small hole in the side, air will be drawn through the hole and into the air stream flowing through the tube, as shown in Fig. 1. If a hose is connected to this hole, and the opposite end of the hose is suspended in a liquid, the liquid will be pulled through the hose and will

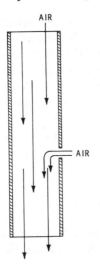

Fig. 1. Air is drawn through a hole in the side of a tube through which a stream of air is passing.

enter the air stream. This is shown in Fig. 2. The amount of liquid passing into the air stream in the tube will depend on how fast the air is moving past the hole in the side of the tube. The greater the velocity of the air, the greater will be the amount of liquid passing into the air stream.

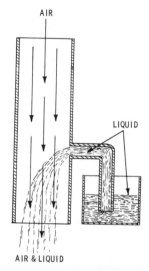

Fig. 2. Liquid from a container can be introduced into the air stream in the tube shown in Fig. 1, if a hose is connected from the liquid to the hole in the side of the tube.

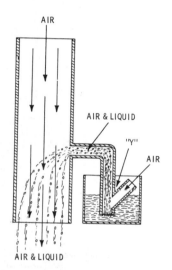

Fig. 3. If a "Y" is added to the hose below the level of the liquid, with the open end of the "Y" exposed to the air, both air and liquid will be drawn into the air stream inside the tube.

If a "Y" is placed in the hose at a point below the level of the the liquid, in a manner such as that shown in Fig. 3, both liquid and air will be pulled through the hose and into the air stream. The introduction of the air into the liquid helps to break up the liquid into smaller particles, making vaporization more complete.

461

For greater efficiency, a portion of the tube can be made with a smaller diameter. The air passing through the tube will speed up in the vicinity of the smaller diameter, and will also create an area of lower pressure at the point where the air is passing on into the normal diameter of the tube. This restriction to the flow of

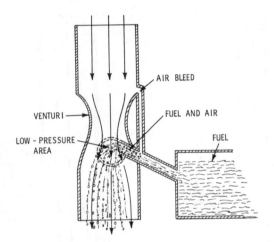

AIR BLEED

VENTURI

FUEL AND AIR

LOW - PRESSURE
AREA

FUEL

Fig. 4. The lower pressure introduced by a venturi in a tube helps to draw fuel and air into the air stream.

air in the tube is known as a *venturi*. The action this restriction has on drawing fuel and air into the air stream is known as the *venturi effect*. Fig. 4 illustrates the principle of a venturi.

With the engine running at idle speed there is not enough air passing through the venturi to draw fuel into the air stream. In addition, the venturi effect is momentarily lost with sudden changes of engine operation, such as rapid acceleration. Other systems are therefore built into the carburetor to overcome these defects. These systems will be discussed later in this chapter.

Float System

The gasoline delivered by the fuel pump to the carburetor is contained in the fuel bowl. The level of the gasoline in the bowl must be kept constant under all conditions of engine operation. The float system in all carburetors operates on the same basic principle. As shown in Fig. 5, the typical carburetor has a float-operated needle valve and seat at the fuel inlet to control the level of the gasoline in the fuel bowl. When the fuel drops below a pre-set level, the float lowers and opens the needle valve, allowing gasoline to enter the bowl. When the fuel reaches the preset level, the rising float forces the inlet needle valve against the seat, shut-

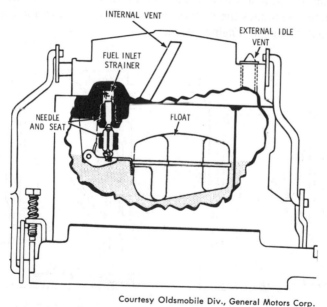

Courtesy Oldsmobile Div., General Motors Corp.

Fig. 5. A typical float system.

ting off the flow of gasoline from the fuel pump. In this manner the gasoline is kept at a constant level in the fuel bowl.

The fuel bowl is vented into the carburetor air horn to provide the proper air pressure to allow the gasoline to enter the passages in the throttle body of the carburetor during engine operation.

Throttle Valve

The throttle valve (Fig. 6) is a round disc, mounted on a shaft and located in the lower part of the throttle body. The throttle valve is pivoted by means of a mechanical linkage from the accelerator either to close off the air-fuel stream through the throttle body or to allow a variable amount of fuel-air to pass through. This action regulates the flow of the fuel-air mixture to the engine, thus controlling the engine speed.

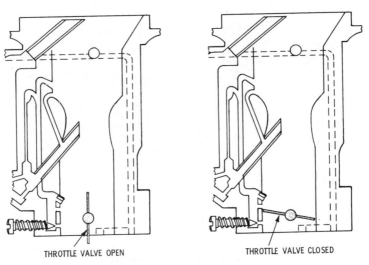

THROTTLE VALVE OPEN   THROTTLE VALVE CLOSED

Fig. 6. The throttle valve controls engine speed.

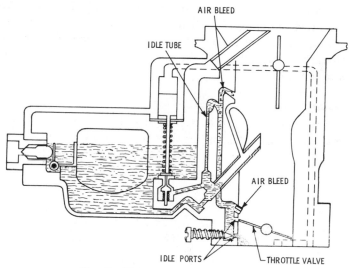

Fig. 7. The carburetor idle system.

Idle System

The idle system supplies the fuel-air mixture to keep the engine running when the throttle valve is completely closed. At idle there is very little air flowing through the venturi because the throttle valve is closed, blocking most of the air flow. Thus, there is no venturi effect to draw fuel from the main fuel nozzle. To allow the engine to operate under this condition, an idle port is placed just below the throttle valve, as shown in Fig. 7. Since the intake vacuum is high at idling speeds, the pressure differential between the air in the fuel bowl and the vacuum below the throttle valve forces fuel through the idle port.

Gasoline flows from the fuel bowl through the idle tube on its way to the idle port. Air bleed holes opening into the idle tube introduce a metered amount of air into the gasoline in the idle system, and also act as vents to prevent siphoning of gasoline from the fuel bowl above idle, at high speeds, or when the engine is stopped. An adjustable needle valve controls the richness of the idle fuel mixture by regulating the amount that passes through the idle port into the engine.

Low-Speed System

When the throttle valve is opened slightly for low-speed operation, there is still insufficient air flow through the venturi to draw

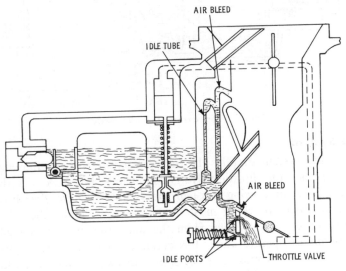

Fig. 8. The carburetor low-speed system.

fuel from the main fuel nozzle. Since more fuel is needed than can be provided by the idle port alone, another port (Fig. 8) is located so that its opening is just above the throttle valve when it is closed, and in the low-pressure area when the throttle valve is in the low-speed position. Fuel is drawn from both ports in low-speed operation to provide the proper air-fuel ratio.

High-Speed System

As the throttle valve is opened further, the air flow through the carburetor increases until, at some point, the venturi effect becomes great enough to draw gasoline from the main fuel nozzle. This action is shown in Fig. 9. Fuel from the slow-speed system starts tapering off as the amount of fuel drawn from the main fuel nozzle increases, until finally the flow from the low-speed system stops completely.

The flow of gasoline during high-speed operation is from the fuel bowl, through the main passageway, through the main nozzle,

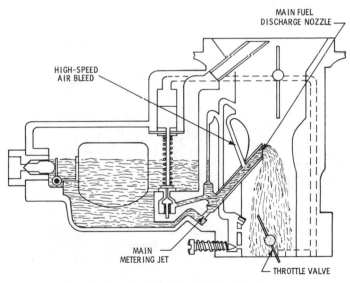

Fig. 9. The carburetor high-speed system.

and out into the air stream in the carburetor throat. An air bleed hole opening into the main passageway provides air to maintain the proper air-fuel ratio. An antisiphon bleed hole is also provided to prevent the gasoline from siphoning out of the fuel bowl when the engine is stopped.

Power System

During periods of increased load on the engine, or full-throttle operation, the ratio of the fuel to the air must be increased to provide a richer mixture. The additional fuel required is supplied by a power fuel system, such as the one in Fig. 10.

The power fuel system is controlled by intake-manifold vacuum on most cars, but may be operated mechanically by accelerator action in a few instances. Manifold vacuum gives an accurate indica-

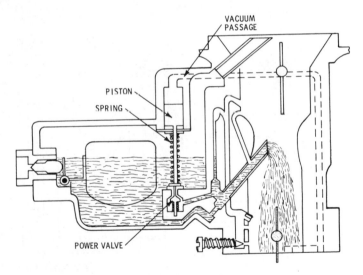

Fig. 10. The carburetor power system.

tion of the power demands placed on the engine, the vacuum being greatest under no-load conditions and decreasing as the load on the engine increases.

Manifold vacuum is transmitted from an opening in the throat at the base of the carburetor, through a passage in the body, to a power-valve chamber, where it acts on a piston or diaphragm. The engine vacuum at idle speeds or normal load conditions is great enough to hold the power valve closed against the tension of a calibrated spring. When the manifold vacuum drops due to an increase load on the engine, the spring opens the valve and allows additional gasoline to flow to the main fuel jet, enriching the mixture. In some carburetors, a metering rod may be lifted instead of a valve being opened. This is shown in the inset of Fig. 10.

Power circuits that are mechanically operated perform the same functions by moving a tapered metering rod in and out of a fixed-size jet. As the rod is moved out of the jet, the opening becomes progressively larger, allowing an increase in the flow of gasoline to the main fuel nozzle.

Accelerator-Pump System

Upon acceleration, the air flow through the carburetor increases almost immediately. There is, however, a brief interval before the fuel (which is heavier than air) can gain speed and maintain the desired balance of fuel and air. Unless this condition is corrected, the air-fuel ratio will become leaner at a time when a richer mixture is actually required for more power. An accelerator pump is therefore provided to momentarily supply additional fuel until the flow from the main fuel-nozzle increases.

The accelerator pump (Fig. 11) is operated by mechanical linkage connected to the throttle. When the throttle is suddenly opened, the spring-loaded plunger forces the required amount of gasoline past the discharge check valve and into the air stream of the carburetor. The spring loading provides for a continuation of fuel flow for a short period after the throttle is opened. Closing the throttle withdraws the pump plunger (Fig. 12), pulling gasoline into the pump cylinder through the inlet valve. This position of the pump

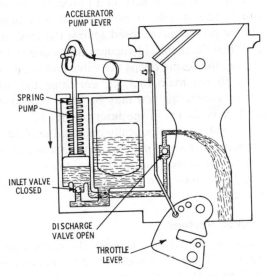

ACCELERATOR
PUMP LEVER

SPRING
PUMP

INLET VALVE
CLOSED

DISCHARGE
VALVE OPEN

THROTTLE
LEVER

Fig. 11. The accelerator pump system during acceleration.

plunger keeps the pump cylinder full of gasoline, ready for immediate use. A diaphragm-type pump is used on some carburetors instead of a plunger-type, but the principle of operation is the same.

Choke System

When a cold engine is being started, most of the gasoline discharged by the carburetor is unable to vaporize before it reaches the engine until the intake manifold heats up sufficiently. This means that a much larger quantity of fuel must be supplied to compensate for this lack of vaporization when starting and running a cold engine. In addition, the speed of the air through the carburetor is slow during starting which lowers the venturi effect, and little or no fuel is drawn from the main fuel nozzle.

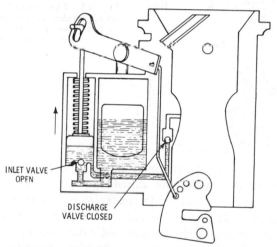

Fig. 12. The accelerator pump system during deceleration.

A choke plate (valve) is placed above the venturi, as shown in Fig. 13. When closed, this choke plate provides a high vacuum above as well as below the throttle valve. This high vacuum draws gasoline from the main fuel nozzle as well as from the idle ports, thus providing the extremely rich mixture needed for cold-engine operation. Choke valves may be operated manually, thermostatically, electrically, or by vacuum.

Most carburetors are equipped with a thermostatically-controlled automatic choke similar to the one in Fig. 14. When the engine is

471

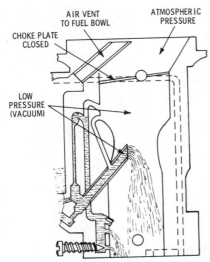

AIR VENT
TO FUEL BOWL

ATMOSPHERIC
PRESSURE

CHOKE PLATE
CLOSED

LOW
PRESSURE
(VACUUM)

*Fig. 13. The vacuum below the
closed choke plate causes gasoline
to flow from the main fuel nozzle
and the idle ports.*

cold, the tension of the thermostatic spring holds the choke plate closed. After the engine has started, the vacuum piston is pulled downward by the vacuum in the intake manifold, partially opening the choke plate to prevent flooding and to allow sufficient air flow for smooth running. Exhaust-manifold gases heat the air in a tube leading into the thermostatic-spring housing. As the spring heats, it gradually loses its tension, allowing the vacuum piston to open the choke plate. When the engine reaches its operating temperature, the choke plate should be completely open. The choke plate in most carburetors is offset on its shaft so that the flow of air through the carburetor after the engine starts helps to hold the choke plate partially open against the thermostatic-spring tension.

Throttle-Return Check (Dashpot)

A dashpot is used on the carburetor of cars equipped with an automatic transmission. The purpose of this unit is to prevent the engine from stalling or hesitating when the throttle is close suddenly. A dashpot (Fig. 15) operates in a manner similar to an automatic door check and this insures that the throttle will close gradually when the accelerator is released suddenly. The con-

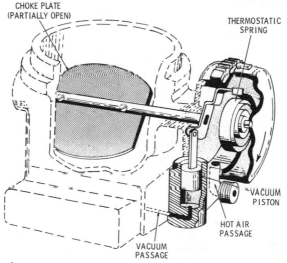

CHOKE PLATE
(PARTIALLY OPEN)

THERMOSTATIC
SPRING

VACUUM
PISTON

HOT AIR
PASSAGE

VACUUM
PASSAGE

Fig. 14. A thermostatic spring and a vacuum piston automatically control the choking action on this carburetor.

struction of dashpots differs depending on the manufacturer, and may be magnetically, hydraulically, or vacuum operated. Most units are sealed and are replaced rather than repaired if they become inoperative.

Throttle Linkage

Engine speed is controlled by the accelerator pedal moving a series of rods, levers, springs, etc., called the throttle linkage. This linkage is different in each particular make and model of car, and will even differ among the same make and model depending on the type of engine, carburetor, and transmission used. Besides opening and closing the throttle valve, the throttle linkage also activates the accelerator pump and the overdrive kickdown, and controls the automatic-transmission shift speeds on cars so equipped.

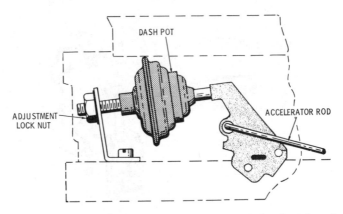

Fig. 15. A dashpot unit prevents sudden closing of the throttle valve.

Adjustments are provided on the throttle linkage to compensate for manufacturing tolerances and normal wear. Improper adjustment can change the idle speed, top speed, dashpot action, and the speeds at which the automatic transmission shifts, even if all other carburetor adjustments are correct.

CARBURETOR TYPES

Carburetors for domestic cars produced in the past ten years have been manufactured by Carter, Holley, Ford, Rochester, and Stromberg. The same basic carburetor may be used for several years on a particular make of car, with only minor changes being made from time to time. In other instances, there may be radical changes made each year with the model number of the carburetor remaining the same.

A carburetor may contain one, two, or four barrels. Also, the carburetor installation on a particular car may include a combination of two or three carburetors, each being a single, dual, or four-barrel unit.

An example of a single-barrel carburetor is shown in Fig. 16. This carburetor is used on the 1964 Tempest with a 215 cu. in.,

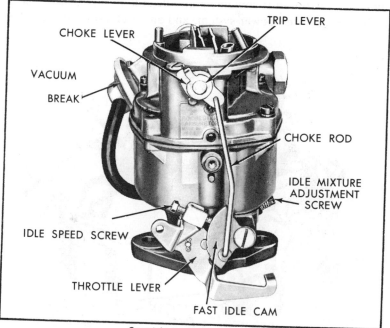

Copyright Pontiac Motor Division, General Motors Corporation

Fig. 16. A Rochester Model BV single-barrel carburetor.

6-cylinder engine. Another example (Fig. 17) of a single-barrel carburetor is used on a 1964 Ford with a 223 cu. in., 6-cylinder engine (Mileage Maker Six, Police Special Six, Taxi Special Six).

An exploded view of a two-barrel carburetor found on some 1963 Dodge Custom 880 V8 engines is shown in Fig. 18. Another two-barrel carburetor of a different make (Fig. 19) is used on some 1960 Mercury automobiles.

Four-barrel carburetors actually consist of two sections—a primary section of two barrels, and a secondary section, also containing two barrels. The primary section is essentially a complete two-barrel carburetor containing an idle system, low-speed system, high-speed system, power system, and an accelerating system. This

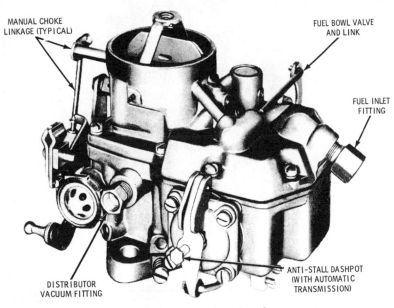

MANUAL CHOKE LINKAGE (TYPICAL)

FUEL BOWL VALVE AND LINK

FUEL INLET FITTING

DISTRIBUTOR VACUUM FITTING

ANTI-STALL DASHPOT (WITH AUTOMATIC TRANSMISSION)

Fig. 17. A Ford single-barrel carburetor.

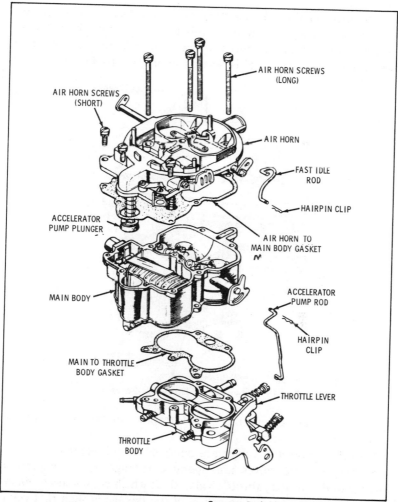

Fig. 18. Exploded view of a Series WWC3 Stromberg two-barrel carburetor.

477

section also contains the automatic-choke mechanism. The secondary section is a supplementary two-barrel carburetor which cuts in to assist the primary section when a predetermined car speed or engine load is reached. This section contains its own high-speed

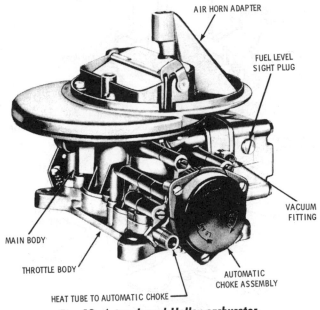

Fig. 19. A two-barrel Holley carburetor.

system, and has a separate set of throttle valves and auxiliary valves.

The primary throttle valves are operated by the accelerator. The secondary throttle valves are operated through a delayed-action linkage to the primary throttle-valve shaft which causes the primary valves to start to open. The action of the linkage is such that both sets of throttle valves reach the wide-open position at the same time.

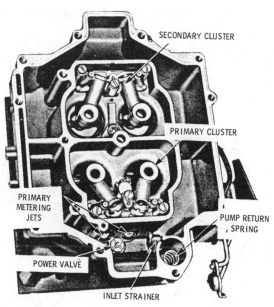

SECONDARY CLUSTER

PRIMARY CLUSTER

PRIMARY
METERING
JETS

PUMP RETURN
SPRING

POWER VALVE

INLET STRAINER

Fig. 20. Internal view of a Rochester Model 4GC four-barrel carburetor.

Fig. 20 is an internal view of a typical four-barrel carburetor that comes as optional equipment on a 1964 Chevelle V8.

Combinations of carburetors are sometimes used to gain increased performance. An example of this is the dual four-barrel carburetor installation that is available as an option on the 1965 Buick 425 cu. in. engine. This installation is shown in Fig. 21. Each carburetor has a primary section (consisting of the two-barrelled forward half) and a secondary section (consisting of the two-barrelled rear half).

Fuel for idling is supplied by the primary section of both carburetors, but the fuel for all other operating conditions except hard acceleration or extreme high speeds is supplied by the primary section of the rear carburetor only. Only the rear carburetor is equipped with an automatic choke.

The primary section of the front carburetor has fixed idle orifices, while the primary of the rear unit has both idle-mixture and idle-speed adjustments. Actually, the design is such that only one air-adjusting screw is used.

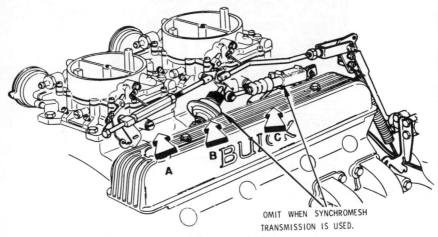

OMIT WHEN SYNCHROMESH
TRANSMISSION IS USED.

Courtesy Buick Motor Div., General Motors Corp.

Fig. 21. Two four-barrel Carter Model AFB carburetors installed on a 425 cu. in. 1965 Buick engine.

The operation of the dual-combination carburetor system from idle to wide open is as follows: As the accelerator pedal is gradually depressed, the primary throttle valves in the rear carburetor start to open. When these valves are approximately half open, the primary throttle valves of the front carburetor start to open. Next, the secondary throttle valves in the rear carburetor start to open, and last, the secondary throttle valves in the front unit start to open.

Each of the four sections opens at such a rate that all throttle valves reach the wide-open position at the same time.

Combinations of three and four carburetors are sometimes used, but these are usually custom installations. The throttle linkage becomes rather complex with each additional carburetor added and adjustments become more critical to achieve proper operation.

CARBURETOR ADJUSTMENTS

Checks and adjustments on carburetors for engine tune-up are comparatively simple. It is often more of a problem to locate the correct rod or screw than it is to adjust it. If, however, the carburetor does not respond correctly to an adjustment, it is usually necessary to disassemble it for repair. This usually requires the use of special tools and gauges, and a thorough knowledge of the procedures. This phase of carburetor service is normally outside the capabilities of the average car owner or service-station operator. For this reason, the disassembly and internal repair of carburetors will not be discussed in detail.

Inlet Fuel Filters

Many carburetors have a filter or screen at the fuel inlet to trap any rust or dirt particles that may have slipped by the sediment bowl and/or fuel-line filters. To service this portion of the carburetor, proceed as follows:

1. Disconnect the fuel line at the carburetor with the correct size wrenches.
2. Remove the filter (or screen) and any gaskets or springs.
3. Wash the filter element or screen in solvent and dry with an air hose.
4. Replace the filter, gaskets, and springs in the correct order

and direction. Some filters or screens are directional (Fig. 22) and should be installed with the larger, or open end toward the fuel inlet.

Throttle-to-Accelerator Linkage

The rods, levers, springs, etc. which make up the throttle linkage should be inspected for looseness and binding. Check for proper ad-

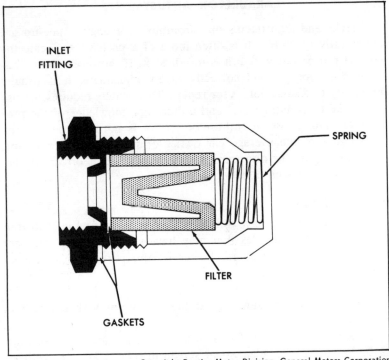

Fig. 22. Cross-sectional view of the components in the fuel inlet of a Rochester Model BV carburetor.

justment of the linkage by completely depressing the accelerator pedal and noting whether the throttle plates are completely open, and whether they close completely when the pedal is released.

NOTE: On cars equipped with an automatic transmission, care must be taken not to disturb the linkage to the transmission. Note the point at which the transmission linkage is connected to the accelerator linkage. Adjustment of the accelerator linkage can usually be made between this point and the accelerator pedal without disturbing the linkage to the transmission. Follow the adjustment procedure recommended by the manufacturer.

An example of the throttle linkage on a car equipped with an automatic transmission is shown in Fig. 23.

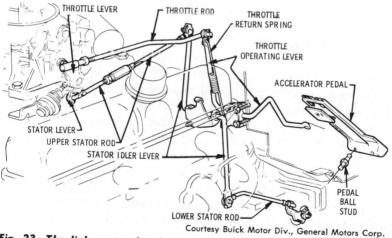

Courtesy Buick Motor Div., General Motors Corp.

Fig. 23. The linkage to the throttle and automatic transmission in this 1961 Buick is typical of the linkage on many automobiles.

Manual Choke

A cable extending from the carburetor to the instrument panel is used to control manual chokes.

Adjustment of a manual choke can be made as follows:

1. Pull the choke control knob fully out and check to see whether the choke plate in the carburetor is fully closed. If not, loosen the setscrew holding the choke cable wire to the choke linkage on the carburetor, and close the choke plate by hand. Tighten the setscrew and proceed to the next step.
2. Push the choke control knob in completely. The choke plate in the carburetor should be in the full-open position.
3. Check for free operation by moving the control knob in and out. If it binds or hangs up at any point, check the entire length of the cable for sharp bends, kinks, or mechanical damage. Reroute the cable to remove any sharp bends, or replace if kinks or cable damage is present.

Choke Rod (Automatic Choke)

On cars equipped with an automatic choke, a choke rod connects the choke-plate lever to a fast-idle cam. This choke rod is sometimes called the fast-idle rod, and is shown on the carburetor in Fig. 24. The linkage shown is the direct type, although an indirect linkage may be found on some carburetors. To locate the choke rod, move the choke plate by hand and observe the movement of the various rods. Adjustment is sometimes required in order to cause the choke plate to open and close properly. This adjustment is usually made by bending the choke rod the necessary amount at the point specified by the manufacturer to lengthen or shorten it. The manufacturer's instructions should be carefully followed when making this adjustment.

An intermediate choke rod that is connected between the choke-plate lever and the automatic-choke mechanism is used in some carburetors. When the carburetor is so equipped, as in Fig. 25, this intermediate rod must be adjusted whenever the fast-idle (main)

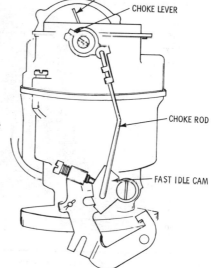

CHOKE PLATE

CHOKE LEVER

CHOKE ROD

FAST IDLE CAM

Fig. 24. An example of a direct choke linkage.

choke rod has been adjusted. Follow the manufacturer's instructions for making this adjustment. The procedure varies depending on the make and model of carburetor, but the general method is as follows:

1. Loosen the cover screws on the automatic-choke housing.
2. Hold the choke valve closed by lifting up on the intermediate choke lever.

3. Line up the specified mark on the automatic-choke cover with the index mark on the housing.
4. Tighten the cover screws on the housing.

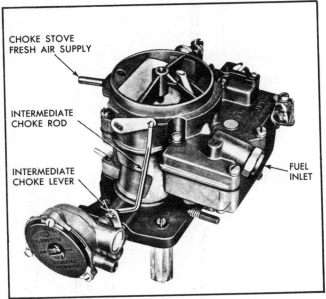

CHOKE STOVE
FRESH AIR SUPPLY

INTERMEDIATE
CHOKE ROD

INTERMEDIATE
CHOKE LEVER

FUEL
INLET

Copyright Pontiac Motor Division, General Motors Corporation

Fig. 25. An example of a carburetor with an intermediate choke rod. This carburetor is a Rochester Model 2GC with two barrels.

Accelerator-Pump Linkage

A pump rod connects the throttle lever to the accelerator-pump lever (or arm). The construction of this linkage varies widely with the make and model of carburetor, but a typical example is illustrated in Fig. 26.

The operation of the accelerator pump can be checked by looking in the air horn and rapidly moving the throttle lever. A

486

noticeable stream of gasoline should spurt into the carburetor throat each time the throttle lever is moved. If no gasoline is noticed, the carburetor must be disassembled to check and repair the accelerator pump.

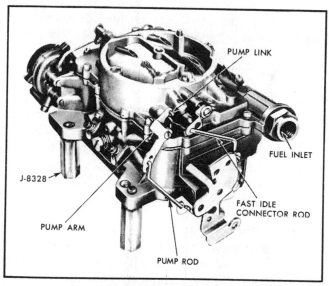

Fig. 26. A Carter Model AFB four-barrel carburetor showing the accelerator pump linkage.

Movement of the throttle lever also allows a check to be made of the linkage to the pump. Some sort of adjustment is provided to lengthen or shorten the pump stroke for different temperature conditions. This adjustment feature is usually in the form of holes in either the throttle lever or pump arm (these holes are in the pump arm in Fig. 26). The pump stroke is changed by moving the accelerator-pump rod from one to another of the holes as specified for the season of the year. The adjustment of the pump stroke is made on some carburetors by bending the linkage rod.

Power-Valve Linkage

The linkage for the power valves does not have an external adjustment. Checking and adjustment requires disassembly of the carburetor and the use of special gauges and tools. The procedures and specifications recommended by the manufacturer must be strictly followed.

Idle Vent-Valve Linkage

An idle vent valve (variously called bowl vent and antipercolator valve) will be found on many late-model carburetors. The purpose of this valve is to vent the vapors from the fuel bowl to the atmosphere when the throttle is closed. An example of the adjustment being made on this valve is pictured in Fig. 27. Some carburetors require partial disassembly to adjust this valve.

Secondary-Throttle Linkage

Four-barrel carburetors are essentially two dual carburetors divided into primary and secondary sides. The primary portion includes all circuits from idle to full power while the secondary side contains a lesser number of circuits and usually does not come into operation until some point between one-half and full-throttle position.

The secondary side of the carburetor is connected by a linkage to the primary side. On some carburetors, this linkage is made by a rod (Fig. 28) which must be bent in making adjustments. On certain other carburetors, the secondary system is not actuated by an external linkage, but by a vacuum-operated diaphragm connected to the secondary system. There are other types of secondary-throttle linkage, but the two just mentioned are the most common.

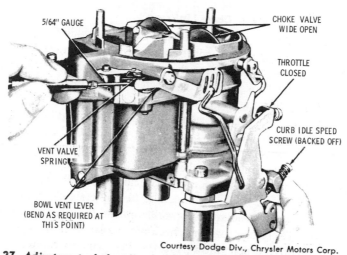

5/64" GAUGE

CHOKE VALVE WIDE OPEN

THROTTLE CLOSED

CURB IDLE SPEED SCREW (BACKED OFF)

VENT VALVE SPRING

BOWL VENT LEVER (BEND AS REQUIRED AT THIS POINT)

Courtesy Dodge Div., Chrysler Motors Corp.

Fig. 27. Adjustment of the idle vent valve on a Stromberg Model WWC3 carburetor.

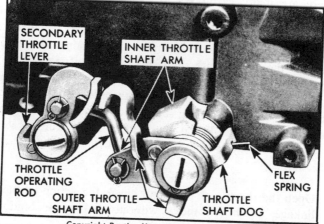

SECONDARY THROTTLE LEVER

INNER THROTTLE SHAFT ARM

THROTTLE OPERATING ROD

OUTER THROTTLE SHAFT ARM

THROTTLE SHAFT DOG

FLEX SPRING

Copyright Pontiac Motor Division, General Motors Corporation

Fig. 28. Secondary throttle linkage on a Carter AFB carburetor.

Choke and Fast-Idle Cam Linkage

To find and trace this linkage on a carburetor that is unfamiliar, the sequence of operation will be helpful. The thermostatic spring in the automatic choke closes the choke valve when the engine is cold. Since the choke rod is connected to the fast-idle cam, the choke closing lifts the cam until the fast-idle screw on the throttle lever contacts the highest point on the cam, providing a faster engine-idle speed. As the engine warms up, the choke opens, dropping the fast-idle cam which causes the idle screw to contact a lower step on the cam. Thus, the idle speed of the engine is reduced.

Anytime the engine temperature is below approximately 70°, the choke will be closed. The choke cannot completely close, however, as long as the fast-idle screw remains on the low step of the fast-idle cam. Therefore, when checking choke action, open the throttle slightly, which allows the fast-idle cam to rotate, closing the choke valve completely.

There are many variations in the choke linkage on different carburetors. The linkage can be traced on unfamiliar units in the following manner: Open the throttle slightly and move the choke plate with your fingers; look for movement of some type of arm at one end of the choke-plate shaft or countershaft; follow the moving parts to the choke linkage which operates the fast-idle cam. The cam is linked with the primary-throttle lever which can be identified by the idle adjusting screw and the connection running to the accelerator pedal. When these parts have been located, the operation of the choke and fast-idle cam linkage can be checked as follows:

1. Open the throttle slightly and check the action of the choke linkage. It should move without sticking or binding and without any looseness or free play.

2. With the engine warm, lift and release the choke rod. It should drop the idle cam of its own accord because of the weight of the choke-rod lever and/or any counterweights provided.

Choke Unloader

If the engine becomes flooded for any reason, the choke valve can be partially opened by depressing the accelerator pedal to the full extent of its travel. This causes an arm or projection (unloader) on the throttle lever to contact and rotate the fast-idle cam which forces the choke valve open. Check the operation of the unloader by opening the throttle fully. The choke plate should open partially under this condition. If adjustment is necessary, it is usually made by bending the unloader tang (Fig. 29) on the throttle lever. Follow the manufacturer's recommendations for proper adjustment.

Automatic Choke

The automatic-choke mechanism on most cars is similar to the one shown in Fig. 30. This type of automatic choke is equipped with a thermostatic spring and a vacuum piston. The thermostatic spring winds up when cold and unwinds when warm. Thus, when the engine is cold, the spring holds the choke piston inward and the choke plate in a closed position (through mechanical linkage) prior to engine start.

When the engine starts, manifold vacuum acting on the piston in the choke housing moves the piston outward against the tension of the thermostatic spring, partially opening the choke plate to prevent stalling. As the engine warms up, manifold vacuum draws warm air from a heat chamber in the exhaust manifold. This warm air enters the choke housing and heats the thermostatic spring, causing it to unwind. Thus, the tension of the spring gradually decreases as the temperature of the air from the heat chamber increases, causing the choke plate to gradually open to the wide-open position when the engine reaches operating temperature.

If this type of choke requires adjustment, the alignment of the scribe marks on the choke cover with the index mark should be checked. Realign to specifications by loosening the three cover-retaining screws and rotating the cover the necessary amount (Fig. 31). If the choke is sticking or sluggish, it may be necessary to remove the cover and free-up the mechanism. Special solvents are available with which to free the choke shaft and piston. If this does not correct the situation, the unit must be removed for repair or replacement.

The automatic choke used on most Chrysler-made cars is a well-type mounted in a cavity at the exhaust crossover passage of

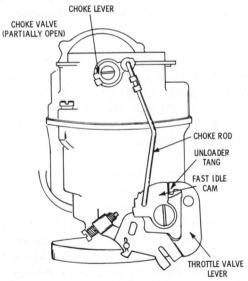

CHOKE LEVER

CHOKE VALVE (PARTIALLY OPEN)

CHOKE ROD

UNLOADER TANG

FAST IDLE CAM

THROTTLE VALVE LEVER

Fig. 29. The unloader partially opens the choke plate at wide-open throttle.

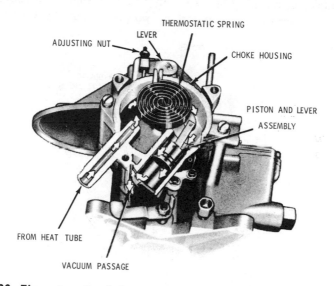

THERMOSTATIC SPRING

ADJUSTING NUT

LEVER

CHOKE HOUSING

PISTON AND LEVER
ASSEMBLY

FROM HEAT TUBE

VACUUM PASSAGE

Fig. 30. The automatic choke system used on the 1964 two-barrel Ford carburetor.

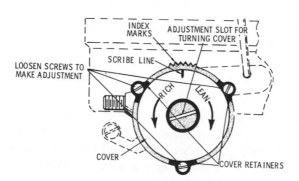

INDEX MARKS

ADJUSTMENT SLOT FOR TURNING COVER

SCRIBE LINE

LOOSEN SCREWS TO MAKE ADJUSTMENT

RICH

LEAN

COVER

COVER RETAINERS

Fig. 31. Automatic choke adjustment.

the intake manifold (Fig. 32). Other than cleaning, the choke requires no service. It is important, however, that the choke unit

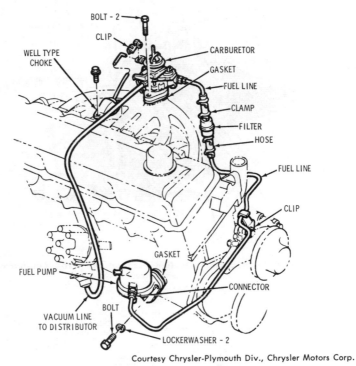

BOLT - 2

CLIP

WELL TYPE CHOKE

CARBURETOR

GASKET

FUEL LINE

CLAMP

FILTER

HOSE

FUEL LINE

CLIP

GASKET

FUEL PUMP

CONNECTOR

VACUUM LINE TO DISTRIBUTOR

BOLT

LOCKERWASHER - 2

Courtesy Chrysler-Plymouth Div., Chrysler Motors Corp.

Fig. 32. Fuel system used on certain 1964 Plymouths and Valiants showing the well-type automatic choke.

works freely in the well and at the choke shaft. Move the choke rod up and down to check for free movement on the pivot. If binding occurs a new choke unit should be installed. **Do not attempt to repair or make any change in the setting of the choke unit.**

Another type of automatic choke uses a temperature-sensing coil mounted in a depression in the exhaust manifold of six-cylinder engines (Fig. 33), and directly over the exhaust cross-

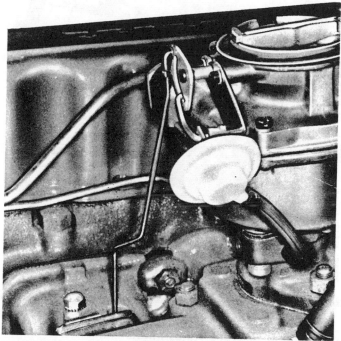

Fig. 33. The automatic choke arrangement on a 1964 Chevelle 6-cylinder engine.

over passage in the intake manifold on V8 engines (Fig. 34). These automatic chokes are adjusted by bending the choke rod at the offset bend according to the instructions of the manufacturer. Lengthening the rod provides a richer mixture, while shortening the rod provides a leaner mixture.

Fig. 34. The automatic choke arrangement on a 1964 Chevelle 8-cylinder engine.

Idle-Speed and Mixture Adjustments

The curb (hot) idle speed and mixture adjustments are relatively simple to make once the correct screw or screws have been located. The curb idle-speed screw is usually located either on the throttle lever, a cam, or in the carburetor body. This screw can be located by moving the throttle linkage and tracing the movement to the screw which stops the movement when the throttle is returned to the closed position (choke valve must be wide open).

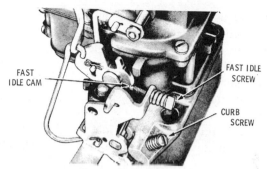

Courtesy Dodge Div., Chrysler Motors Corp.

Fig. 35. Some carburetors have a separate fast-idle adjustment in addition to the curb-idle adjustment.

Do not confuse this screw with a separate fast-idle screw used on some carburetors (Fig. 35). The curb idle speed is always set with the engine at operating temperature (choke valve wide open).

The fast idle-speed screw is located by tracing the choke-rod linkage to the fast-idle cam. The fast-idle screw is the stop screw which contacts the highest step or point on the fast-idle cam when the throttle and choke are in the closed position. Some carburetors have only a single idle-speed screw (Fig. 36). With this type, the fast idle will be correct when the correct curb-idle adjustment has been made with the idle screw contacting the lowest step or point on the fast-idle cam.

Fig. 36. A single idle-speed screw is used on some carburetors. When the curb-idle speed is adjusted correctly, the fast-idle speed will automatically be correct.

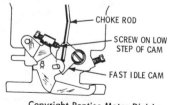

Copyright Pontiac Motor Division, General Motors Corporation

Screws for adjusting the idle fuel mixture are provided in the carburetor throttle body, usually near the lower edge. Only one idle fuel-mixture screw is used on single-barrel carburetors (Fig. 37), while Fig. 38 shows two idle-mixture screws on a four-barrel unit. The two mixture screws on some Holley carburetors are recessed in the carburetor body, as shown in Fig. 39, one on the left side and one on the right.

The actual adjustment of the curb idle speed, the fast idle speed, and the idle fuel mixture should not be made until all other systems

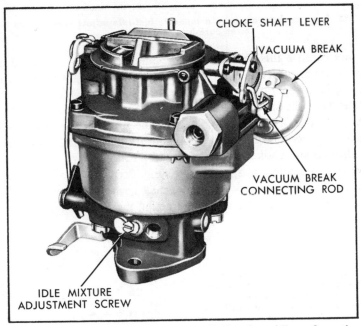

CHOKE SHAFT LEVER

VACUUM BREAK

VACUUM BREAK
CONNECTING ROD

IDLE MIXTURE
ADJUSTMENT SCREW

Fig. 37. A single-barrel carburetor has only one idle fuel-mixture adjusting screw.

that might affect engine performance have been checked and corrected. These include compression, fuel-pump operation, manifold heat-control valve, throttle linkage, and ignition timing. After these have all been checked and corrected, use the following procedure to set the curb-idle speed and idle fuel mixture:

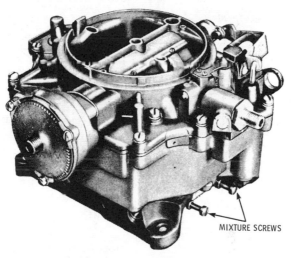

MIXTURE SCREWS

Fig. 38. A four-barrel carburetor has two idle fuel-mixture adjusting screws.

1. Slowly turn the idle fuel-mixture screw clockwise until it gently seats. **Do not use a screwdriver—use fingers only.** Then turn the screw out (counterclockwise) the recommended number of turns. Backing the screw out from 1 to 1½ turns, unless otherwise specified, will usually give an average starting point for the adjustment.
2. Start the engine and set the hand brake. Allow the engine to run until it reaches its normal operating temperature. Follow the car manufacturer's recommendations as to the

position of the shift lever, whether lights should be on or off, whether certain vacuum lines to accessories should be disconnected and taped, etc.

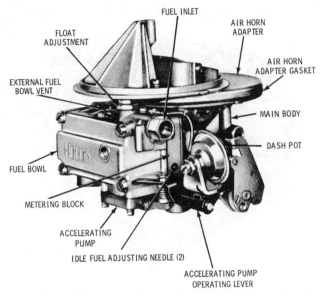

Fig. 39. The idle-mixture screws on two- and four-barrel Holley carburetors are located differently than on other makes. Shown is the location on a two-barrel unit. The screws on a four-barrel Holley carburetor are in a similar position.

3. Turn the curb idle-speed screw slowly in or out until the engine is running at the idle speed specified by the manufacturer.
4. Turn the idle fuel-mixture screw slowly clockwise (toward a lean mixture) until the engine just starts to lag or run unevenly.

5. Now turn the screw slowly counterclockwise (toward a richer mixture) until the engine begins to run evenly.
6. Finally, set the idle fuel-mixture screw to a position midway between the lean and rich positions. If this is not the smoothest running idle position, compromise toward the rich (counterclockwise) position.

   NOTE: When the carburetor has two idle-mixture screws, perform Steps 4, 5, and 6 for each screw.
7. If the idle speed of the engine has changed due to these adjustments, reset the idle-speed screw to obtain the specified speed.

Some carburetors have no fast-idle adjustment. When the curb-idle speed is correct, the fast idle speed will automatically be correct. For those carburetors, however, that do have a fast-idle adjustment, use the following procedure:

1. Open the throttle enough to permit moving the fast-idle cam until the fast-idle screw contacts the high step on the cam.
2. Turn the fast-idle screw to obtain the specified fast-idle speed.

Compound-Carburetor Adjustments

Some cars are equipped with compound carburetors, such as three two-barrel carburetors, or two four-barrel units. The basic checks and adjustments described for single carburetors are applicable here, with the following variations.

On a three two-barrel installation, the center carburetor is a standard two-barrel unit and is adjusted in the normal manner. The front and rear carburetors are controlled from the center unit by a combination of vacuum and mechanical linkage. Since the front and rear units do not contain choke, idle, or part-throttle systems, no idle speed or idle fuel-mixture adjustments are necessary.

Check the vacuum connections for tightness, and the mechanical connections for free and smooth operation. Remove the air cleaners and, with engine running, open the throttle all the way. The throttle plates on all three carburetors should be fully opened under this condition. If they are not, adjustment of the vacuum valves or the front-to-rear carburetor throttle rod should be made as recommended by the manufacturer.

Each carburetor of a dual four-barrel installation is basically the same as the carburetor of a single four-barrel installation. Both contain idle-speed and mixture screws which must be adjusted until the best engine performance is obtained at the correct idle speed.

Linkage adjustments vary because some dual four-barrel installations are designed so both carburetors operate together from idle to full throttle. In other installations, the second carburetor starts to open when the first carburetor is at about half throttle. Thus, the manufacturer's instructions should be referred to when making linkage adjustments.

Dashpot Adjustments

The location of the dashpot varies on cars so equipped. Some are mounted on the body of the carburetor (Fig. 40), some are mounted either on the firewall in the engine compartment or at some point on the engine, as in Fig. 41, and in a few instances the dashpot is a built-in component inside the carburetor. The adjustment of all but the built-in units is similar. With the built-in dashpot, adjustment is made by bending the external lever that connects with the throttle linkage.

The adjustment of all but the built-in type dashpots is adjusted similar to the following procedure:

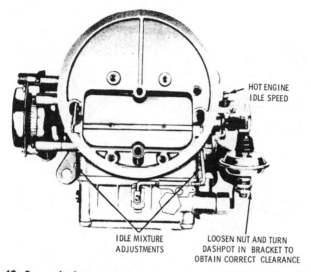

HOT ENGINE
IDLE SPEED

IDLE MIXTURE
ADJUSTMENTS

LOOSEN NUT AND TURN
DASHPOT IN BRACKET TO
OBTAIN CORRECT CLEARANCE

Fig. 40. Some dashpots are located on the body of the carburetor.

1. Complete the idle-speed and mixture adjustments and have the engine at operating temperature.
2. Hold the dashpot plunger in as far as possible with a screwdriver and measure the clearance between the plunger and the contact connected to the throttle mechanism (Fig. 42).
3. Adjust the clearance, if necessary, by loosening the locknut and turning the dashpot assembly in or out of its bracket to obtain the specified clearance. Tighten the locknut.

Check for correct adjustment as follows:

1. Test drive the car. Make a fast start, then release the accelerator suddenly, braking to a quick stop at the same time.
2. The engine should not hold at a high rpm, nor should it stall.

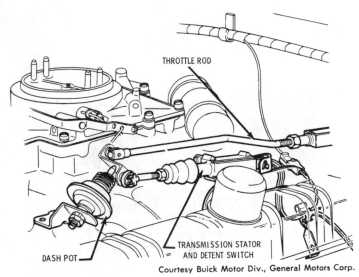

THROTTLE ROD

TRANSMISSION STATOR
AND DETENT SWITCH

DASH POT

Courtesy Buick Motor Div., General Motors Corp.

**Fig. 41. The dashpot on this 1965 Buick is mounted on the engine instead
of the carburetor.**

3. If the engine stalls, reduce the clearance between the dashpot
    plunger and throttle linkage.

4. If the engine rolls or surges, increase the clearance.

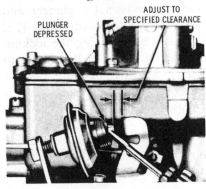

ADJUST TO
SPECIFIED CLEARANCE

PLUNGER
DEPRESSED

**Fig. 42. Adjusting the dashpot
clearance on a Ford two-barrel
carburetor.**

Complete carburetor servicing requires the disassembly of the unit and the use of special tools and gauges. Follow the manufacturer's instructions for this type of service.

CARBURETOR TROUBLES AND REMEDIES

Symptom and Possible Causes   *Possible Remedy*

Flooding or Leaking Carburetor

(a) Cracked carburetor body. — (a) Replace cracked unit.

(b) Defective main-body and/or fuel-bowl gasket. — (b) Replace defective gasket(s).

(c) High fuel level or float setting. — (c) Adjust float level.

(d) Fuel inlet needle not seating properly. — (d) Inspect for dirt or wear. Remove dirt or replace worn parts.

(e) Rupture of accelerator-pump diaphragm. — (e) Replace diaphragm.

(f) Excessive fuel-pump pressure. — (f) Repair or replace fuel pump.

(g) Defective power-valve gasket. — (g) Replace gasket.

(h) Ruptured power-valve diaphragm. — (h) Replace diaphragm.

(i) Leaking carburetor float. — (i) Repair or replace float.

Hard Starting

(a) Improper starting procedure causing engine flooding. — (a) Use correct starting procedure.

(b) Improper fuel level in carburetor. — (b) Adjust float level.

Symptom and Possible Causes	Possible Remedy
(c) Improper idle adjustments.	(c) Adjust low- and high-speed idle.
(d) Fuel-inlet valve sticking or improperly seating.	(d) Free-up or replace needle.
(e) Incorrect fuel-pump pressure.	(e) Repair or replace fuel pump.
(f) Improper carburetor gasket and spacer combinations.	(f) Replace with correct combination.
(g) Automatic choke set incorrectly.	(g) Adjust automatic choke.
(h) Choke plate or linkage binding.	(h) Free-up and adjust plate or linkage.
(i) Broken or binding manual-choke linkage.	(i) Repair or replace linkage.
(j) Restrictions or air leaks in the vacuum or hot-air passages to the automatic choke.	(j) Remove restrictions and repair air leaks.
(k) Dirty carburetor air-cleaner element.	(k) Service or replace air-cleaner element.
(l) Incorrect fast-idle adjustment.	(l) Adjust fast idle.
(m) Incorrect accelerator-pump stroke.	(m) Adjust accelerator pump.

Stalling (Engine Cold)

(a) Incorrect idle fuel mixture.	(a) Adjust idle fuel mixture.
(b) Engine idle speed too slow.	(b) Adjust fast idle.
(c) Dirt, water, or ice in fuel filter.	(c) Clean or replace filter element.

Symptom and Possible Causes

(d) Positive crankcase-ventilation system defective.

(e) Fuel lines restricted or leaking air.

(f) Fuel-tank vent restricted.

(g) Intake manifold or carburetor gaskets leaking.

(h) Carburetor icing.

(i) Incorrect throttle-linkage adjustment.

(j) Clogged air bleeds or idle passages.

(k) Defective fuel pump.

(l) Defective or misadjusted automatic choke.

Stalling (Engine Hot)

(a) Improperly adjusted or defective dashpot.

(b) Idle speed too slow.

(c) Incorrect idle fuel mixture.

(d) Worn or bent tip on idle fuel-mixture screw.

(e) Defective fuel pump.

(f) Coolant thermostat defective.

(g) Dirt, water, or ice in fuel filter.

Possible Remedy

(d) Repair or replace defective parts.

(e) Remove restrictions, tighten fittings, or replace defective part.

(f) Remove restriction or replace gas cap.

(g) Tighten bolts or replace defective gasket.

(h) Use anti-icing fluid.

(i) Adjust throttle linkage.

(j) Disassemble carburetor and clean thoroughly.

(k) Repair or replace.

(l) Repair or adjust automatic choke.

(a) Adjust, repair, or replace.

(b) Adjust slow-idle speed.

(c) Adjust idle fuel mixture.

(d) Replace screw.

(e) Repair or replace.

(f) Replace thermostat.

(g) Clean or replace fuel-filter element.

Carburetors

Symptom and Possible Causes	Possible Remedy
(h) Fuel-tank vent clogged.	(h) Remove restriction or replace gas cap.
(i) Fuel lines clogged or leaking air.	(i) Remove restriction and tighten fittings or replace defective parts.
(j) Carburetor icing.	(j) Use anti-icer fluid in fuel.
(k) Throttle shaft too loose in body of carburetor.	(k) Repair or replace parts as needed.
(l) Incorrect throttle linkage.	(l) Adjust throttle linkage.
(m) Clogged air bleeds or idle passages.	(m) Disassemble carburetor and clean thoroughly.
(n) Leaking intake-manifold or carburetor gasket.	(n) Tighten bolts or replace gaskets.

Rough Idle

(a) Idle speed too slow.	(a) Adjust idle speed.
(b) Incorrect idle fuel mixture.	(b) Adjust idle fuel mixture.
(c) Damaged or worn idle-mixture screws.	(c) Replace screws.
(d) Dirt in idle fuel passages or air passages.	(d) Disassemble and clean carburetor thoroughly.
(e) Air leaks in fuel intake or intake manifold.	(e) Find and eliminate air leaks.
(f) Defective coolant thermostat.	(f) Replace thermostat.
(g) Incorrect fuel level in carburetor.	(g) Adjust float level.
(h) Throttle plates or shafts bent or misaligned.	(h) Repair or replace damaged parts.

Symptom and Possible Causes	*Possible Remedy*
(i) Worn or damaged main metering jet.	(i) Replace jet.
(j) Fuel pump defective.	(j) Repair or replace fuel pump.

Poor Acceleration

(a) Incorrectly installed or adjusted accelerator-pump linkage.	(a) Install properly or adjust.
(b) Defective check valves in accelerator pump.	(b) Repair or replace valves.
(c) Dirt, water, or ice in fuel filter.	(c) Clean or replace fuel-filter element.
(d) Leaking accelerator-pump diaphragm.	(d) Replace diaphragm.
(e) Defective fuel pump.	(e) Repair or replace fuel pump.
(f) Automatic choke malfunctioning.	(f) Repair or adjust as needed.
(g) Clogged vent in gas cap.	(g) Remove restriction or replace cap.
(h) Clogged fuel line.	(h) Remove restriction.
(i) Air leak in fuel line.	(i) Tighten fittings or replace defective part.
(j) Low fuel level in carburetor.	(j) Adjust float level.
(k) Defective accelerator pump.	(k) Repair, adjust, or replace pump.

Symptom and Possible Causes   *Possible Remedy*

Choke Plate Jammed

(a) Engine backfires.

(b) Starting fuel mixture too lean.

(c) Accelerator not fully depressed before starting, causing engine to backfire.

(a) Set engine timing.

(b) Adjust carburetor for richer mixture.

(c) Use correct starting procedure.

Severe Transmission Engagement After Cold Start

(a) Fast-idle speed set too high.

(b) Throttle operating on highest point of the fast-idle cam.

(c) Binding or sticking throttle linkage, throttle valves or shafts, or accelerator pedal.

(a) Adjust fast-idle speed.

(b) Check automatic-choke adjustment.

(c) Repair or replace defective parts as needed.

Surging (Cruising Speed or Higher)

(a) Clogged main jets.

(b) Undersize main jets.

(c) Low fuel level in carburetor.

(d) Low fuel-pump pressure or volume.

(a) Disassemble and clean carburetor. Replace jets if needed.

(b) Replace with proper size jets.

(c) Adjust float level.

(d) Repair or replace fuel pump.

510

Symptom and Possible Causes

(e) Clogged air bleeds.

(f) Clogged fuel filter.

(g) Vacuum passage to distributor clogged.

Reduced Top Speed

(a) Incorrect fuel level in carburetor.

(b) Incorrect fuel-pump pressure or volume.

(c) Improper size or clogged main jet.

(d) Automatic choke not operating properly.

(e) Improper throttle linkage adjustment.

(f) Clogged vacuum passage to venturi.

(g) Secondary throttle system defective.

Possible Remedy

(e) Disassemble and clean carburetor.

(f) Clean or replace fuel-filter element.

(g) Remove restriction.

(a) Adjust float level.

(b) Repair or replace fuel pump.

(c) Clean or replace main jet.

(d) Repair, adjust or replace automatic choke.

(e) Adjust throttle linkage.

(f) Clean or repair.

(g) Inspect secondary system for binding, sticking, bent shafts, wedged throttle plates, etc. Repair or replace as needed.

CHAPTER 18

Cooling Systems

All domestic automobiles are equipped with a liquid-type cooling system. The principle of operation is the same for all cars and the actual construction features differ only slightly. The cooling system is necessary because of the high temperature generated during engine operation. Efficient combustion requires a relatively high temperature, but it is not possible to use all of the heat generated without harming the engine. The temperature within the combustion chambers rises to about twice the amount needed to melt iron, so it can be seen that something must be done to remove some of this heat to prevent damage. If the engine is not cooled during operation, valves will burn and warp, lubricating oil will break down, pistons and bearings will overheat, and pistons will seize in the cylinders.

COOLANTS

Water is universally used as the coolant in domestic automobiles. Only clean soft water should be used. Hard water contains minerals which forms a scale on the inside surfaces of the cooling system, reducing its efficiency. Inhibitors are available to reduce or prevent the formation of scale and rust, and should always be used when water only is used as the coolant.

The main objection to using water alone is its relatively high freezing point of 32°F. Automobiles in most sections of the country will be operated in temperatures below this point at some time during the year, making the use of water alone impractical.

Additives

Besides the inhibitors used to prevent scale and rust, the most well-known additive is antifreeze. The most common antifreeze solutions are methyl alcohol, ethyl alcohol, and ethylene glycol. The first two are the least expensive, but are subject to evaporation caused by boiling at temperatures at which the engine operates most efficiently. Ethylene glycol, however, has a boiling point (330°) well above normal operating temperatures, and so is well suited for engine cooling purposes. It is noncorrosive, has no appreciable odor, and offers complete protection from freezing when used in the proper amount. The maximum protection from freezing is obtained with a mixture of approximately 40% water and 60% ethylene glycol.

This mixture offers protection from freezing at temperatures down to −65°F. A higher concentration of ethylene glycol will only raise the freezing point of the mixture. In fact, pure ethylene glycol has a freezing point that is not much below that of water alone. Methyl alcohol and ethyl alcohol do not show this increase in their freezing point, however, as the concentration is increased. Methyl alcohol has a freezing point of −144°F, while ethyl alcohol will freeze at −174°F.

Most antifreeze solutions now available contain an inhibitor. This is not permanent protection against scale and rust formation, however, and the antifreeze solution should be drained and discarded each spring. The system should be flushed and cleaned, and fresh soft water added when all danger of freezing is over. An inhibitor should be added to the water at this time for the summer and fall driving seasons. As the first freezing weather approaches, this water and inhibitor should be drained and discarded, the system flushed and cleaned, and antifreeze added to fresh water for the winter driving.

Coolant Flow

The basic automobile cooling system consists of a radiator, coolant (water) pump, flexible hose, fan, thermostat, and a system of passages and water jackets in the cylinder head and cylinder block through which the coolant circulates. This is shown in Fig. 1. Cooling of the engine parts is accomplished by keeping the coolant circulating and in contact with all of the metal surfaces to be cooled.

The pump draws the coolant from the bottom of the radiator, forces it through the passages and water jackets in the engine, and ejects it into the tank at the top of the radiator. From here, the coolant passes through tubes to the bottom of the radiator and is again circulated through the engine by the water pump. A fan draws air over the outside surfaces of the radiator tubes and cools the liquid as it travels through them.

WATER JACKETS

The water passages in the cylinder block and head form the engine water jacket. In the cylinder block, the water jacket completely surrounds all the cylinders along their full length. In addition, narrow passages are provided between the cylinders for coolant circulation. In L-head engines, still other passages are provided in the cylinder block around the valve seats and any other hot parts that might be present.

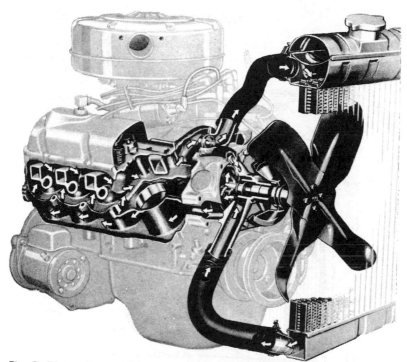

Fig. 1. The cooling system on a 1964 Ford Challenger 289 V8 engine is typical of all cooling systems.

In the cylinder head, water passages surround the combustion chambers. If the engine is of the overhead-valve type, passages around the valve seats will also be provided. The coolant flows from the cylinder block up into the head through openings called water transfer ports. A tight seal at the ports between the cylinder block and head is very important. This seal must be watertight at the ports and gas tight at the combustion chamber openings, and is obtained by using a single large gasket, called the head gasket.

RADIATORS

Automobile radiators consist of two general types—the vertical-flow (Fig. 2) and cross-flow (Fig. 3). Both types contain two

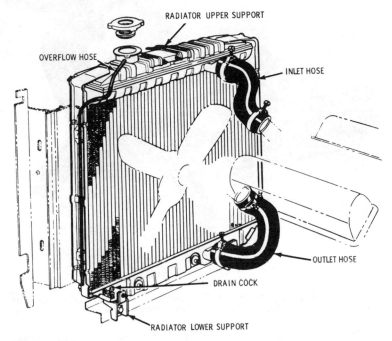

Fig. 2. A typical vertical-flow radiator.

tanks with cores between them to form the radiating portion. The inlet tank contains an opening with a fitting to which is attached a flexible inlet hose. This tank is at the top of the radiator (on vertical-flow types) and usually contains a baffle located above the inlet opening. Most radiators of this type also have a filler neck

516

located on the inlet tank. An overflow pipe is generally a part of the filler neck.

The outlet tank also has an opening and a fitting to which the flexible outlet hose is connected. In addition, a drain cock is pro-

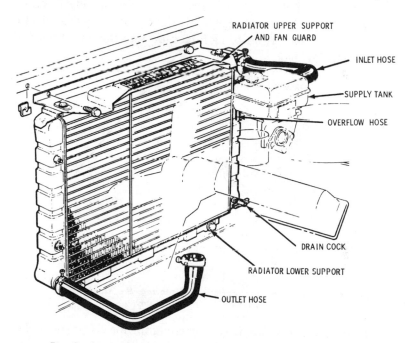

RADIATOR UPPER SUPPORT AND FAN GUARD

INLET HOSE

SUPPLY TANK

OVERFLOW HOSE

DRAIN COCK

RADIATOR LOWER SUPPORT

OUTLET HOSE

Fig. 3. A cross-flow radiator with a separate supply tank.

vided in the bottom of this tank for draining the radiator. The radiators on later model cars with automatic transmissions will also have oil-cooler connections in the outlet tank. Transmission fluid is pumped through pipes to a coil inside the outlet tank to dissipate some of the heat built up in the automatic transmission.

The radiator connections for cooling the transmission fluid in a 1964 Ford 289 V8 is shown in Fig. 4, and is typical of many cars so equipped.

The inlet tank collects the incoming coolant and distributes it across the top of the radiator cores (or along the side in cross-flow radiators). The baffle helps distribute the coolant and also prevents the coolant from being forced up into the filler neck and out the overflow pipe.

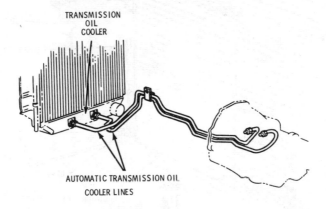

TRANSMISSION
OIL
COOLER

AUTOMATIC TRANSMISSION OIL
COOLER LINES

Fig. 4. Typical connections for cooling the fluid in an automatic transmission.

The overflow pipe provides an opening for the escape of coolant or steam that might otherwise cause excessive pressure which could rupture the thin metal walls of the radiator.

The radiating portion of the radiator consists of many water tubes to which are attached air fins. The passage in the tubes is divided into many very thin columns, which exposes a larger radiating surface to the cooler air passing through the radiator than a single large passage would provide.

WATER PUMPS

The water pumps on all domestic cars are very similar in operating principles and construction. The pump is usually located at the front of the engine block and powered by the same shaft as the fan. Coolant from the lower part of the radiator is drawn into the pump through the lower radiator hose, and is forced through the water jacket into the upper part of the radiator.

The pump is a centrifugal type, having an impeller with blades which force the coolant outward as the impeller rotates. The impeller may be made of metal or plastic.

A cross-sectional view of a typical water pump is shown in Fig. 5. The bearings shown are ball bearings and are permanently lubricated. Some water pumps on older-model cars have sleeve bearings that require periodic lubrication with a special water-pump grease. A seal assembly around the shaft prevents the coolant from leaking out around the shaft. Should any liquid escape, however, a slinger rotating with the shaft throws the leakage away from the shaft by centrifugal force and it drains out of the pump body through a hole provided for this purpose. Thus, any coolant leaking past the seal assembly is prevented from entering the bearings where it could cause damage. Excessive leakage indicates the need for a new seal assembly.

FANS

The fan circulates a large amount of air through the radiator core to rapidly dissipate the heat carried by the coolant. In addition to removing heat from the radiator, this flow of air also provides some direct air cooling of the engine. Fans may have from four to eight blades, the number depending somewhat on the size of the motor and whether or not the car has air conditioning.

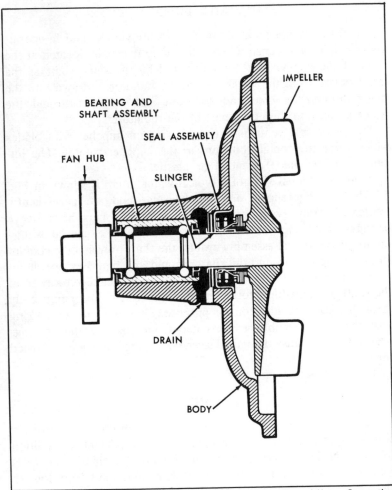

Fig. 5. The construction features of this water pump is similar to all late model pumps.

A rather recent development is a fan driven by a torque- and/or temperature-sensitive clutch. This clutch is a fluid coupling containing silicone oil. The fan speed is regulated by the amount of the silicone oil in the coupling—the more oil, the greater the fan speed. The amount of oil entering the coupling is regulated by some form of thermostatic device. As the air passing through the radiator becomes hotter, the thermostatic element opens a valve which admits more silicone oil into the coupling. Thus, the fan is driven at a faster speed to draw more air through the radiator to lower the temperature. As the temperature drops, the thermostatic valve closes, and the silicone oil in the coupling returns to a reserve chamber through bleed holes provided for that purpose. Radiating fins are an integral part of the assembly to dissipate the heat generated by the shearing action of the silicone oil. The top speed of this type of fan is somewhat lower than the top speed of the engine, since at high speeds enough air is passing through the radiators due to the forward motion of the car to provide adequate cooling without the benefit of the fan. Fig. 6 shows the fan-drive clutch used on some 1964 Fords.

THERMOSTATS

Without a thermostat, the water pump would start circulating the coolant through the system as soon as the engine is started, no matter how low the temperature. Thus, a thermostat is included in the cooling system of an automobile to insure rapid warmup and to prevent overcooling in cold weather. The thermostat regulates the engine temperature by automatically controlling the amount of coolant flowing from the engine block to the radiator core. With the thermostat closed, water circulates through the engine block and head, but not through the radiator. This is possible because of a bypass through which the coolant returns directly to the water

FAN DRIVE

Fig. 6. A typical fan-drive clutch installation.

pump for recirculation when the thermostat valve has the circulation blocked through the radiator.

Two general types of thermostats are in use today—the bellows type and the pellet type. The bellows type may be found in some older-model cars and consists of a flexible-metal bellows attached to a valve. The sealed bellows, which is expandable, is filled with a highly volatile liquid, such as ether. When this liquid is cold, the

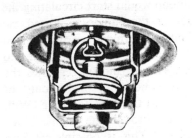

Fig. 7. A pellet-type thermostat.

Courtesy Dodge Div.,
Chrysler Motors Corp.

bellows chamber is contracted and the valve is closed. When heated, the liquid vaporizes and expands the chamber, opening the valve.

The pellet-type thermostat is found in nearly all late-model cars. This type of thermostat uses a pellet containing a paste. As the temperature rises, the paste turns to a liquid, expanding the pellet and opening the valve against the tension of a spring. A typical unit of this type is shown in Fig. 7.

Thermostats are available to maintain the engine at various operating temperatures. When nonpermanent antifreeze is used, a low-temperature thermostat should be installed. This type of thermostat usually starts to open in the range of 150°-160°F. For more efficient operation of the engine and heater, permanent antifreeze should be used and a high-temperature thermostat installed. This type of thermostat usually starts to open in the range from 180°-190°F.

A thermostat may fail either in the closed position (most unlikely) or the open position (most likely). When it fails closed, engine overheating, loss of coolant, and eventual engine damage will result. When it fails open, slow engine warmup, low engine efficiency, and poor heater operation will result. **A defective thermostat cannot be repaired. Always replace with a new unit.**

RADIATOR CAPS

The cooling system on all late-model cars is non-pressurized and requires a pressure radiator cap similar to the one in Fig. 8. A pressure of from 12 to 15 lbs. is maintained in the cooling system during the time the engine is operating normally. This pressure is maintained in order to raise the boiling point of the coolant, allowing the engine to operate at a higher temperature without overflow and loss of coolant.

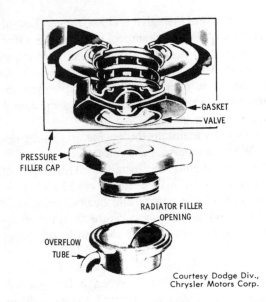

GASKET

VALVE

PRESSURE
FILLER CAP

Fig. 8. A typical pressure radiator cap.

RADIATOR FILLER
OPENING

OVERFLOW
TUBE

Courtesy Dodge Div.,
Chrysler Motors Corp.

The cap contains two valves, as shown in Fig. 9, which are normally closed, sealing the system. The pressure or blowoff valve is the larger of the two, and acts as a safety valve to relieve the pressure in the system if it should increase above the safe level. The smaller valve opens only when the pressure in the system

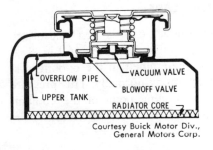

VACUUM VALVE

OVERFLOW PIPE

BLOWOFF VALVE

UPPER TANK

RADIATOR CORE

Fig. 9. Cross-sectional view of a typical pressure-type radiator cap.

Courtesy Buick Motor Div.,
General Motors Corp.

becomes less than the atmospheric pressure as the system cools off. When this vacuum valve opens, air is drawn into the system through the overflow pipe.

Care should be taken when removing the cap from a pressurized system while the coolant is still hot. If the cap is removed too rapidly, the coolant may suddenly start boiling and gush out the filler neck, resulting in serious burns to the individual. To properly remove this type of cap, either wait until the engine has cooled, or rotate the cap counterclockwise to the stop, wait until the pressure has been relieved through the overflow pipe, then again turn counterclockwise until the cap is released.

OVERFLOW TANKS

Overflow or radiator supply tanks are provided on some cars, such as the 1964 Ford 352, 390, and 427 V8's (Fig. 10). A

Fig. 10. A radiator supply tank is provided on some makes and models of automobiles.

pressure-type radiator cap is placed on the supply tank instead of the radiator. The radiator itself may or may not have a separate cap—usually it does not.

The use of an overflow or supply tank is made necessary on some engines having a larger-than-normal coolant capacity to offer greater protection for prolonged high-speed driving in high temperatures.

DRAINING THE SYSTEM

If it is found necessary to completely drain the cooling system of coolant to prevent damage by freezing, special precautions must be taken. The drain cock located at the bottom of the radiator does not completely drain the entire system in most cars. Drain plugs are provided on the side of the engine block to completely drain the water jackets in the engine. Most four- and six-cylinder in-line engines will have one drain plug, while V-type engines usually have two—one on each side of the engine.

If the car is equipped with a heater, it will be necessary to disconnect the heater hose on some cars to drain the coolant that remains even after the rest of the system has been completely drained.

COOLING-SYSTEM TROUBLES AND REMEDIES

Symptom and Possible Cause	*Possible Remedy*
External Leakage	
(a) Loose hose clamp.	(a) Tighten or replace clamp.
(b) Hose leaking.	(b) Replace hose.
(c) Radiator leaking.	(c) Repair or replace radiator as required.
(d) Worn or damaged water pump.	(d) Replace water-pump seal or packing.
(e) Loose freeze or core-hole plug.	(e) Replace with new plug.
(f) Damaged gasket (dry gasket if car has been stored).	(f) Replace gaskets as necessary.
(g) Cylinder-head bolts loose or tightened unevenly.	(g) Replace cylinder-head gasket and tighten head bolts in the correct sequence.

Symptom and Possible Causes	*Possible Remedy*
(h) Leak at heater connection.	(h) Clean the heater connections and replace hose and clamps as necessary.
(i) Leak at water-temperature sending unit.	(i) Tighten sending unit.
(j) Leak at the water-pump attaching bolts.	(j) Torque bolts to specifications.
(k) Leak at exhaust-manifold stud.	(k) Torque bolts to specifications.
(l) Cracked thermostat housing.	(l) Replace housing.
(m) Dented radiator inlet or outlet tube.	(m) Straighten tube as necessary.
(n) Leaking radiator core.	(n) Repair or replace radiator core.
(o) Warped or cracked water-pump housing.	(o) Replace water-pump assembly.
(p) Cracked cylinder block.	(p) Replace block.
(q) Cracked or warped cylinder head.	(q) Replace head.
(r) Sand holes or porous condition of head or block.	(r) Replace head or block as necessary.

Internal Leakage

(a) Defective head gasket.	(a) Install new gasket.
(b) Crack in head into valve compartment.	(b) Replace head.
(c) Cracked valve port.	(c) Replace head or block as required.

Symptom and Possible Causes	*Possible Remedy*
(d) Crack in block into push-rod compartment.	(d) Replace block.
(e) Cracked cylinder wall.	(e) Replace block.
(f) Leaking oil cooler.	(f) Repair or replace oil cooler.

Poor Circulation

(a) Low coolant level.	(a) Fill radiator to correct level.
(b) Collapsed radiator hose. (Bottom hose may collapse at driving speeds only).	(b) Replace hose and internal spring if so equipped.
(c) Fan belt glazed, oil soaked, or loose.	(c) Tighten or replace fan belt as required.
(d) Air leak through bottom hose.	(d) Reposition hose clamps or replace hose.
(e) Defective thermostat.	(e) Replace thermostat.
(f) Broken or loose water-pump impeller.	(f) Replace impeller assembly.
(g) Water passages in radiator clogged.	(g) Reverse flush and clean radiator.
(h) Water jackets in engine clogged.	(h) Reverse flush and clean cooling system.

Overheating (Apparent or Actual)

(a) Low coolant level.	(a) Fill radiator to correct level.
(b) Air passages in radiator blocked.	(b) Blow air passages out with compressed air.
(c) Incorrect ignition timing.	(c) Time ignition system.

Symptom and Possible Causes	*Possible Remedy*
(d) Engine oil level low.	(d) Add oil to correct level.
(e) Incorrect valve timing.	(e) Correct valve timing.
(f) Faulty temperature gauge.	(f) Replace temperature gauge.
(g) Overflow tube clogged.	(g) Remove restriction in overflow tube.
(h) Defective pressure radiator cap.	(h) Replace cap.
(i) Heat-control valve stuck.	(i) Free up heat-control valve.
(j) Brakes dragging.	(j) Adjust brakes.
(k) Prolonged engine idling.	(k) Stop engine.
(l) Coolant frozen.	(l) Thaw cooling system and add antifreeze as required.
(m) Defective fan drive unit.	(m) Repair or replace fan drive unit.
(n) Defective temperature sending unit.	(n) Replace unit.

Radiator Overflows

(a) Radiator overfilled.	(a) Adjust coolant to correct level.
(b) Coolant foaming.	(b) Flush cooling system and add antifreeze or inhibitor as required.
(c) Air leak at bottom radiator hose.	(c) Reposition hose clamp or replace hose.
(d) Blown head gasket.	(d) Replace head gasket.

Symptom and Possible Causes	*Possible Remedy*

Corrosion

(a) Use of water that is too hard.

(a) Use only clean soft water.

(b) Low coolant level.

(b) Fill radiator to correct level.

(c) Insufficient inhibitor.

(c) Fill with fresh antifreeze or inhibitor as required.

(d) Prolonged use of antifreeze.

(d) Drain cooling system and replace with fresh antifreeze.

(e) Air leak at bottom radiator hose.

(e) Reposition hose clamps or replace hose.

Low Engine Temperature

(a) Defective thermostat.

(a) Replace thermostat.

(b) Defective temperature gauge.

(b) Replace gauge.

(c) Defective temperature sending unit.

(c) Replace unit.

Noisy Water Pump

(a) Defective seal.

(a) Replace seal and lubricate as required.

(b) Defective bearing.

(b) Replace bearing or pump assembly as required.

CHAPTER 19

Engine Lubricating Systems

One of the most important systems in an automobile is the one that lubricates the engine. Failure of this system will result in serious damage to the engine in a very short time. In the early days of automobiles, the engine was lubricated entirely by the splash-system. This was satisfactory for the comparatively loose-fitting parts then in use, provided the oil level was not allowed to get too low. As the power of engines was increased and greater precision used in fitting parts, the splash-system was found to be inadequate. Thus, a combination of splash and pressure was used to distribute the oil to the various engine parts. Finally, the full-pressure system of lubrication was adopted and is used almost universally in the modern automobile engine.

ENGINE LUBRICATION

The lubrication in an engine actually performs four functions— (1) it prevents metal-to-metal contact between the moving parts; (2) it assists in carrying heat away from the engine; (3) it cleans the engine parts, and (4) it provides a seal between the piston rings and cylinder walls to prevent blow-by of combustion gases.

The primary function of engine lubrication is to reduce the friction between moving parts. Friction not only uses power that would otherwise be available to drive the automobile, but it is also destructive and creates heat that can destroy the moving parts. Moving parts that are deprived of oil will either melt, fuse, or seize after a very short period of operation. It is lubrication that makes possible the use of relatively simple and thin bearings and bushings in a modern engine.

The bearings at the crankshaft, connecting rods, wrist pins, camshaft, etc., are important points that must be constantly lubricated. In addition, other parts must be provided with an adequate supply of oil. For example, the valve stems must operate under stress and a wide range of temperature, and so require lubrication. Valve tappets and cams, gears, timing chains, and accessory drives also require a constant oil bath. In fact, any moving part must be bathed in oil while the engine is operating or else it will fail.

The engine oil is heated through contact with the pistons and cylinder walls, after which it returns to the oil pan. Air flowing around the outside surface of the oil pan serves to cool the oil.

ENGINE OILS

The oil industry has kept pace with the higher-horsepower, high-compression engines in use today by producing oils to meet the more rigid requirements demanded by these engines. Engine oils today are graded and classified to standards recommended by the Society of Automotive Engineers (SAE) and the American Petroleum Institute (API).

Most readers will remember when it was recommended that engine oil be changed every 1,000 miles. This change interval has been greatly extended by the improved design of modern automobile engines and by the use of the proper type of oil designed for the heavy-duty requirements of these engines. Change intervals of 4,000 to 6,000 miles or more are common, depending on the make and model of car, and on the driving conditions. Always follow the car manufacturer's recommendations for the correct change interval.

Viscosity

The viscosity of an oil refers to its resistance to flow. When oil is hot, it will flow more readily than when it is cold. In cold weather, therefore, oil should be thin (low viscosity) to permit easy flow and, consequently, easier engine starting. In hot weather, oil should be heavier (high viscosity) to retard the rate of flow.

Oils are graded according to their viscosity by a series of SAE numbers. The higher the SAE number, the more viscous, or heavy, is the oil. This viscosity number has no connection with the lubricating qualities of the oil.

The oil most frequently used in automobile engines has SAE numbers of 10W, 20, and 30. For extreme cold conditions, SAE 5W is available, but when this weight is used, sustained high speeds (above 65 mph) should be avoided because of possible increased oil consumption.

Multi-viscosity oil is also available and becoming more and more popular. This type of oil is produced in two grades (5W-20 and 10W-30) which provides the starting ease of low-viscosity oil and the protection of high-viscosity for sustained driving. These multi-viscosity oils are generally acceptable by most car manufacturers.

The viscosity (SAE number) of the oil should be selected for the lowest anticipated temperature at which engine starting will be required, and not for the temperature at the time of oil change. The following temperatures and recommended viscosities are generally acceptable.

Lowest Anticipated Temperature	Recommended Single-Viscosity	Recommended Multi-Viscosity
Above 32° F	SAE 20W-20	SAE 10W-30
Above 0° F	SAE 10W	SAE 10W-30
Below 0° F	SAE 5W	SAE 5W-20

These viscosities are suggested for use in cars in good condition. A higher viscosity, such as SAE 30, may be required in high-mileage cars to decrease oil consumption.

Classification

There are several types of oil manufactured for use in automobile engines. For maximum engine protection and performance under all driving conditions, it is recommended that only a heavy-duty type oil marked "For Service MS" or "For Service DG" be used. The term "MS" or "DG" should appear on the oil container singly or in combination with other designations. This oil is a heavy-duty, detergent type formulated to withstand all service conditions in modern automobile engines.

Oils designated as "ML" and/or "MM" are not recommended for use in high-compression engines and should not be used except in emergencies when "MS" oil is not available.

Changing Oil

Oil does not wear out, but it does become contaminated and diluted. For this reason, the oil should be changed at the recommended intervals as determined by the car manufacturer for specific driving conditions.

Probably the most serious cause of engine oil deterioration is that of dilution. Dilution is caused by fuel vapor (and, in some cases, raw gasoline) leaking past the piston rings and mixing with the oil. Another cause of dilution is the condensation of moisture on the cylinder walls and crankcase. Leakage of fuel vapors into the oil pan occurs mostly during engine warm up when the fuel is not completely vaporized and burned. Water vapor enters the crankcase through normal engine ventilation and through the blow-by of exhaust gases. When the engine is not completely warmed up, these water vapors condense and combine with condensed fuel vapors and exhaust gases to form acid compounds in the crankcase. The acid thus formed can cause serious etching or pitting, resulting in rapid wear of wrist pins, bearings, and other moving parts of the engine.

Another result of water condensation is the emulsification that takes place when this water combines with the oil and any dirt or foreign matter present. In this way, sludge is formed that may clog oil lines and lubricating passages.

Raw gasoline drawn into the cylinders by excessive choke action or unvaporized fuel remains in a liquid state and drains past the piston rings into the oil pan. Here it is mixed with the oil. This mixture decreases the viscosity of the oil and causes it to lose some of its lubricating qualities. Presence of gasoline will not lower the oil level but will maintain or even raise it.

Many devices incorporated in the modern automobile engine help to minimize engine-oil dilution. The coolant thermostat, heat-control valve in the exhaust manifold, automatic choke, and crankcase ventilation are among the items that help control dilution.

Probably the greatest contributor to dilution is stop-and-go driving. Longer continuous driving allows the engine to reach operating temperature and evaporate any water or raw gasoline that may have mixed with the engine oil. For this reason, the oil should be changed at shorter intervals when the driving is principally stop-and-go or slow, short-time drives.

It is advisable to drain the crankcase only after the engine has become thoroughly warmed up to its normal operating temperature. Otherwise, the benefit of changing the oil is largely lost, as some of the suspended foreign material will cling to the sides of the oil pan and will contaminate the new oil.

Filters

An oil filter is standard equipment on most late-model automobiles. This unit filters the oil, removing most of the impurities that have been picked up by the oil as it circulates through the engine. There are two general types of filters on automobile engines at present—the full-flow and the partial-flow type.

An internal view of a full-flow filter is shown in Fig. 1. In this type, all of the circulating oil passes through the filter element before entering the main oil gallery. If the filter element should become so clogged that the oil cannot pass through it readily, a

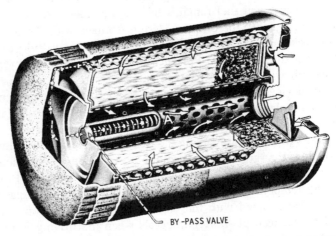

BY-PASS VALVE

Fig. 1. Internal construction features of a full-flow type of oil filter.

spring-loaded by-pass valve will open to allow oil to circulate freely. Under this condition, of course, no filtering action will take place. Regular replacement of the filter will prevent this sequence of operation from ever occurring.

In the partial-flow filter, only a portion of the total circulating oil passes through the filter element. The remainder is by-passed around the element.

In some cars, only the filter element and gasket needs replacement at the prescribed intervals. In other cars, the entire filter is discarded and a new unit installed. Follow the car manufacturer's instructions for changing the filter.

Most filter assemblies also contain an antidrain valve. This valve closes when the engine stops and holds the oil in the passages instead of allowing it to drain back to the oil pan. Thus, when the engine is started, oil is immediately available and engine lubrication starts at once.

OIL PUMPS

Oil pumps are of two general types—the meshed-gear and the rotor type. The meshed-gear type, shown in Fig. 2, consists of a driven gear and an idler gear enclosed in a housing. The two gears are rotated by a shaft that is usually coupled to the camshaft. In some instances, the oil-pump shaft is an extension of the distributor shaft. Maximum oil pressure is regulated by means of a pressure-regulator valve. Oil is drawn into the pump through a screened intake which prevents any foreign material from entering the circulating oil system. As a safety precaution, some means is provided to by-pass the screen if it should become clogged. This pickup screen assembly is designed to float in some cars to prevent its picking up any sludge or sediment that may settle to the bottom of the oil pan.

The rotor-type oil pump (Fig. 3) differs very little from the meshed-gear type. An off-center inner rotor is the driven element, and as it turns, it causes an outer rotor to rotate. This action draws

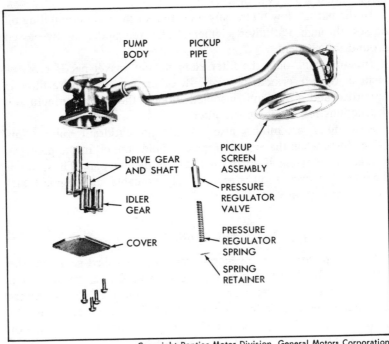

Fig. 2. A meshed-gear type oil pump.

oil into the pump and forces it out into the oil circulating system. A pressure-relief valve and inlet oil strainer is also included.

To service either type of oil pump requires the removal of the oil pan on all but a few models of cars. The inlet screen should be cleaned at this time and any worn parts in the oil pump re-

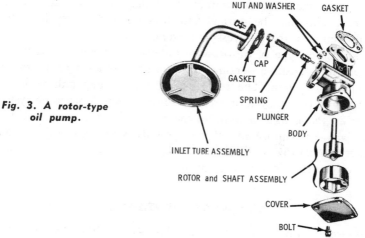

NUT AND WASHER   GASKET

CAP

GASKET

SPRING

PLUNGER

BODY

INLET TUBE ASSEMBLY

ROTOR and SHAFT ASSEMBLY

COVER

BOLT

Fig. 3. A rotor-type oil pump.

placed. The entire meshed-gear assembly or the rotor assembly should be replaced, even though only one part is worn or defective. Always use new gaskets when reassembling the pump. Refer to the manufacturer's instructions for removal and reassembly.

OIL-PRESSURE INDICATORS

Two different types of oil-pressure indicators are in use on automobiles. The most common type is the oil-pressure warning light that comes on only if the oil pressure drops below a predetermined level. In this system, a pressure-sensitive switch is wired in series with the ignition switch, the warning bulb, and the car battery. With no or with low oil pressure, this switch is closed and the bulb lights. As pressure builds up, the switch opens and the warning light goes out. Thus, when the ignition switch is turned on, the warning light comes on. After the engine starts, the oil pressure increases and opens the pressure-sensitive switch, and the light goes out. On some cars, the warning light may come on at slow idle speeds. This may be normal and does not necessarily indicate a malfunction of the oil pressure system.

The other type of oil-pressure indicator is a gauge actuated by a pressure-sensitive sending unit located somewhere in the oil circulating system. The resistance of the sending unit varies according to the amount of pressure in the engine lubricating system, causing the gauge to indicate the comparative pressure existing. The gauge is calibrated either in pounds per square inch or some other comparative units to indicate the relative pressure with which the oil is being forced through the system.

CRANKCASE VENTILATION

Gasoline vapor and steam are harmful if they are allowed to remain in the engine oil. Steam will condense and mix with the oil to form a sludge, while gasoline vapor will condense and dilute the oil. Two different methods are used to remove these vapors from the crankcase. The first method consists of a breather tube which depends on the flow of air past its open end to remove the vapors. The second method, known as positive crankcase ventilation, utilizes the intake manifold pressure to circulate air through the crankcase, returning the vapors to the combustion chamber for removal.

Breather-Tube Type

One end of the breather tube opens into the crankcase above the oil level, and the other end extends down under the vehicle into the air stream. As air rushes past, a low pressure is created at the open end of the tube sufficient to draw any vapors out of the crankcase. An opening in the valve cover or in the oil-filler cap allows air to enter to replace that drawn out of the breather tube.

A screen is often placed in the end of the breather tube, and nearly always in the oil-filler breather cap. These screens must be kept clean. If they become clogged, pressure may build up in the crankcase causing excessive oil consumption. The screen in the

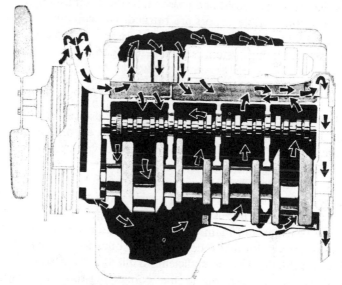

Fig. 4. Breather-tube type crankcase ventilation.

breather tube is nearly always neglected, due to its inaccessibility or due to the fact that its existence is unknown. Many cases of excessive oil consumption or abnormal sludge formation has been traced to a clogged breather tube. The screen or filtering material in the breather cap and/or outlet breather tube should be periodically cleaned by rinsing in a suitable solvent and saturating with engine oil. Fig. 4 shows a typical breather-tube type of crankcase ventilation.

Positive Type

Intake manifold vacuum draws air into the crankcase through a filter in the oil-filler cap. From here, the air moves through the engine, picking up any vapors that may be present. Finally, the air enters the intake manifold and passes into the combustion chamber where any combustible vapors are burned. Noncombustible vapors are forced out through the exhaust system. A typical positive crankcase-ventilating system is shown in Fig. 5.

PRESSURE LUBRICATING SYSTEMS

All domestic cars manufactured today use a pressure-type engine lubricating system (Fig. 6). Oil from an oil-pan sump is delivered under pressure by an oil pump to various parts of the engine. Oil passages in the engine block deliver a constant flow of oil to the main bearings and connecting rod bearings. In order to direct the oil to the connecting-rod bearings, oil passages are drilled in the crankshaft. The oil enters these passages from openings in the main bearings and main journals. In some engines, these openings are merely holes that index (line up) once for every revolution of the crankshaft. This is sufficient to fill the oil passages in the crankshaft and furnish oil to the connecting-rod bearings. In other engines, annular grooves are machined in the bearings through which oil can constantly pass into the passage through the crankshaft.

The cylinder walls are lubricated in most engines by means of a small groove or a drilled hole in the connecting-rod bearing that indexes with a matching hole in the connecting-rod journal once for every revolution of the crankshaft. This method is used most often in V8 engines where oil from the squirt hole in one connecting-rod bearing lubricates the opposite cylinder wall. For

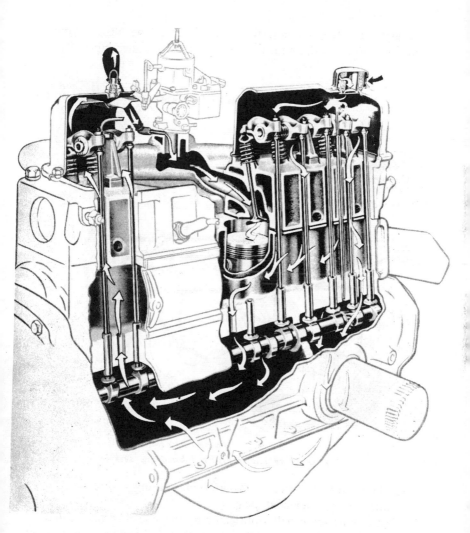

Fig. 5. Positive crankcase ventilation.

example, the No. 1 connecting rod lubricates the No. 5 cylinder, etc. As the crankshaft turns, the hole in the connecting-rod bear-

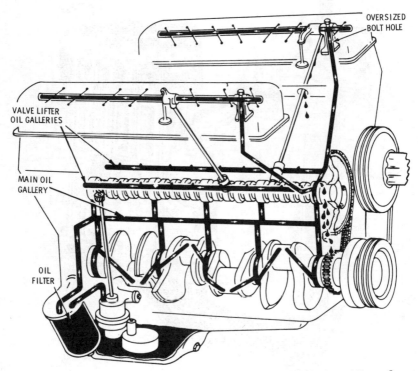

Courtesy Buick Motor Div., General Motors Corp.

Fig. 6. A typical pressure lubricating system.

ing aligns with the hole in the journal, causing a direct squirt of oil onto the cylinder wall (Fig. 7).

Piston pins are usually lubricated by the splash of oil created by the crankshaft. Moving parts not lubricated either by splash or by

544

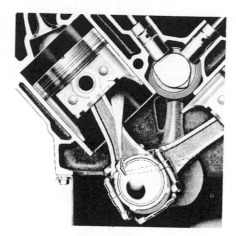

Fig. 7. A common method of lubricating the cylinder walls in a V8 engine.

oil under pressure will be lubricated by dripping oil on its way back to the oil pan.

The formation of sludge will often clog the drain passages provided in the engine block to return the oil from the rocker-arm lubrication to the oil pan. Positive crankcase ventilation and the use of detergent oil has done much to minimize this formation.

LUBRICATING-SYSTEM TROUBLES AND REMEDIES

Symptom and Possible Causes   *Possible Remedy*

Oil-Pressure Drop

(a) Low oil level.

(b) Faulty oil-pressure sending unit or oil warning-light switch.

(a) Fill crankcase to correct level.

(b) Install new sending unit or warning-light switch.

Symptom and Possible Causes	*Possible Remedy*
(c) Thin or diluted oil.	(c) Drain oil and refill crankcase with oil of the correct viscosity.
(d) Relief valve in oil pump stuck.	(d) Remove valve, and clean and repair as necessary.
(e) Oil-pump suction tube loose or cracked.	(e) Remove oil pan and install new tube or oil-pump assembly as necessary.
(f) Clogged oil filter.	(f) Install new oil filter.
(g) Excessive bearing clearance.	(g) Measure bearing for correct clearance and repair as necessary.

Main Bearing Noise

(a) Insufficient oil supply.	(a) Check engine oil level and add oil if necessary. Check relief valve in oil pump for correct operation. Repair or replace as necessary.
(b) Low oil pressure.	(b) Check oil level and all possible causes under preceding symptom (Oil-Pressure Drop).
(c) Thin or diluted oil.	(c) Drain oil and refill crankcase with oil of the correct viscosity.
(d) Excessive bearing clearance.	(d) Measure bearings for correct clearance and repair as necessary.

Symptom and Possible Causes	*Possible Remedy*

(e) Excessive end play of crankshaft.

(e) Check main bearings for flange wear. Correct as necessary.

(f) Main-bearing journal(s) out-of-round or worn.

(f) Remove crankshaft and re-grind journal(s).

(g) Loose flywheel or torque converter.

(g) Tighten to the correct torque.

Connecting-Rod Noise

(a) Insufficient oil supply.

(a) Check oil level and correct as necessary. Check relief valve in oil pump for correct operation, and repair or replace as necessary.

(b) Low oil pressure.

(b) See preceding symptom (Oil-Pressure Drop).

(c) Thin or diluted oil.

(c) Drain oil and refill crankcase with oil of the correct viscosity.

(d) Excessive bearing clearance.

(d) Measure bearing clearance and correct as necessary.

(e) Connecting-rod journal(s) out-of-round.

(e) Remove crankcase and re-grind journals(s).

(f) Connecting rod bent.

(f) Replace defective rod.

Noisy Valves

(a) High or low oil level.

(a) Add or remove oil to bring to the correct level.

(b) Thin or diluted oil.

(b) Drain and refill with oil of the correct viscosity.

Symptom and Possible Causes	*Possible Remedy*
(c) Low oil pressure.	(c) See preceding symptom (Oil-Pressure Drop).
(d) Dirt in valve tappets.	(d) Clean valve tappets.
(e) Bent push rod(s).	(e) Replace defective push rod(s).
(f) Worn rocker arm(s).	(f) Replace defective rocker arm(s).
(g) Worn tappets.	(g) Install new tappets.
(h) Worn valve guides.	(h) Ream guides and install new valves with oversize stems, or replace guides and valves as necessary.
(i) Excessive run-out of valve faces or seats.	(i) Grind the valve faces and seats.

Oil Pumping at Rings

(a) Worn, scuffed, or broken piston rings.	(a) Hone cylinders and install new rings.
(b) Carbon in oil-ring slots.	(b) Install new rings.
(c) Rings fitted too tight in grooves.	(c) Remove rings and check the groove width. If too narrow, replace the piston.

CHAPTER 20

Pistons and Rings

The pistons and rings in an automobile are designed to withstand severe punishment. They must be able to operate effectively over a very wide range of temperatures and pressures. The area at the top of the piston must be sealed from the crankcase to prevent combustion blow-by and loss of compression, and also to prevent oil on the cylinder walls from entering the combustion chamber. All this must be done at temperature extremes ranging from below zero (when the engine is started in winter cold) to several hundred degrees after the engine has reached operating temperature. Pressure extremes range from the vacuum existing on the fuel-intake stroke to the several hundred pounds per sq. in. pressure exerted as the fuel-charge fires.

PISTON CONSTRUCTION

The majority of pistons in late-model cars are made of an aluminum alloy, and usually plated with tin to decrease friction and wear. Some cast-iron pistons will be found, especially in older-model cars.

The aluminum-alloy pistons are generally cam-ground, as shown in Fig. 1. This means that the piston, when cold, is not perfectly round; instead, it is slightly elliptical. As the temperature of this piston rises, the expansion along the diameter which passes through the piston-pin axis is greater than the expansion along the diameter across the thrust axis. Thus, the piston becomes circular at its operating temperature.

Aluminum-alloy pistons should never be ground or honed in any way. If a piston is found to be oversize, the cylinder must be rebored or honed to obtain the proper fit.

Cast-iron pistons found in some older-model cars can be machined slightly in most cases. Care must be taken if this operation is performed, however, to make sure the piston is not weakened, especially in the skirt area.

Pistons are designed for a particular make and model of car and cannot be used in other cars. This is true, even if the piston di-

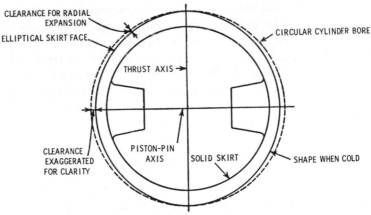

Fig. 1. Bottom view of a cam-ground piston showing its elliptical shape exaggerated for clarity.

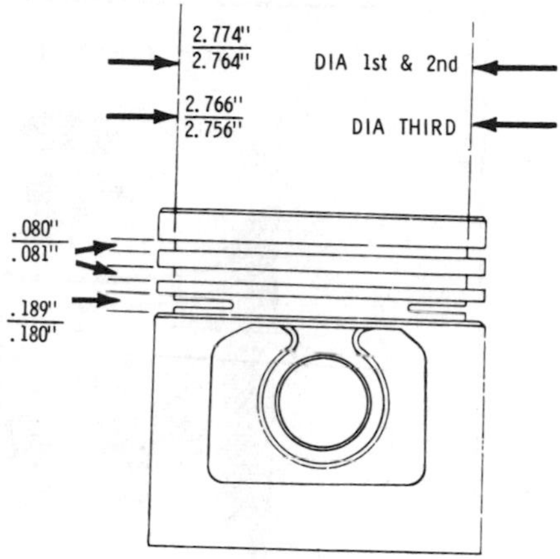

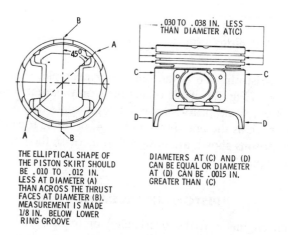

2.774" / 2.764" DIA 1st & 2nd

2.766" / 2.756" DIA THIRD

.080" / .081"

.189" / .180"

Fig. 2. A full-skirted piston.

Courtesy American Motors Corp.

B

A

45°

A

B

THE ELLIPTICAL SHAPE OF
THE PISTON SKIRT SHOULD
BE .010 TO .012 IN.
LESS AT DIAMETER (A)
THAN ACROSS THE THRUST
FACES AT DIAMETER (B).
MEASUREMENT IS MADE
1/8 IN. BELOW LOWER
RING GROOVE

.030 TO .038 IN. LESS
THAN DIAMETER AT (C)

C   C

D   D

DIAMETERS AT (C) AND (D)
CAN BE EQUAL OR DIAMETER
AT (D) CAN BE .0015 IN.
GREATER THAN (C)

Courtesy Dodge Div., Chrysler Motors Corp.

Fig. 3. A piston with a partial skirt.

551

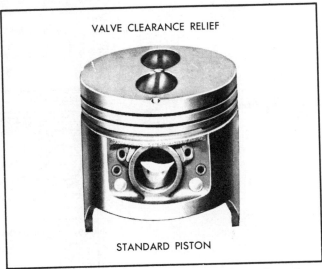

Copyright Pontiac Motor Division, General Motors Corporation

Fig. 4. A piston with recessed top to give clearance to the valves.

ameter and wrist-pin size is the same. For example, some pistons have full skirts (Fig. 2), while others have only partial skirts (Fig. 3). In addition, some pistons have flat tops, while others have recessed tops, such as the one shown in Fig. 4, or dome tops (Fig. 5). Both of the pistons shown are designed to increase the compression ratio of the engine.

PISTON REPLACEMENT

When an engine is to be overhauled or to be inspected for a possible ring and/or piston replacement, the following procedure for removing the pistons is suggested:

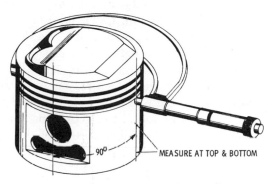

90° — MEASURE AT TOP & BOTTOM

Courtesy Buick Motor Div., General Motors Corp.

Fig. 5. A piston with a domed top to increase the compression ratio.

1. Remove any ridge that may be present around the top of the cylinders before removing the pistons from the cylinder block. Keep the piston tops covered during this operation.
2. Rotate the crankshaft so that the connecting rod to the piston to be removed is centered in the cylinder bore. (The pistons and connecting rods in most cars must be removed from the top of the cylinder block.)
3. Remove the connecting-rod cap.
4. Push the piston and rod assembly out of the cylinder bore. Take extra care to prevent the connecting-rod bolts from contacting and damaging the connecting-rod journal on the crankshaft.
5. Install the connecting-rod bearing cap on the rod.

INSPECTION

All deposits should be removed from the surface of the pistons. Any gum or varnish should be cleaned from the piston skirt, wrist pin, and rings with a suitable solvent. **Do not use a wire brush or a caustic cleaning solution.** Clean the ring grooves on the pistons with a ring-groove tool, such as the one shown in Fig. 6. Make sure the oil-ring slots (or holes) are clean.

Inspect the pistons for cracks at the ring lands, skirts, and pin bosses, and for scuffed, rough, or scored skirts. If any of these conditions exist, the affected piston or pistons should be replaced. Other conditions that call for piston replacement are excessive wear, a high stop on the lower inner portion of the ring grooves, spongy or eroded areas near the top of the piston, and wavy ring lands.

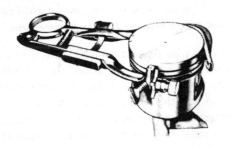

Fig. 6. A ring-groove tool being used to clean a piston.

Wrist Pins

Replace any wrist pins that show signs of cracks or etching and/or wear. Check the wrist pin fit as recommended by the manufacturer. This is usually given as a light thumb-press fit with both the piston and wrist pin at a normal temperature of approximately 70°F. If the fit of the wrist pin is not correct, new units should be installed. Most manufacturers supply oversize pins to be used if the old pins are loose. This means the wrist-pin hole in the piston must be reamed or honed to the correct size to accept the oversize pin. Some manufacturers do not recommend reaming or honing, or the use of oversize pins. Instead, they recommend replacement of both the piston and wrist pin.

The correct method of reaming a piston for an oversize wrist pin is to place the reamer in a vise and revolve the piston around the reamer. Set the reamer to the size of the existing pin bore, then expand the reamer slightly and make a trial ream. **Take a light cut.** Use a pilot sleeve of the nearest correct size in order to maintain alignment of the bores.

Check the hole size, using a new wrist pin to be installed. If the bore is too small, expand the reamer slightly and make another light cut. Continue this procedure until the proper fit is obtained. Check the fit of the wrist pin in the connecting rod and, if necessary ream or hone the rod until the pin fits according to specifications.

Cylinder Block

After removing the cylinder head, remove all the old gasket material from the machined surfaces of the cylinder block, and thoroughly clean the block with solvent. Remove any pipe plugs which seal oil passages, and blow out the passages, bolt holes, etc., with compressed air. Make sure the threads in all bolt holes are clean. Dirt in the threads may cause binding and result in an incorrect torque reading. Use a tap to true-up the threads and to remove any deposits.

Inspect the block for cracks after it has been thoroughly cleaned. Small cracks that are not readily visible may be detected by coating the suspected area with a mixture of 25% kerosene and 75% light engine oil. Wipe the area dry and immediately apply a coating of zinc oxide dissolved in wood alcohol. If cracks are present, the coating will become discolored at the defective area, indicating that the block should be replaced.

Check all machined gasket surfaces for burrs, nicks, scratches, and scores. Remove any minor imperfections with an oilstone.

Check the flatness of the cylinder-block gasket surface. Regrind this surface if the flatness is not within the limits set up by the manufacturer. Do not remove more metal than recommended, for to do so will upset the compression ratio and may result in damage to the engine after a short period of operation.

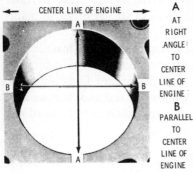

A AT RIGHT ANGLE TO CENTER LINE OF ENGINE

B PARALLEL TO CENTER LINE OF ENGINE

1. OUT-OF-ROUND = DIFFERENCE BETWEEN **A** AND **B**
2. TAPER = DIFFERENCE BETWEEN THE **A** MEASUREMENT AT TOP OF CYLINDER BORE AND THE **A** MEASUREMENT AT BOTTOM OF CYLINDER BORE

Fig. 7. Checking the out-of-round and taper conditions of a cylinder.

Inspect the cylinder walls for roughness, scoring, glazing, or other signs of wear. Check the cylinder bore for out-of-round and taper, making the measurements as shown in Fig. 7. Measure the diameter of each cylinder bore at the top, bottom, and middle, one set of readings with the gauge placed at right angles to the center line of the engine and another set of readings with the gauge parallel to the center line.

Reboring

Rebore and hone any cylinders that are deeply scored or that exceed the out-of-round and/or taper limits specified by the manufacturer. Before reboring any cylinder, all main-bearing caps must be in place and torqued to specifications so that the crankshaft bearing bores will not be distorted by the reboring operation.

Rebore and hone only the cylinder or cylinders that require it. **All pistons are the same weight (for a given car) whether they are standard or oversize; therefore, one or more different size pistons can be used without upsetting engine balance.** Rebore the cylinder with the most wear first to determine the maximum oversize necessary. If the cylinder cannot be refinished to fit the maximum oversize piston available, the block will have to be replaced.

Rebore the cylinder to within approximately 0.0015 inch of the required oversize diameter. This will allow enough stock for the final honing step to give the proper surface finish and pattern. Use the clean sharp 220- to 280-grit hones for the final operation.

Honing

Honing the cylinder walls is necessary after reboring, or to remove minor imperfections and glaze. This operation cannot be used to correct an excessive out-of-round or taper condition of the cylinder, however. Usually, a few strokes of the hone will produce a satisfactory finish on the cylinder walls and within the required limits.

Before honing, stuff clean rags under the cylinders and over the crankshaft to keep the abrasive material from entering the crankshaft area. Honing should be done by moving the rotating hone up and down in the cylinder fast enough to produce a crosshatch pattern on the walls similar to the pattern in Fig. 8. Place the hone in the cylinder and expand the stones until the assembly can just be turned by hand. Connect a ½″ electric drill to the hone and drive at drill speed while moving the hone up and down the entire length of the cylinder until the hone begins to run free. During this operation a liberal amount of kerosene, or other suitable cutting fluid, should be used to keep the stones clean. Move the hone up and down slowly with the first-cut rough stones, but more rapidly with the finish-cut fine stones. The final bore finish should show very fine and uniform scratches in a cross-hatch pattern having approximately a 45° to 60° included angle.

Expand the stones against the cylinder walls and repeat the honing operation until the desired bore diameter is obtained. The cylinder should be cleaned occasionally during the honing operation and the piston selected for that cylinder checked for the correct fit. **Allow the cylinder to cool and be sure it is clean and dry before the piston fit is checked.**

Fig. 8. A cross-hatch pattern on a correctly-honed cylinder wall.

Mark each piston, after the correct fit has been obtained, to correspond with the cylinder to which it has been fitted. **Handle the pistons with care and do not attempt to force them into the cylinder.** Using force may permanently distort some types of pistons, making them unfit for use.

After the honing is completed, all abrasives must be removed from the engine parts. Hot water and soap is recommended to clean the cylinder walls. Scrub well with a stiff bristle brush, rinse with hot water, and dry thoroughly. The cylinder bores can be considered clean when they can be wiped with a white cloth without any dirt or particles appearing on the cloth. If any of the abrasive material is allowed to remain on the cylinder walls, it will rapidly wear the new rings and cylinder bores in addition to the bearings that are lubricated with the contaminated oil. The cylinder walls should be swabbed several times with light engine oil and a clean cloth and then wiped with a clean dry cloth. **The cylinders should not be cleaned with gasoline or kerosene.** Remove all abrasive material from other parts of the engine block.

Piston Fitting

The fit of each piston can be checked in the following manner:

1. Invert the piston (skirt end up) and insert in the top of the cylinder with a ½"-wide feeler ribbon of the recommended gauge between the piston and the cylinder wall. The gauge should be positioned on the side of the piston 90° from the wrist-pin holes, and connected to a spring scale.

   CAUTION: Handle the pistons with care and do not attempt to force them into the cylinder. Unless the cylinder has been bored or honed to the correct size, the pistons may be distorted and permanently damaged by careless handling.

2. Insert the feeler ribbon and inverted piston into the cylinder so that the center of the wrist-pin hole is flush with the top of the cylinder block. See Fig. 9. Keep the feeler ribbon straight up and down and keep the wrist-pin hole parallel with the crankshaft axis.

3. Pull the feeler ribbon straight up and out from between the piston and cylinder wall, noting the amount of pull registered on the spring scale necessary to remove the ribbon.

   NOTE: The thickness of the ribbon and the recommended pull necessary to remove it depends on the car manu-

USE .0015 FEELER STRIP

Fig. 9. Checking the fit of a piston.

facturer's specifications. The ribbon is usually 0.0015″ thick and the pull required varies from around 7 to 18 lbs. Check the specifications for the correct figure.

4. If the scale reading is greater than the maximum pull specified, try another piston or lightly hone the cylinder to obtain the proper fit.

5. If the scale reading is less than the minimum pull specified,

try another piston, or if standard size, try a standard high-limit piston if available. If the proper fit cannot be obtained, the cylinder must be rebored to the next oversize piston size.

6. Mark each piston, after fitting, to correspond with the cylinder to which it has been fitted.

PISTON RINGS

If new piston rings are installed without reboring the cylinders, the glaze on the cylinder walls should be removed. This is accomplished by using very fine stones in a hone and honing the walls very lightly. Be sure to remove all abrasives from the cylinder after this operation.

Select rings comparable in size to the piston being used. For example, use standard-size rings with standard-size pistons; use 0.010″ oversize rings with 0.010″ oversize pistons, etc. The rings must be checked for the correct clearance in the piston grooves and for the correct gap. The cylinders and piston grooves must be clean, dry, and free of carbon and burrs.

Nearly all cars, especially late models, use a three-ring piston. The two top rings are compression rings and the bottom ring is an oil-control ring. This oil ring is usually an assembly of three or four separate parts—a top and bottom rail, a spacer, and often an expander. A set of typical piston rings is shown in Fig. 10.

The clearance of the rings in the piston grooves may be checked as shown in Fig. 11. The gauge should be inserted between the ring and its lower land, because any wear that has taken place will form a step at the inner portion of the lower land. If a relatively high step has been worn in the land, the piston should be discarded; installing new rings will be unsatisfactory because of excessive ring clearance. Rings are not available in oversize widths to compensate for ring-groove wear. The specified thickness of

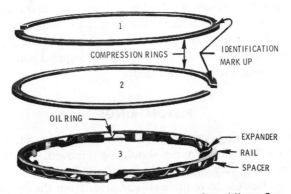

COMPRESSION RINGS

IDENTIFICATION MARK UP

OIL RING

EXPANDER
RAIL
SPACER

Courtesy Buick Motor Div., General Motors Corp.

Fig. 10. A set of typical piston rings.

feeler gauge (usually 0.0015 to 0.003 inch for compression rings and 0.001 to 0.009 inch for oil rings) should slide freely around the entire ring circumference without binding.

The ring gap can be checked as shown in Fig. 12. Place the ring in the cylinder and, using the head of an inverted piston, press the ring down into the cylinder approximately 2 inches. Using the inverted piston insures that the ring will be square with the cylinder.

Fig. 11. Checking piston-ring clearance.

Measure the gap between the ends of the ring with a feeler gauge. The gap should be from 0.010 to 0.015 inch on most cars. (Check the specifications for the correct gap.) If the gap is too wide, try another ring set. If the gap is too narrow, carefully file the ends of the ring until the correct gap is obtained.

It is important that each ring be fitted to its individual piston and cylinder. Clearly mark each ring set so that it will be installed in the proper cylinder. The oil ring should be installed first, following the specific instructions given on the package. The middle compression ring is installed on the piston next, followed by the top compression ring. A piston-ring expander should be used to install each ring with the identification mark on the ring toward the top of the piston.

Before installing the pistons in the cylinders, position the gaps in the two compression rings so they are staggered and so that neither gap is in line with the gap in the oil ring. In addition, the gaps in the oil ring rails should be positioned so that they are not in line with each other or with the gap in the spacer. At least 1″ should separate the gaps.

Fig. 12. Checking piston-ring gap.

To install the piston ring and assembly in the cylinder, a ring-compression tool, such as the one in Fig. 13, should be used. Lightly coat the pistons, rings, and cylinder walls with light engine oil. Install each piston in its respective cylinder with the identifying

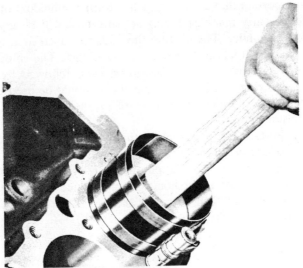

Fig. 13. Using a ring-compressor to install a piston assembly.

mark on the top of the piston toward the front of the engine. Push the piston through the ring compressor and into the cylinder by means of a wooden hammer handle placed in the center of the piston face. **Do not pound the piston into place. Use a steady push.**

Be sure to install the pistons in the same cylinders for which they were fitted. Carefully guide the connecting-rod bearing into place on the crankshaft journal to avoid damage to the journal.

Install the connecting-rod bearing caps and tighten to the specified torque.

IMPORTANT: After installation of new pistons and rings, care should be taken in starting and running the engine for the first hour. Avoid high speeds until the parts have had a reasonable amount of break-in time so that scuffing or scoring will not occur.

CHAPTER 21

Crankshafts
and Connecting Rods

The crankshaft and connecting rods transform the reciprocating motion of the pistons into the rotary motion necessary to drive the car. These parts are subjected to extreme stresses and strains, which means they must be constructed of special materials and with great precision if they are to perform satisfactorily.

CRANKSHAFTS

The crankshaft is cast or forged from a special alloy, after which its bearing surfaces are machined. A final grinding operation finishes the crankshaft to the close tolerances necessary in the modern automobile. The unit is then carefully balanced to prevent vibration at high engine speeds.

Replacement of the crankshaft or any of its bearings calls for the same precision as the original installation if satisfactory operation is to be expected.

Main Bearings

The crankshaft rotates in main bearings located at both ends and at certain intermediate points. The main bearings are supported by webs in the lower part of the engine block. The number of main bearings may vary between different makes and models of cars. Usually, however, 6-cylinder in-line engines (Fig. 1) will have four main bearings while 8-cylinder V-type engines (Fig. 2) will have five.

Notice in Figs. 1 and 2 that one of the main-bearing inserts has a lip and is marked thrust bearing. The purpose of this bearing is to take the end thrust of the crankshaft. This thrust bearing is usually the 3rd main bearing back from the front of the engine.

All modern engines in domestic automobiles use bearing inserts in the main-bearing assemblies. Most manufacturers use a steel shell insert lined with babbit, although some late-model cars use other material, such as aluminum. One half of the shell fits into the bearing cap and the other half into a fixed recess in the lower part of the cylinder block. This type of shell insert has the advantage of being easily replaced (often without removing the crankshaft on certain cars) and does not require scraping and fitting. Its main disadvantage is that it cannot be line-bored or reamed to compensate for a warped crankshaft or block.

Notice that one-half of each bearing insert set is channeled to allow oil under pressure to enter from holes drilled in the crankshaft. In this way, the bearing is constantly supplied with oil to keep it lubricated.

Bearing Failure

Failure of the main-bearing inserts may be due to any one of a number of causes. The appearance of the defective insert will often provide the clue to the cause of failure. Fig. 3 shows the

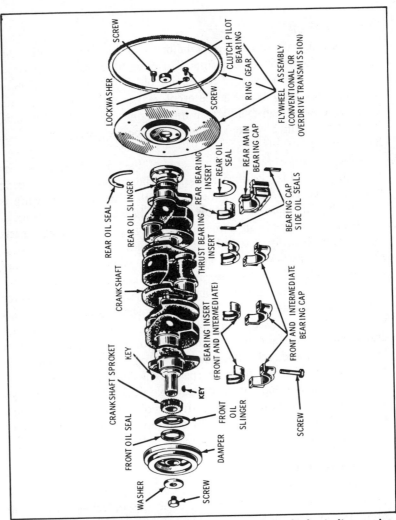

Fig. 1. Crankshaft and related parts of a typical 6-cylinder in-line engine.

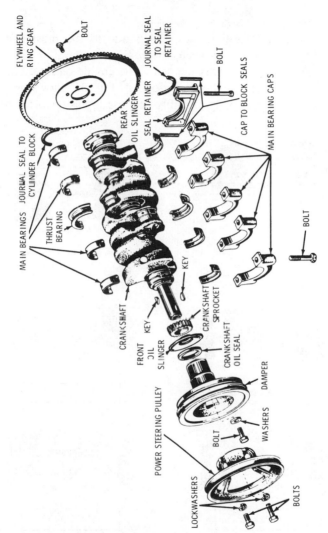

Fig. 2. Crankshaft and related parts of a typical 8-cylinder V-type engine.

appearance of inserts that have failed due to the most common causes. Fig. 3A shows the results of abrasive material or dirt in the oil. Fig. 3B shows what may happen if the engine oil level becomes to low or if oil passages become clogged. Fig. 3C shows an insert that was seated improperly, possibly because it was distorted before

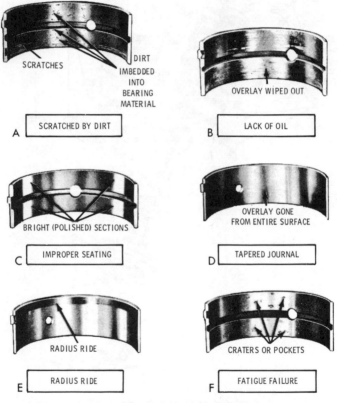

SCRATCHES
DIRT IMBEDDED INTO BEARING MATERIAL
A — SCRATCHED BY DIRT

OVERLAY WIPED OUT
B — LACK OF OIL

BRIGHT (POLISHED) SECTIONS
C — IMPROPER SEATING

OVERLAY GONE FROM ENTIRE SURFACE
D — TAPERED JOURNAL

RADIUS RIDE
E — RADIUS RIDE

CRATERS OR POCKETS
F — FATIGUE FAILURE

Fig. 3. Typical bearing failures.

installation or because dirt was present between it and the bearing seat. A tapered or out-of-round journal might cause the overlay material to be wiped out from the entire insert surface, as in Fig. 3D. An improperly ground journal might result in the type of failure shown in Fig. 3E. Fig. 3F shows what may happen when the bearing material becomes fatigued. This may be caused by defective material, sustained high-speed driving, continual engine overload, etc.

Any of the above conditions requires replacement of the defective inserts and correction of the fault that caused the failure. Sound judgment and proper inspections are necessary when evaluating bearing failure. Clean and inspect each bearing insert carefully. Remove any gum or varnish from the insert with a suitable solvent; do not remove by scraping. Clean and inspect the respective main-bearing journals on the crankshaft for cracks, scratches, grooves, or score marks. Dress any minor imperfections with a fine oil stone. If the journal is damaged, has a taper, or is out-of-round, it will have to be ground to size for the next undersize bearing.

Bearing Clearance

The clearance of main (and connecting-rod) bearings can be accurately checked by using *Plastigage*. This material consists of a wax-like plastic which compresses evenly between the bearing and journal surfaces without damaging either surface. *Plastigage* is manufactured by Perfect Circle Corporation and is available from most parts supplier's and car manufacturer's warehouse. *Plastigage* is manufactured in a variety of ranges, with type PG-1 (green) being the proper type for measuring the clearance of most main bearings.

To measure the clearance of a bearing, remove the cap and clean all oil from the bearing and journal surfaces (*Plastigage* is soluble in oil). Make sure all other main bearings are tightened to their specified torque. (If the engine is in the car, support the crankshaft with a jack to prevent its weight from giving an improper clearance reading.) Place a piece of *Plastigage* lengthwise along the bottom center of the bearing cap, as shown in Fig. 4. Install the bearing cap and tighten to the specified torque. DO NOT TURN THE CRANKSHAFT WITH THE *PLASTIGAGE* IN THE BEARING.

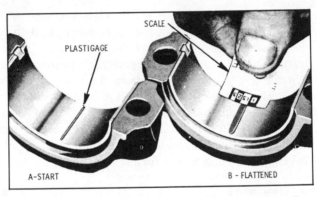

Courtesy Buick Motor Div., General Motors Corp.

Fig. 4. Checking bearing clearance with Plastigage.

Remove the bearing cap; the *Plastigage* will be found adhering to either the bearing shell or the crankshaft journal. Do not remove it. Measure the flattened *Plastigage* with the scale printed on the *Plastigage* envelope. The number within the graduation which most closely corresponds to the width of the flattened *Plastigage* indicates the bearing clearance in thousandths of an inch. The measurement in Fig. 4 indicates a clearance of 0.0015". If the bearing is not within the specified clearance, it should be replaced.

Measure the *Plastigage* at its widest point for the minimum clearance and at its narrowest point for the maximum clearance. If the

Plastigage tapers toward the middle or ends, a difference in clearance exists, indicating a tapered condition, a low spot, or other irregularity of the bearing or journal. If the difference in clearance is 0.001" or more, consideration to grinding the journal and installing undersize bearing inserts should be given. If no taper or out-of-round condition exists, and the clearance is not over 0.003" to 0.004", or under 0.001", the bearing fit is usually considered to be satisfactory. Consult the manufacturer's specifications for the recommended clearance limits.

Bearing Replacement

The main bearings on most cars can be replaced without removing the crankshaft. Special insert removal and installer tools are available to remove and install the upper inserts. Such a tool is shown in Fig. 5. The upper inserts are removed by placing the

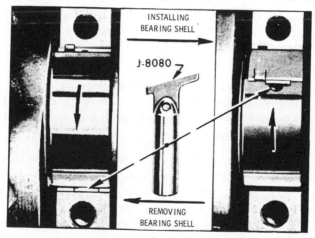

Courtesy Buick Motor Div., General Motors Corp.

Fig. 5. A main-bearing insert removal and installer tool used on certain models of Buick cars.

tool in the crankshaft journal oil hole and rotating the crankshaft in the proper direction. This causes the tang on the tool to engage the bearing insert and rotate it out of its seat. Care must be taken when removing inserts on the front and rear bearings to prevent the oil seal from also rotating out of position. Replace one bearing insert at a time, leaving the other bearings securely fastened.

When the inserts are installed, the ends extend slightly beyond the parting surfaces. This is normal in order that the inserts will be clamped tightly in place to insure positive seating and to prevent their turning. **The ends of the inserts must never be filed to bring them flush with the parting surfaces.**

Before installing the new bearing inserts, make sure the crankshaft journal and the bearing seats in the crankcase and cap are clean. Coat the inside surface of the upper bearing insert with engine oil and place it against the crankshaft journal so that any tang that is present will engage the notch in the crankcase when the insert is rotated into place. Rotate the insert into place as far as possible by hand. Use the installer tool (Fig. 5) to complete the installation.

> **NOTE: The bearing insert should slide into place with very little pressure. If heavy pressure is required, the insert was not started squarely and will be distorted if forced into position.**

Place the lower bearing insert in the cap and check the clearance with *Plastigage* as previously described. The clearance should be between 0.005″ and 0.0025″ for most cars. If the clearance is greater than this, try the next undersize inserts, and check again with *Plastigage*. When the proper size insert has been determined, clean out all *Plastigage*, oil the insert, and reinstall the bearing cap. Tighten the cap bolts to the specified torque. **Under no circumstances should the ends of the bearing caps be filed to** adjust for wear in old inserts or to obtain the proper clearance of new inserts. Neither do most car makers recommend shims to obtain proper clearance.

If a thrust bearing has been disturbed or replaced, it is necessary to align the thrust surfaces of the inserts before the cap bolts are tightened. This is done on most cars by moving the crankshaft fore and aft the limit of its travel several times with the cap bolts finger-tight. The end play of the crankshaft should be checked with a feeler gauge between the thrust bearing and its mating surface on the crankshaft. If outside the specified limits (usually from 0.002″ to 0.010″), a new thrust bearing should be installed.

Oil Seals

Seals are pressed into grooves in the crankcase and rear bearing cap to seal against leakage of oil around the crankshaft. These

Fig. 6. Typical rear-bearing oil seals.

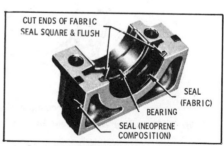

Courtesy Buick Motor Div., General Motors Corp.

seals can be replaced in some cars without removing the crankshaft but not in others.

Fig. 6 shows typical rear bearing oil seals. These are used on 1965 Buicks and consist of a braided fabric inner seal and neoprene composition side seals. Other makes and models may use other materials and different shape seals, but all are similar.

The seals are pressed into their grooves with a smooth object, such as a hammer handle or with an oil-seal installing tool (Fig. 7). The seal is placed in position and that portion trimmed off that protrudes above the cap.

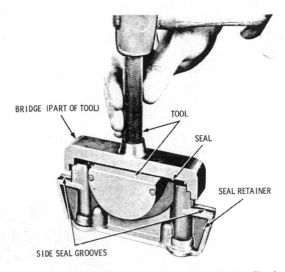

Courtesy Chrysler-Plymouth Div., Chrysler Motors Corp.

Fig. 7. Installing an oil seal in a 1964 Plymouth rear-bearing cap.

Neoprene composition seals swell in the presence of oil and heat. Thus, they are undersize when first installed and may even leak for a short time until they have had time to swell and seal the opening.

CAUTION: The engine must be operated at a slow speed for a short time after braided-type seals have been installed.

CONNECTING RODS

The same general procedure is used in replacing rod bearings as for main bearings. The same type of bearing failure can occur and the same general procedure for checking bearing clearance is used.

A bent or twisted rod may cause bearing damage and eventual failure. In addition, piston and ring wear will almost surely take

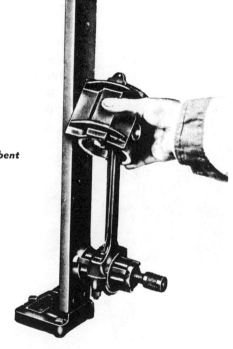

Fig. 8. A tool for detecting a bent or twisted connecting rod.

Courtesy American Motors Corp.

place, resulting in excessive oil consumption. Therefore, if such a condition is indicated or suspected, the rod should be checked. Fig. 8 shows a connecting rod being checked. The instructions that accompany the tool should be carefully followed.

To replace or inspect a connecting-rod bearing, turn the crankshaft until the bearing is at the bottom of its travel. The cap bolts are easily reached in this position. Follow the procedure described for main bearings to inspect, replace, and measure clearances. Remove only one cap at a time and replace it before continuing to the next one. **Never interchange the caps or connecting rods.**

After new bearing inserts have been installed, it should be possible to move the rod freely endways on the crankshaft journal, as allowed by the side clearance. If the rod cannot be moved,

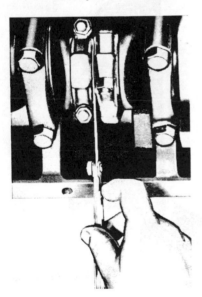

Fig. 9. Checking connecting-rod side clearance.

either the bearing is too much undersize or the rod is bent or twisted.

Side clearance of the connecting rods should be checked with a feeler gauge, as shown in Fig. 9. The clearance in V8 engines, where two connecting rods share the same journal, is measured between the two rods. On 6-cylinder engines, the clearance is measured between the connecting rod and shoulder on the crankshaft. The allowable clearance varies between different makes and models but is usually somewhere between 0.005″ to 0.030″.

CHAPTER 22

Camshafts

The main purpose of the camshaft is to open and close the intake and exhaust valves at the correct time to provide efficient engine operation. In addition, other cams and gears may be included to operate the fuel pump and distributor. The camshaft is always rotated at one-half the speed of the crankshaft, either by means of a pair of meshing gears or by two sprockets and a chain.

The camshaft has a cam lobe for each valve. As the camshaft rotates, the lobes move up under push rods or tappets that cause the respective valves to open. When the cam lobes rotate from under the push rods or tappets, valve springs return the valves to their original closed position.

CONSTRUCTION FEATURES

The general construction features of all camshafts are similar, regardless of whether they are designed for 6-cylinder in-line engines or for V8 engines. The number and location of the cams and any gears they might have may be different, but the general appearance and material will be very similar.

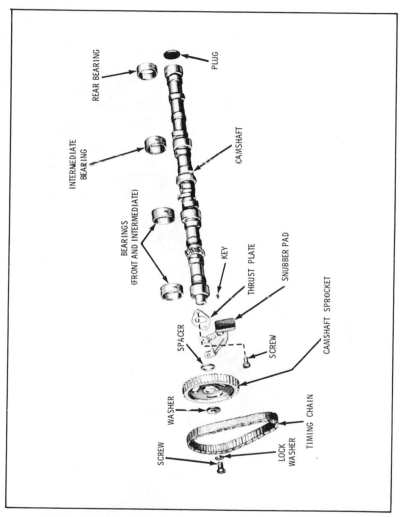

Fig. 1. A typical camshaft used on a 1964 6-cylinder Ford.

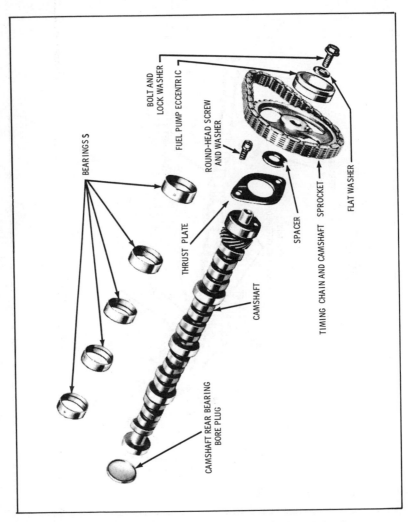

Fig. 2. A typical camshaft used on a 1964 V8 Ford.

BOLT AND LOCK WASHER

FUEL PUMP ECCENTRIC

ROUND-HEAD SCREW AND WASHER

BEARINGS S

THRUST PLATE

SPACER

TIMING CHAIN AND CAMSHAFT SPROCKET

FLAT WASHER

CAMSHAFT

CAMSHAFT REAR BEARING BORE PLUG

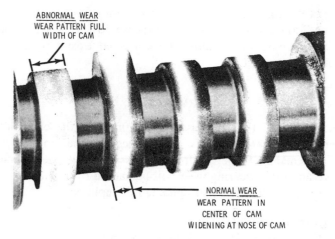

ABNORMAL WEAR
WEAR PATTERN FULL
WIDTH OF CAM

NORMAL WEAR
WEAR PATTERN IN
CENTER OF CAM
WIDENING AT NOSE OF CAM

Courtesy Oldsmobile Div., General Motors Corp.

Fig. 3. Examples of normal and abnormal cam-lobe wear.

Fig. 1 shows a camshaft used in a 6-cylinder engine, while Fig. 2 shows one for a V8. The principle difference between the two units is the number of bearing surfaces (4 for the 6-cylinder and 5 for the V8) and the number of cams (12 for the 6-cylinder and 16 for the V8). Even though camshafts may appear to be the same, they are seldom interchangeable from model to model and often not even from year to year in the same model. The reason for this is the many variables such as bearing journal diameters, cam lift and spacing, length of shaft, etc.

The journals and cams are precision ground and specially treated to produce a tough, wear-resistant surface. The shape and size of the cam lobes are critical and any appreciable wear that changes either of these factors will result in poor engine performance. Typical normal and abnormal wear patterns of cam lobes are shown in Fig. 3. Excessive wear of the cam will cause late opening of the valve and a decrease in the amount of total lift. The latter condition can normally be compensated for by adjustment, but a late-opening valve cannot be corrected except by replacement of the camshaft.

SERVICING

The most usual type of service performed on the camshaft is replacement of bearing inserts. Cam lobes may become so worn that replacement of the shaft is necessary, and, occasionally, excessive and rapid bearing wear will be caused by a camshaft that is bent, requiring that it be straightened or replaced.

Bearing Replacement

Most camshaft bearings are of the steel-backed, babbit-lined, insert variety. Replacement of these units requires the removal of the camshaft. The removal procedure differs somewhat depending on the make and model of engine, but certain steps must be taken regardless of make or model.

The camshaft on most cars can be removed with the engine in the car provided the grille, radiator, fan, etc., are removed. On some cars, however, the engine must be removed before it is possible to extract the camshaft.

The camshaft is usually supported by 4 steel-backed, babbit-lined bearings in 6-cylinder engines, and 5 bearings in V8 engines. These bearings are pressed into the block and may or may not be line-reamed, depending on the make and model. The bearings on most camshafts are step-bored, being larger at the front bearing than at the back. This feature permits easier removal and replacement of the camshaft. A few cars, however, use the same size bearings throughout. Drilled galleries in the engine block supply oil under pressure to lubricate the camshaft bearings. It is therefore important that the oil hole in each bearing insert is lined up with the drilled hole in the block.

Camshaft Removal—The following steps should be followed to remove the camshaft (with engine out of the car).

1. Remove the cover from the timing chain and sprockets.
2. Remove the timing chain and sprockets, using the proper tools and procedure as recommended by the car manufacturer.
3. Remove the valve cover or covers.
4. Remove the valve push rods in sequence and place them in order in a rack so that they can be installed in their original positions.
5. Remove the hydraulic valve lifters or valve tappets through the push-rod openings, using a magnet or special tool if required. Place the tappets or lifters in a rack in the correct order so they can be installed in their original positions.
6. Remove the distributor and shaft from the engine, following the procedure of the manufacturer.
7. Remove the oil pump and shaft, if driven directly from the camshaft.
8. Remove the fuel pump and push rod if driven by an eccentric on the camshaft.
9. Remove the camshaft thrust plate and spacer, if so equipped.
10. Carefully remove the camshaft by pulling it toward the front of the engine. *Use caution to avoid damaging the camshaft bearings, especially on those cars in which the bearing diameters are all the same.*

Inspection—Inspect the camshaft for scored or worn bearings. Bearing wear can be checked with inside and outside micrometers. Most manufacturers specify a maximum limit of from 0.004″ to 0.006″ before bearing replacement is necessary. If only one exceeds the limit, all bearings should be replaced.

The camshaft journals should be checked for an out-of-round condition. If the journals are more than 0.001″ out-of-round, either the camshaft should be replaced or the journals reground to a smaller diameter. (NOTE: Undersize bearings are available for some cars but not for others.)

The camshaft should also be checked for alignment, especially if excessive bearing wear is evident. This is best done by the use of V-blocks and a dial indicator, as shown in Fig. 4. If the camshaft is more than 0.002″ out of true, as read on the dial indicator as the camshaft is rotated, the camshaft should be straightened or replaced. **Use care in attempting to straighten the camshaft as it can be broken easily.**

Fig. 4. Checking camshaft alignment.

Bearing Removal—If it is found necessary to replace the bearings, the following procedure is suggested for use on most cars:

1. Remove the crankshaft, if necessary.
2. Drive out the bore or expansion plug, in line with the camshaft and located at the rear of the engine block.
3. Remove the camshaft bearings using the special tool available for the particular engine being serviced.
4. Position the new bearings at the bearing bores such that the oil holes will align when the bearings are pressed into place.

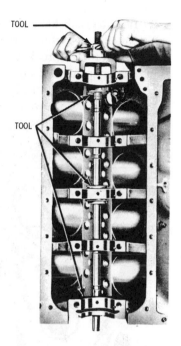

Fig. 5. Installing camshaft bearings in a 1964 V8 Ford engine, using special tools.

5. Use the special tool (Fig. 5) to press the bearings into place. Follow the correct sequence as specified by the manufacture. Also make sure the correct size bearing (for taper-bored camshafts) is pressed into the correct bore.

6. Line-bore and ream the new bearings in engines requiring this operation.

7. Clean the rear expansion-plug recess thoroughly. Coat a new plug with oil-resistant sealer and install the plug with the flange facing out.

8. Coat the camshaft with engine oil and install, using caution not to damage the bearing surfaces.

9. Install crankshaft (if removed) and other parts (flywheel, clutch housing etc.) that may have been removed.
10. Position the sprockets and timing chain (or timing gears) on the camshaft and crankshaft (Fig. 6). Make sure the timing marks are positioned correctly, as specified by the manufacturer. Fig. 7 shows the correct alignment for most cars using

Fig. 6. Installing timing chain and sprockets.

a timing chain. An exception to this is shown in Fig. 8 for a 6-cylinder 1964 Ford. Here, the number of chain pins between timing marks determines the correct position of the sprockets. Fig. 9 shows the correct alignment of timing marks when timing gears are used instead of sprockets and a timing chain.
11. Position the No. 1 piston on TDC after the compression stroke. Position the distributor and shaft in the block with the rotor at the No. 1 firing position and the breaker points open. Secure the distributor in place.

12. Install the oil pump and shaft. Follow the manufacturer's procedure for priming the pump. This varies, but requires either filling the pump with engine oil or packing it with a special lubricant before final assembly.

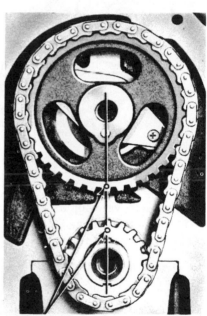

Fig. 7. Correct alignment of timing marks.

TIMING MARKS

13. Install fuel pump and push rod.
14. Install valve tappets (or hydraulic lifters) and valve push rods in their correct former positions. Perform any valve adjustment necessary.
15. Replace the rocker-arm covers, using a new gasket.

589

CAMSHAFT SPROCKET
TIMING MARK

12 PINS BETWEEN
MARKS

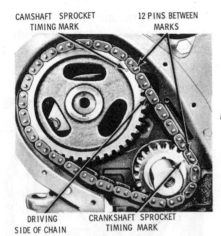

*Fig. 8. Timing mark alignment on
a 1964 6-cylinder Ford.*

DRIVING
SIDE OF CHAIN

CRANKSHAFT SPROCKET
TIMING MARK

HYDRAULIC VALVE LIFTERS

Hydraulic valve lifters are used in most overhead-valve engines. These lifters ride on the cams of the camshaft and, along with solid one-piece push rods, operate the rocker arms and valves.

*Fig. 9. Example of timing mark
alignment on cars using timing
gears.*

TIMING MARKS

On most cars, this system requires no lash adjustment at the time of assembly or in service; therefore, no adjusting studs or screws are provided in the valve train.

The normal function of the hydraulic lifter is that of a cam follower. However, each lifter also serves as an automatic adjuster which maintains zero lash in the valve operating linkage under all operating conditions. In addition, the hydraulic lifter provides a cushion of oil to absorb operating shocks, thus promoting quiet valve operation. Periodic valve adjustment to compensate for wear of parts is completely eliminated.

The hydraulic lifters for the different makes and models of cars may vary slightly in construction features (Fig. 10), but the operating principles are virtually the same for all.

Operating Principles

The hydraulic lifter action on the camshaft is shown in Fig. 11. As shown, all parts of the lifter are housed in the main body, which is the cam follower. During manufacture, the body and plunger are machined to very close limits, with the plunger selectively fitted to each body to insure free movement with a minimum of clearance. The push-rod seat moves with the plunger and has a spherical seat to accept the end of the push rod.

The plunger is forced toward the upper end of the lifter body by a coil spring which also holds a check ball (or valve) retainer against the lower end of the plunger. A spring-wire retainer holds all the parts in the body when the push rod is removed from the seat.

When the valve lifter is installed in the engine, the push rod holds the plunger well below the spring-wire retainer ring at all times. In addition, the push rod also causes the entire assembly to press against the camshaft with a load of several pounds (usually from 5 to 10 pounds). This pressure is sufficient to take up all lash

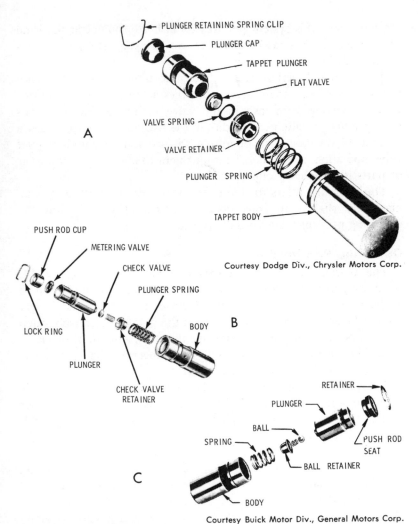

PLUNGER RETAINING SPRING CLIP

PLUNGER CAP

TAPPET PLUNGER

FLAT VALVE

VALVE SPRING

A

VALVE RETAINER

PLUNGER SPRING

TAPPET BODY

Courtesy Dodge Div., Chrysler Motors Corp.

PUSH ROD CUP

METERING VALVE

CHECK VALVE

PLUNGER SPRING

BODY

B

LOCK RING

PLUNGER

CHECK VALVE
RETAINER

RETAINER

PLUNGER

BALL

PUSH ROD
SEAT

SPRING

C

BALL RETAINER

BODY

Courtesy Buick Motor Div., General Motors Corp.

Fig. 10. Hydraulic valve lifters; (A) 63 Dodge; (B) 64 Ford; (C) 65 Buick.

clearances between the parts of the valve linkage without affecting the positive seating of the valve.

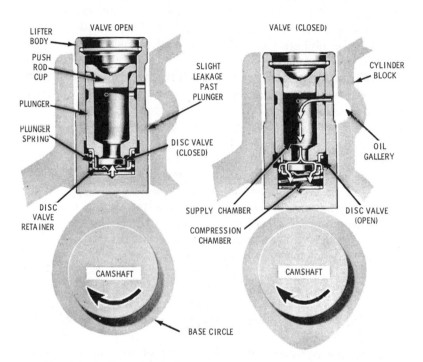

Fig. 11. Action of a hydraulic lifter as the camshaft rotates.

Oil is fed under pressure to all lifters through galleries in the crankcase. The oil enters the lifters through grooves and oil holes in the lifter body and plunger, and flows down into the chamber below the plunger through a feed hole. In the first few moments of operation after the engine starts, all air is forced out and the plunger and lower chamber is completely filled with oil.

At the start of each cycle of valve operation, the lifter body rests on the base circle of the camshaft. In this position, the plunger spring holds all lash clearance out of the valve linkage, and the check ball (or valve) rests on its retainer. Thus, conditions are such that the plunger feed hole is open to permit passage of oil into the lower chamber.

As the camshaft rotates, the cam starts raising the valve lifter body, and the oil in the lower chamber starts flowing up through the feed hole into the plunger. This action causes the ball or valve to seat against the plunger, preventing an appreciable loss of oil from the lower chamber. The lifting force against the body is thus transmitted through the entrapped oil to the check ball or valve and plunger so that the push-rod seat moves upward as a unit to operate the linkage to open the engine valve.

As the camshaft rotates further to close the engine valve, the valve spring forces the linkage and lifter to follow the cam down. When the engine valve seats, the linkage and the lifter plunger stop moving, but the plunger spring now causes the lifter body to follow the cam down. Oil pressure holding the check ball or valve closed ceases when the plunger stops, allowing the ball or valve to drop down against its retainer. This action opens the feed hole in the plunger and permits the passage of oil once again into the lower chamber.

During the opening and closing action of the engine valve, a slight amount of oil escapes from the lower chamber through the clearance between the plunger and the body of the lifter. This oil returns to the crankcase. The slight loss of oil (called *leakdown*) is beneficial because it provides a gradual change of oil in the lifter. The opening of the plunger feed hole at the end of each cycle not only permits replacement of the oil lost from the lower chamber because of leakdown, but also permits control of the amount of oil in the lower chamber. The amount of oil compensates for expansion and contraction of valve linkage parts as the temperature of the engine changes.

When the temperature of the engine (and the oil) increases, the valve linkage parts expand, and the plunger in the lifter must move to a slightly lower position in the body to insure full closing of the engine valve. When the temperature of the engine decreases, the valve linkage parts contract, and the plunger must move to a slightly higher position to maintain zero lash in the valve linkage train.

HYDRAULIC LIFTER TROUBLES

Before disassembling any part of the engine to correct hydraulic lifter noise, check the oil pressure and oil level. The pressure should be within the specified limits (usually from 40 to 60 pounds at 1000 to 2000 rpm). The oil level should never be above the "full" mark on the dipstick, or below the "add oil" mark. Either of these two conditions can be the cause of noisy lifters.

An oil level above the "full" mark may result in the connecting rods dipping into the oil while the engine is running, causing the oil to foam. This foam will enter the lifters causing them to lose length, thus resulting in noisy operation.

Too low an oil level may allow the oil pump to take in air which, when fed to the lifters, again cause them to lose length, resulting in noisy operation. Any air leaks on the intake side of the oil pump will cause the same noisy lifter operation. Lifter noise due to air in the oil may be intermittent or constant, but will usually affect more than one lifter. When the fault has been corrected, the engine should be operated at fast idle for sufficient time to allow all the air in the lifters to bleed out.

The following is a list of noises that may be encountered, their probable cause, and the suggested remedy:

Rapping Noise Only When Engine Is Started—Any lifter that is on a camshaft lobe when the engine is stopped is under pressure of the valve spring. This will cause leakdown or escape of the oil in the lower chamber of the lifter. Thus, when the engine is started, a few seconds may be required to fill the lifter, especially in cold weather when the oil is sluggish. Noise from this source that occurs only occasionally is considered to be normal and requires no correction. If this noise occurs each time the engine starts, check for: (1) Oil too heavy for prevailing temperatures; (2) Excessive varnish in lifter. The remedy here is to: (1) Change to the recommended viscosity of oil for the prevailing temperatures; (2) Remove and clean varnish from valve lifter.

Intermittent Rapping Noise—A lifter noise that comes and goes every few seconds indicates leakage at the check ball or valve seat due to foreign particles, varnish, or defective valve or seat. Recondition the noisy lifters, checking carefully for the presence of grit or metal particles. If such foreign particles are present, a complete change of oil and filter is necessary, along with a thorough flushing of the system to remove the offending material.

Noisy Lifter Operation at Low or Idle Speeds—If one or more lifters are noisy at idle or at speeds up to 25 mph, but quiet at higher speeds, excessive leakdown or faulty check valve or seat is indicated. Faulty lifters may be detected by pushing down with equal pressure on each rocker arm while the engine is idling. Recondition the noisy lifters.

Noisy Lifter Operation at All Speeds—Check for high or low oil level in the crankcase. With the engine idling, strike each rocker arm on the push-rod side several sharp blows with a rawhide mallet. If the noise disappears, it indicates that foreign material was keeping the check valve from seating. Stop the engine and place the suspected lifters on the camshaft base circle (engine valve closed). If any lash clearance exists in any valve linkage, it indicates a stuck lifter plunger, a worn lower end on the lifter body, or a worn camshaft lobe. Recondition or replace the defective lifter or replace the camshaft as necessary.

Noisy Lifter Operation at Normal Engine Temperature Only—If a lifter (or lifters) is noisy only when the engine is at normal operating temperature, excessively fast leakdown or a scored lifter plunger is indicated. Recondition the defective lifter.

Locating a Noisy Valve Lifter

A noisy hydraulic lifter can usually be located by operating the engine at idle speed and placing a finger on the face of each valve spring retainer in turn. If a lifter is not operating properly, a shock will be felt each time the valve seats.

NOTE: Worn valve guides or cocked springs are sometimes mistaken for noisy lifters. If these parts are at fault, the noise may be dampened by applying a side thrust to the valve spring. If this does not appreciably reduce the noise, it can be assumed the lifter is at fault.

Another method of identifying a noisy lifter is by the use of a piece of hose. With the engine idling, place one end of the hose near the end of the valve stem and the other end to your ear. Listen for a metallic click. Repeat this procedure on each intake and exhaust valve until the noisy lifter or lifters have been located.

Valve Lifter Service

The most common causes of hydraulic lifter troubles are dirt, gum, varnish, carbon deposits, and air bubbles. Less common troubles are caused by worn parts. If any of these causes exist (except the presence of air bubbles), it will be necessary to remove the lifter for cleaning, repair, or replacement.

Dirt, gum, and varnish can prevent the check valve (or ball) from seating, causing a loss of hydraulic pressure. The plunger will force oil back through the unseated valve into the plunger chamber during the time the push rod is being lifted. Dirt, gum, or varnish can also cause the plunger to stick or become sluggish, resulting in noisy operation. In the same manner, the body of the lifter may also stick in the bore. This will result in the engine valve remaining open at all times.

When it is necessary to remove one or more lifters, certain precautions should be observed. The following general procedure should be used:

1. Clean all dirt from cylinder heads, rocker-arm and valve-lifter covers, and any adjacent area. *It is of the utmost importance to avoid getting dirt into the hydraulic valve lifters.*

2. Remove the rocker-arm and valve-lifter covers as necessary to gain access to the valve lifters.

3. Remove the valve lifters that require service, following the procedure for the particular make and model of car being repaired.

4. Place the lifters in a wooden block having numbered holes or use another suitable method of identifying them according to their original position in the engine.

5. If less than a full set of lifters is being removed, immediately disassemble and inspect one or two lifters for the presence of dirt, gum, or varnish. If any dirt, gum, or varnish is found, all lifters should be removed for cleaning and inspection; otherwise it is necessary to service only those lifters that are not operating properly.

6. Examine the cam contact surface at the lower end of each

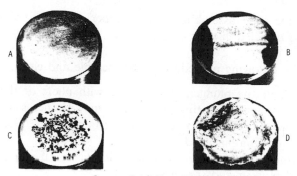

Courtesy Buick Motor Div., General Motors Corp.

Fig. 12. Lifter body wear patterns; (A) Rotating—normal; (B) Not rotating —normal; (C) Galled. Should be replaced; (D) Soft, worn. Should be replaced.

lifter body. If this surface is excessively worn, galled or otherwise damaged, discard the lifter assembly and replace with a new unit. Fig. 12 shows the appearance of the wear patterns on typical lifters. A lifter that has been rotating will have an overall wear pattern as shown in Fig. 12A, while a lifter that has not been rotating will have a pattern similar to the one in Fig. 12B. Either of these two conditions may be considered normal and such bodies may continue to be used. If any lifter shows the condition illustrated in Fig. 12C or D, it should be discarded and the mating camshaft lobe examined for excessive wear or damage.

Disassembly and Cleaning—Observe the utmost cleanliness when disassembling and assembling a hydraulic valve lifter. *Never perform this operation on a dirty workbench.*

NOTE: The internal parts of each hydraulic lifter are matched sets. Do not interchange with parts of other lifters. It is advisable to work on only one lifter at a time to avoid mixing the parts.

Keep the lifter assemblies in the proper sequence so that they can be installed in their original bores.

Use the following procedure to disassemble and clean.

1. Remove the plunger retainer ring with pliers or the special tool designed for this purpose. It may be necessary to depress the plunger to release the retainer ring. This can be done with a push rod.
2. Remove the push-rod cup, metering valve (if so equipped), and plunger and spring assembly.
3. Invert the plunger and spring assembly and remove the check-valve retainer. Next remove the check valve (ball or disc type) and spring.
4. Clean all parts in a suitable solvent that will remove all varnish and carbon.
5. Thoroughly wipe off all parts with a clean lint-free cloth, using a hard wiping action to remove any deposits. Rinse in clean kerosene.
6. Inspect the parts and discard the entire lifter assembly if any part shows signs of pitting, scoring, or galling. Replace the entire assembly if the plunger is not free in the body. The plunger should drop to the bottom of the body by its own weight.
7. Reassemble the lifter if all parts appear to be in good condition.

Checking Leakdown Rate—Any reassembled hydraulic lifter or any unit suspected of being defective should be checked for correct leakdown rate. This is a test of how rapidly or slowly the oil from the lower chamber leaks past the plunger, allowing the plunger to settle toward the bottom of the lifter body. A certain amount of leakage is desirable in order that fresh oil will gradually be supplied to the lifter. Too rapid a leakdown, will result in noisy operation. Check for leakdown as follows:

1. Remove the push-rod cup and completely submerge the lifter in an upright position in clean kerosene, or other liquid that might be recommended by the car manufacturer.
2. Allow the lifter to completely fill with kerosene.
3. Remove the lifter and replace the push-rod cup.
4. Hold the lifter upright and force the plunger down with either a push rod or with special pliers (Fig. 13). If the plunger collapses almost instantly as pressure is applied, disassemble the lifter, clean and test again.
5. If the lifter still does not operate satisfactorily, replace with a new unit.

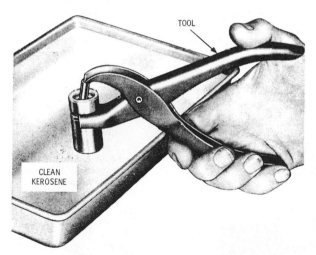

Courtesy Chrysler-Plymouth Div., Chrysler Motors Corp.

Fig. 13. Testing a hydraulic lifter for proper leakdown.

An alternate (and more accurate) test of the leakdown rate can be made by using one of the testers available commercially (Fig. 14). Proceed as follows:

1. Place the hydraulic lifter in the tester with the plunger facing upward. Pour hydraulic testing fluid into the test cup to a level that will cover the lifter assembly. (Fluid for the tester can be purchased from the tester manufacturer. **Do not use kerosene as it will not provide an accurate test.**)
2. Lower the ram on the tester until it rests in the push-rod seat of the lifter. Adjust the length of the ram (if adjustable) until the pointer is in line with the starting mark as the ram contacts the push-rod cup.
3. Pump the tester up and down through the full travel of the lifter plunger to force all air out of the lifter unit. Continue the pumping until considerable resistance is built up in the lifter.

Fig. 14. A commercial tester being used to check the leakdown rate of a hydraulic valve lifter.

4. Raise the weight arm of the tester to allow the lifter to completely fill with fluid, and then allow the ram and weight to force the lifter plunger downward. Measure the exact time it takes for the pointer to travel from the "Start Timing" mark to the "Stop Timing" mark.
5. Compare the time with the specifications of the car manufacturer. Usually, a time of at least 10 seconds but less than 100 seconds indicates a satisfactory leakdown rate.
6. If the leakdown rate is not within specifications, disassemble the lifter and clean and inspect it. Reassemble and test the lifter again. If it still does not meet specifications, replace it with a new lifter. *Always test a new lifter before installing it in the engine.*
7. Bleed all fluid from the lifter before installing it in the engine.

MECHANICAL VALVE LIFTERS

Cars equipped with mechanical valve lifters require periodic adjustment of the valve train mechanism to maintain the correct clearances. This adjustment is usually made on overhead-valve engines by means of an adjusting screw on the rocker arm (Fig. 15). The valve adjustment on an L-head engine is usually made

Fig. 15. Valve clearance adjustment on an overhead-valve engine that is equipped with mechanical lifters.

Courtesy American Motors Corp.

directly below the valve stem by means of an adjustable stud (Fig. 16).

The valve adjustment is usually made with the engine running at normal operating temperature. A feeler gauge of the specified thickness is inserted between the rocker arm and valve stem (overhead-valve engines) or between the adjusting stud and valve stem (L-head engines). The adjusting screw is turned in the proper di-

Fig. 16. Adjusting the valve clearance on an L-head engine equipped with mechanical lifters.

Courtesy American Motors Corp.

rection until the correct clearance is obtained. This will be the point where the feeler gauge is a snug sliding fit during the time the valve is closed. When the correct clearance is obtained, the adjusting screw is locked in place by means of the locking nut provided.

NOTE: *It is very important that the correct valve clearance be maintained. If the clearance is too small, the valve will open early and close late, causing rough engine idle and eventual warping and burning of the valve. If the clearance is too great, the valve will open late and close early, causing valve bounce and possible damage to the camshaft.*

Fig. 17. Using a step-type feeler gauge to adjust valve clearance.

STEP-TYPE FEELER GAUGE

A more accurate valve clearance setting can be made by using a step-type ("go" and "no-go") feeler gauge, as shown in Fig. 17, instead of the common type. For example, if the desired valve

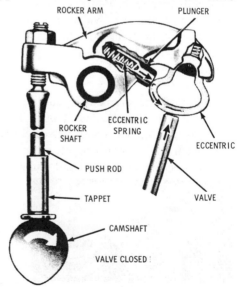

Fig. 18. Silent-lash rocker arm used on some models of Ford cars.

ROCKER ARM

PLUNGER

ROCKER SHAFT

ECCENTRIC SPRING

ECCENTRIC

PUSH ROD

VALVE

TAPPET

CAMSHAFT

VALVE CLOSED

ADJUSTING SCREW   ECCENTRIC

ADJUSTMENT MARK

Fig. 19. Depressing the rocker-arm eccentric.

clearance is 0.017 inch, a step-type gauge of 0.016 inch ("go") and 0.018 inch ("no-go") would be used. The "go" step should enter but the "no-go" step should not when the clearance is 0.017 inch.

Certain models of Ford cars have a zero-lash rocker arm that is used with mechanical lifters. This type of rocker arm, shown in Fig. 18, provides zero valve lash and minimizes valve train noise and wear. Adjustment of the valves differs somewhat when this type of rocker arm is used. The procedure is as follows, with the engine not operating:

1. Rotate the crankshaft until the piston associated with the valve to be adjusted is near TDC at the end of the compression stroke (both valves closed).
2. Push the rocker-arm eccentric toward the rocker arm until the eccentric spring (and plunger) is pushed completely into

PLUNGER

Fig. 20. Correct position of the eccentric.

606

its bore (Fig. 19). Turn the adjusting screw clockwise until the eccentric and plunger are held in that position.

3. Slowly turn the adjusting screw counterclockwise until the adjustment mark on the eccentric is exactly centered over the valve stem (Fig. 20). Tighten the lock nut to lock the adjustment.

4. Repeat the above procedure on all rocker arms, making sure the associated piston is at TDC at the end of the compression stroke.

5. Start the engine and operate it at normal idle speed. Observe the position of the adjustment mark on each eccentric. Make minor adjustments, as necessary, with the engine idling.

CHAPTER 23

Valves

Each cylinder in an automobile engine has two valves—an intake valve to permit the fuel mixture to enter the cylinder, and an exhaust valve to allow the burned gases to escape. The exhaust valve is made of a different material than that used for the intake valve. This is because the exhaust valve must withstand a higher temperature.

When the valves are closed, they must effectively seal the cylinder to prevent the escape of gas. This seal is made possible by the very accurate fit between the valve face and the valve seat. Valve grinding or refacing is necessary from time to time to renew the seal between the valve and its seat. Valve inserts are used in some engines to aid in maintaining a good seal over prolonged periods of time.

The valves are kept in alignment with the valve seats by guides through which the valve stem extends. The valve guides and stems are precision fit to allow the valve stem to move freely up and down without any side play or passage of appreciable lubricant from one end of the guide to the other. The guides may be integral parts of the cylinder block or head, or they may be removable sleeves that can be replaced when worn.

The valves are opened by lobes on the camshaft rotating and applying pressure to the valve stem through the valve train linkage. The valves are closed by the pressure of valve springs that act to move the valve when the camshaft lobes rotate out from under the valve tappets or lifters.

Valve heads and seats are cooled by the transfer of heat to adjacent metal and thence to the water circulating through the engine water jacket.

VALVE ASSEMBLIES

A typical valve assembled and in place is shown in Fig. 1. An exploded view of both an intake and exhaust valve assembly appear in Fig. 2. The particular valves shown indicate the heads are of different diameters. This is true of this particular model of car (1963 Dodge) but is not necessarily true in all makes of cars.

VALVE SEATS

Valve seats are present in an automobile engine to provide a perfect seal with the valves when the valves are closed. Any wear or distortion of either the valve face or the valve seat will destroy this perfect seal and make repair or replacement of these parts necessary.

The valve seats in most engines are an integral part of the engine block or cylinder head, having been machined into either of these units. When this type of seat becomes damaged or excessively worn, it becomes necessary to regrind it to effect a repair. Repeated regrinding will eventually result in the removal of too much metal, in which case the engine block or cylinder head will have to be discarded. This rarely happens, however, if care is taken in the grinding process, and if the valve train clearances are maintained.

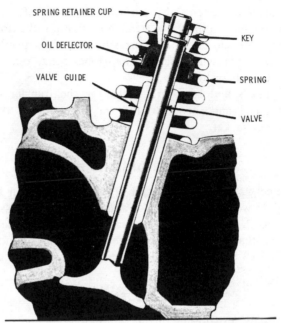

SPRING RETAINER CUP

OIL DEFLECTOR

VALVE GUIDE

KEY

SPRING

VALVE

Courtesy Oldsmobile Div., General Motors Corp.

Fig. 1. An example of a valve assembly in place.

A few cars have valve seat inserts, which means that those seats that cannot be reground to specifications can be removed and new units installed. In many cases it will be found that only the exhaust valve in each cylinder will have a valve seat insert—the intake valve will not.

The angle at which the valve seat is ground, as well as the width of the refinished face, is very important and must be maintained to specifications. Refacing the seat will always result in a greater seat width. This width can be brought back to specifications by removing metal either from the bottom of the seat with a grind-

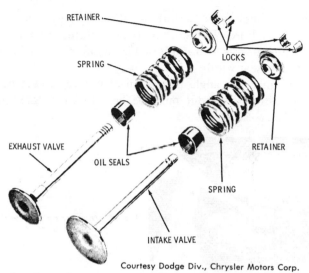

RETAINER

SPRING

LOCKS

EXHAUST VALVE

OIL SEALS

RETAINER

SPRING

INTAKE VALVE

Courtesy Dodge Div., Chrysler Motors Corp.

Fig. 2. Exploded view of an intake and exhaust valve assembly.

ing wheel having a greater angle than the wheel used to grind the face, or from the top of the seat with a wheel having less of an angle than the wheel used to grind the face. Fig. 3 shows the

Fig. 3. Valve-seat refacing.

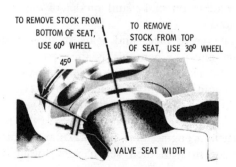

TO REMOVE STOCK FROM BOTTOM OF SEAT, USE 60° WHEEL

TO REMOVE STOCK FROM TOP OF SEAT, USE 30° WHEEL

45°

VALVE SEAT WIDTH

611

recommended angles for performing this operation on the valve seats in a 1964 Ford. **Remember, these angles may be different for other makes and models.** Fig. 4 shows a scale being used to measure the seat width.

Not only must the angle and width of the valve seat be maintained, but also the runout must be held to close tolerances. A

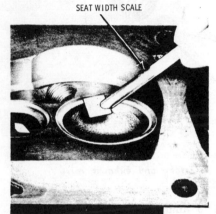

SEAT WIDTH SCALE

Fig. 4. Measuring the width of a valve seat.

special gauge (Fig. 5) is used to check runout. If the reading exceeds the allowable limit (usually from 0.001 to 0.002 inch, depending on make and model of engine), the face must be reground.

The valve faces and seats in most engines are ground at the same angle. When this is the case, the final grinding operation can be accomplished by means of valve-grinding compound. It is becoming more prevalent, however, to reface the valve at a slightly different angle than the valve seat to provide what is known as an *interference fit*. An example of this is shown in Fig. 6. In this particular engine, both the intake and exhaust valves have an interference fit with their seats. Some other cars may have this type of fit only on the exhaust valve. It is obvious that with the different angles between the valve face and seat, grinding compound cannot be used to finish the surfaces. Instead, refacing equipment must be utilized.

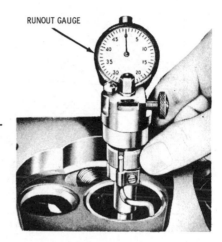

RUNOUT GAUGE

Fig. 5. Checking runout (concentricity) of a valve seat.

When refacing the valve seats, it is important to use the correct size valve-guide pilot for the refacing stones. This will insure a true and complete surface. After the refacing operation, measure the concentricity (runout) of the seat with the proper gauge (see Fig. 5). The total runout should not exceed the allowable limit (usually 0.002 inch).

The overall contact of the valve face with the seat can be checked by lightly coating the valve seat with Prussian blue. Set the valve in place and rotate while applying a light downward pressure. If the blue is transferred to the center or upper half of the valve face (nearest the top of the head), the fit is satisfactory. If the blue is transferred to the extreme top edge, lower the valve seat with a stone of the proper angle (usually 30°). If the blue is transferred to the bottom edge of the valve face, raise the seat by using a stone of the recommended angle (usually 60°). When

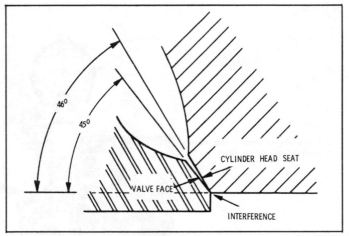

Fig. 6. Relation of valve-face and valve-seat angle in a 1964 Chevelle V8 engine.

the seat is properly positioned, its width must be within the recommended specifications (usually from 3/64 to 3/32 inch).

VALVE GUIDES

Valve guides allow the valves to move up and down and provide accurate positioning of the valve face on the valve seat. The guides may be an integral part of the engine block or head, or may be in the form of inserts.

For those engines in which the guides are an integral part, valves with oversize stems are available when the guides (or valve stems) become excessively worn. For those engines with valve-guide inserts, wear can be corrected by replacement of the guides and/or valves.

When wear either of the valve stem or the guide is suspected, both should be checked. The valve stem diameter can be measured with a micrometer. If the wear exceeds the specifications (usually 0.002 inch), the valve should be replaced.

The valve guide can be checked for wear by means of a gauge such as shown in Fig. 7. With this method, the sleeve (Fig. 7A) places the valve at the correct position to obtain the proper measurement with the dial indicator. The gauge is fastened to the cylinder head and at right angles to the valve stem being measured. Move the valve to and from the indicator. The total reading should not exceed specifications (usually 0.010 to 0.015 inch).

If the valve-guide wear is excessive, the guide should be reamed for a valve with an oversize stem. Select the correct size reamer and slowly turn it by hand in the valve-guide bore. Clean the guide thoroughly before installing the new valve. **Never attempt to ream a valve guide from a standard size directly to the maximum oversize. Instead, ream in steps using successively larger reamers so the guide will be reamed true in relation to the valve seat.**

Valve-guide insert replacement (in cars so equipped) is necessary when the old insert is worn beyond specifications. The insert can be removed and a new one installed by means of special tools and an arbor press, or by special tools and a hammer (for Buicks, shown in Fig. 8). After a new guide has been installed, it must be hand reamed to the correct size.

VALVE SPRINGS

Whenever the valves have been removed for inspection, reconditioning, or replacement, the valve springs should be tested.

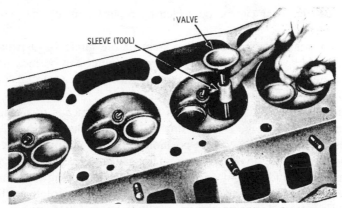

(A) Special sleeve necessary for measuring valve-guide wear.

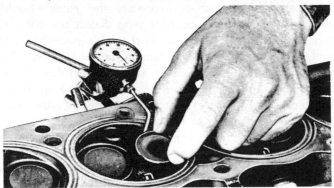

(B) Dial indicator used to check valve-guide wear.
Courtesy Chrysler-Plymouth Div., Chrysler Motors Corp.
Fig. 7. Checking valve-guide wear.

This is often overlooked, but the valve springs play a very important part in proper engine operation. A weak valve spring may cause unsatisfactory seating of the valve, resulting in rough engine idling and possible damage to the valve. A distorted spring or one

DRIVE OLD GUIDE OUT FROM COMBUSTION CHAMBER SIDE

DRIVE NEW GUIDE IN FROM TOP SIDE OF HEAD

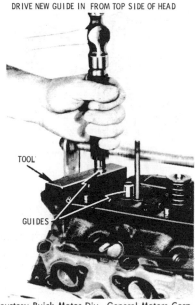

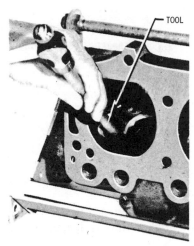

Courtesy Buick Motor Div., General Motors Corp.

Fig. 8. Removing and installing a valve guide in a Buick engine.

with too much tension may cause excessive wear of the camshaft lobes. Therefore, testing the valve springs for correct pressure and squareness should be a part of every valve reconditioning operation.

Valve Spring Pressure

Each valve has only one spring on most cars. There are a few exceptions to this, however, one being certain Buick models that have two—one inside the other. The spring pressure is different for each car, ranging from as low as 70 pounds to as high as 280 pounds. The usual pressure, however, is from 100 to 150 pounds.

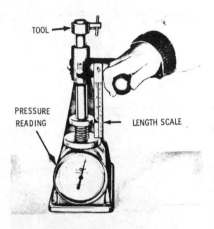

TOOL

PRESSURE
READING

LENGTH SCALE

*Fig. 9. Checking valve-spring
pressure.*

Special tools are available for checking the valve spring pressure,
one type being shown in Fig. 9.

To measure the pressure, the spring is compressed to a specified
length, and the force necessary to hold it at this length is the

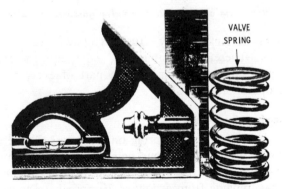

VALVE
SPRING

Courtesy Chrysler-Plymouth Div., Chrysler Motors Corp.

Fig. 10. Checking valve-spring squareness.

valve spring pressure. A reading that varies more than 10 pounds from the specifications indicates the spring should be replaced.

Squareness

The valve spring should also be tested for distortion by using the method shown in Fig. 10. An ordinary machinist's or carpenter's square is placed on a flat surface with the valve spring positioned as shown. The length is measured as the spring is rotated. If the measurements vary by more than 1/16 inch, install a new spring. The overall length of the spring can also be measured with this setup and should agree with the specifications.

Installation

Installation (or removal) of the valve spring requires the use of a compressor tool. These are available in different designs, many

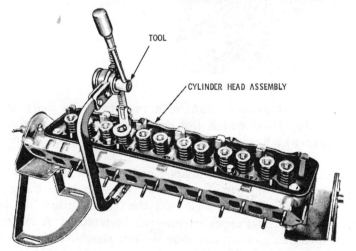

Courtesy Chrysler-Plymouth Div., Chrysler Motors Corp.

Fig. 11. Compressing the valve spring for removal or installation.

of them being made specifically for a particular make and model of engine. A typical tool for this purpose is illustrated in Fig. 11. This type of tool is used when the cylinder head is removed from the engine.

The valve springs can be installed in or removed from most engines with the cylinder head in place. To do this, the spark plug is removed from the cylinder that requires valve spring service and a threaded compressed-air adapter is inserted.

Fig. 12. Using a plier-type spring compressor to remove or install a valve spring.

Courtesy American Motors Corp.

NOTE: This adapter can be made from the body of a spark plug from which the porcelain has been removed and into which an air-hose adapter has been threaded.

Connect an air hose to the adapter and maintain at least 90 lbs. of air pressure in the cylinder while the valve spring is being removed. The air pressure will hold the valve against its seat so the valve lock and upper retainer can be removed. A different type of spring compressor tool than the one shown in Fig. 11 will have to be used with this method. A plier-type tool (Fig. 12) is usually the handiest to use in this case.

UNDERSIDE OF SPRING RETAINER

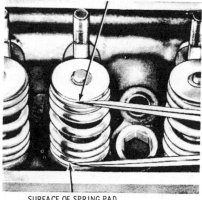

Fig. 13. Measuring the installed height of a valve spring.

SURFACE OF SPRING PAD

New oil seals should always be installed on the valve stems when the valve springs have been removed. In addition, replace any damaged spring shields (if used), or retainers.

Valve Spring Installed Height

The installed height of the valve spring should be checked especially if the valves or seats have been reground. This measurement is made from the top of the spring seat (or shim, if used) to the bottom of the spring retainer (Fig. 13). If the installed height is greater than the specifications, add the necessary number of spacers between the spring and its seat to bring the assembly to the recommended height.

621

CHAPTER 24

Manual Transmissions and Clutches

Manual transmisisons are still preferred by many people and are available for most makes and models of cars being manufactured at present. In addition, most manufacturers can provide either a 3-speed or 4-speed type.

3-SPEED TRANSMISSIONS

All 3-speed transmissions differ very little from the ones that have been used in cars for the past 25 to 30 years. Improvements have naturally been made to keep up with the greater stresses placed upon this part of the automobile by the greater horsepower of the later-model engines. The operating principles, however, have remained practically the same. The shift pattern for the 3-speed units has not changed from that used for years. Progress in the automotive field has seen the gear-shift lever moved from the floor to the side of the steering column and back to the floor. Ford manual transmissions manufactured in recent years have all gears (except reverse) synchronized to permit quicker shifts, reduce gear clash, and to permit down-shifting for better car control. Most other manufacturers synchronize only second and third gears.

Fig. 1. A typical 3-speed transmission.

A typical 3-speed transmission is shown in Fig. 1. This particular unit is available on 1964 Fords and Mercurys.

Operation

All forward-speed shifting is accomplished through the action of synchronizer sleeves (Fig. 2). These sleeves allow all forward-speed gears to be in constant mesh at all times, thus preventing one source of gear clash.

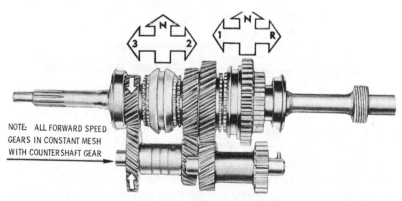

NOTE: ALL FORWARD SPEED GEARS IN CONSTANT MESH WITH COUNTERSHAFT GEAR

Fig. 2. Internal gear arrangement of a typical 3-speed transmission.

623

When the first speed is selected, the shift lever moves the reverse gear and sleeve forward and forces the conical surface of the synchronizer blocking ring against the matching cone on the first gear located on the output shaft. If the car is moving, the internal teeth of the reverse gear and sleeve will not mesh with the first gear until the speed of the first gear is increased or decreased to match the speed of the reverse gear and sleeve which are rotating with the output shaft.

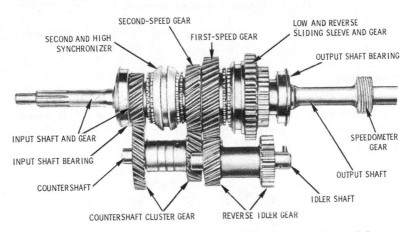

Fig. 3. Power flow in the 3-speed transmission of Figs. 1 and 2.

The reverse gear and sleeve have internal splines that will slide over the teeth on the blocking ring and engage with the external clutch teeth on the first gear when the speed of the two assemblies match. Since first gear is always in mesh with the countershaft cluster gear, the action just described causes the power flow to be from the input shaft (and gear), through the countershaft gear, to the first gear through the reverse gear and sleeve, to the output shaft. See Fig. 3 to follow the power flow.

Selection of second and third gears are similar to first, except a different synchronizer is used. This synchronizer, like the reverse gear and sleeve, is splined to the output shaft.

Those 3-speed transmissions in which first gear is not synchronized usually have only one gear for both first and reverse gears. This single gear is slipped forward or backward along the splined output shaft until it meshes with one or the other of two countergears. Thus, either first or reverse is selected. A system of mechanical interlocks prevents the selection of more than one gear at a time.

Gear Ratios

The ratio between the rotational speed of the input shaft and the output shaft in the transmisison is different for each gear selected. The ratio is determined by the size of the engine, weight of the car, type of differential, size of rear tires, type of service to which the car will be subjected, etc. This means that, for a given make and model of car, the transmisison gear ratios might be different depending on the size of the engine, for example. Cars of different manufacture will also likely have different gear ratios. One ratio, however, that all seem to have in common is that of third speed. Here, the ratio is always 1 to 1.

The ratio for first gear may be as low as 2.25 to 1 to as high as 3.25 to 1. The higher the ratio, the greater the power multiplication, but the lower the speed multiplication. Typical ratios for second gear are from 1.5:1, to 1.85:1. Third gear is always 1:1. Reverse may range all the way from 2.25:1 to 4.15:1.

4-SPEED TRANSMISSIONS

Most cars are now available with 4-speed transmisisons as optional equipment. The four forward speeds and reverse offer the driver more complete control and better performance than the 3-speed units. All 4-speed transmissions have all forward speeds synchronized, permitting downshifting without gear clash or the necessity of double clutching. Reverse gear, of course, is not synchronized.

Fig. 4 shows a typical 4-speed transmission cross section. Power flow in the various gears is shown in Fig. 5.

Operation

The principal of operation for 4-speed transmissions is like that for the 3-speed types except for the fourth gear that has been added. Synchronizing ring and clutch assemblies provide the means for shifting into any forward gear at any speed without gear clash or the necessity for double clutching.

> **NOTE:** Downshifting into first gear above 45 mph, and into second above 65 mph causes extra work for the synchronizers and will require more time and force on the shift lever to complete. *There is danger of overspeeding the engine if first or second gear is used at high car speeds. It is not recommended, therefore, to downshift into first and second at speeds above 45 mph and 65 mph, respectively.*

Gear Ratios

The gear ratios in 4-speed transmissions are closer spaced than in 3-speed units. This provides a better engine-to-car speed ratio with a minimum loss of engine speed at the shift points. Typical ratios in 4-speed units are around 3:1 for first gear, 1.9:1 for second gear, 1.4:1 for third, with direct (1:1) drive in fourth. Reverse gear will always have a ratio the same as or near that of first gear.

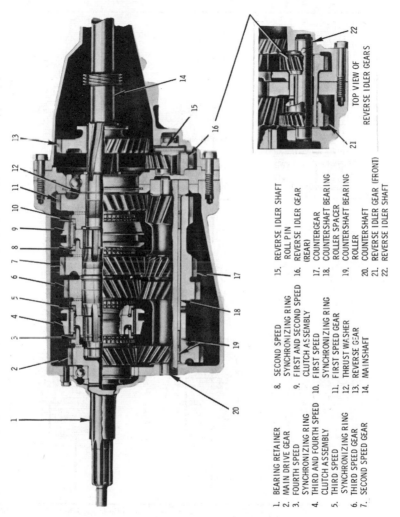

1. BEARING RETAINER
2. MAIN DRIVE GEAR
3. FOURTH SPEED SYNCHRONIZING RING
4. THIRD AND FOURTH SPEED CLUTCH ASSEMBLY
5. THIRD SPEED SYNCHRONIZING RING
6. THIRD SPEED GEAR
7. SECOND SPEED GEAR
8. SECOND SPEED SYNCHRONIZING RING
9. FIRST AND SECOND SPEED CLUTCH ASSEMBLY
10. FIRST SPEED SYNCHRONIZING RING
11. FIRST SPEED GEAR
12. THRUST WASHER
13. REVERSE GEAR
14. MAINSHAFT
15. REVERSE IDLER SHAFT ROLL PIN
16. REVERSE IDLER GEAR (REAR)
17. COUNTERGEAR
18. COUNTERSHAFT BEARING ROLLER SPACER
19. COUNTERSHAFT BEARING ROLLER
20. COUNTERSHAFT
21. REVERSE IDLER GEAR (FRONT)
22. REVERSE IDLER SHAFT

TOP VIEW OF REVERSE IDLER GEARS

Fig. 4. A typical 4-speed transmission.

627

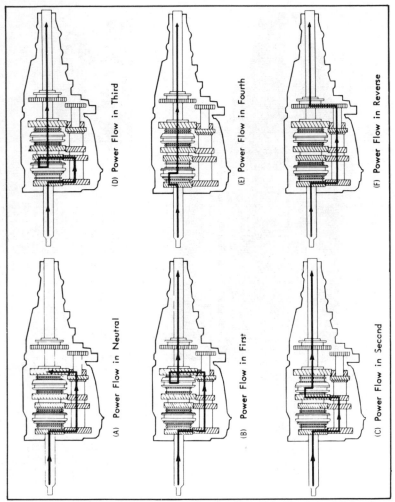

Courtesy Oldsmobile Div., General Motors Corp.

Fig. 5. Power flow in the transmission of Fig. 4.

MANUAL TRANSMISSION SERVICE

Each make of transmission differs somewhat in design and service procedure necessary. Specific repair instructions as outlined in the manufacturer's service manual should therefore be followed when disassembly of the unit is required. Special tools designed for each make are also required, without which service is impossible. The following list may prove helpful, however, in diagnosing trouble in the transmission assembly.

TROUBLE	POSSIBLE CAUSE
Noisy in One or More First Through Third Gear Speeds (4-speed units only)	First, second, and/or third gear worn or damaged. Counter gear worn or damaged. Counter-gear bearings worn or damaged. Synchronizers worn or damaged.
Noisy in All Gear Speeds	Low oil level. Wrong type of oil. Countershaft gear or bearings worn or damaged. Input shaft bearings worn or damaged. Transmission misaligned or loose.
Noisy in High Gear	Synchronizer worn or damaged. Input shaft bearing or gear worn or damaged. Output shaft bearing worn or damaged.

TROUBLE	POSSIBLE CAUSE
Noisy in Reverse	Reverse idler or shaft worn or damaged.
	Reverse sliding gear worn or damaged.
	Shift linkage improperly adjusted.
	Bent, damaged, or loose shift linkage; shift levers, shafts, or forks worn.
Hard Shifting	Clutch improperly adjusted.
	Clutch parts worn or damaged.
	Shift linkage out of adjustment.
	Bent, damaged, or loose shift linkage.
	Shift levers, shafts, or forks worn.
	Incorrect lubricant.
	Synchronizers worn or broken.
Jumping Out of Gear	Shift linkage out of adjustment, worn, or loose.
	Detent mechanism worn, or springs weak or broken.
	Misalignment or loose transmission case or clutch housing.
	Worn input shaft pilot bearing.
	Bent output shaft.
	Worn or broken high-gear synchronizer.

TROUBLE	POSSIBLE CAUSE
	Worn clutch teeth on input shaft and/or on synchronizer sleeve.
	Bent or worn shift fork, lever, or shaft.
	Input shaft bearing retainer loose or broken.
	Shift cover loose or gasket damaged (4-speed only).
Sticks in Gear	Clutch not fully releasing.
	Burred or battered teeth on synchronizer sleeve or input shaft.
	Frozen synchronizer blocking ring on input shaft gear cone.
	Lack of lubrication.
	Improper lubrication.
	Corroded shift levers or shafts.
	Binding input shaft pilot bearing.
Gear Clash When Shifting Into Gear From Neutral (car not in motion)	Clutch not fully releasing.
	Binding input shaft pilot bearing.
	Shifting too soon after clutch is released.

OVERDRIVES

Overdrive units are available as optional equipment on some makes of automobiles if they are equipped with 3-speed transmissions. Essentially, the overdrive unit is a two-speed planetary transmission attached to the rear of the conventional 3-speed transmission. This provides four forward speeds instead of three. In overdrive, the engine speed is approximately 30% lower at a given road speed. This is made possible by the planetary gears which provide a lower overall gear ratio than that obtained in high gear with the conventional transmission. A typical overdrive unit is shown in Fig. 6.

An electrical system controls the operation of the overdrive unit and consists of a solenoid, a relay, a speed-sensitive governor switch, a manual kickdown switch, and the circuit wiring.

Operation

When the overdrive control handle is pushed in, the power flow from the transmission up to a speed of approximately 28 mph is direct (1:1) and free-wheeling (Fig. 6A). This drive is said to be free-wheeling because the overrunning clutch permits the transmission output shaft to drive the overdrive main shaft, but it does not permit the rear wheels to drive the engine.

While the overdrive unit is in the free-wheeling condition, the planetary gearing is in neutral, because the sun gear can run free. It can rotate in either direction or stand still depending on the relative speeds of the planet carrier and the internal ring gear.

At a speed of approximately 28 mph, the solenoid energizes and the pawl is pushed in against the balk ring. However, as long as the engine is driving the car, the overdrive will still not engage. This is because the balk ring is in the position shown in Fig. 7A, and will not allow the pawl to engage. All elements of the planetary gearing are revolving as a unit in a counterclockwise (from the rear) direction which rotates the balk ring against the pawl.

When the driver releases the throttle above the 28-mph speed, the main shaft of the overdrive overruns the output shaft of the

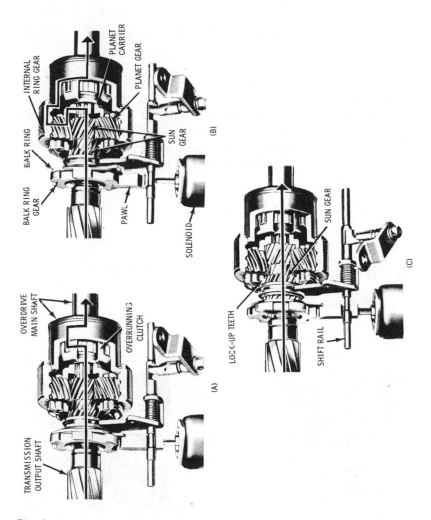

Fig. 6. A typical overdrive unit; (A) Direct (free-wheeling) drive; (B) Overdrive; (C) Lock-out drive.

633

transmission. When this overrun exceeds a ratio of 0.7:1, the sun gear and balk ring reverse direction, allowing the pawl to slide into the slot in the balk ring (Fig. 7B).

In this condition, the power flow is from the output shaft of the transmission to the planet carrier splined to it, through the planet gears, and to the sun gear. With the sun gear held from rotating, the planet gears are forced to "walk around" the sun gear and thus drive the internal ring gear. The transmission will then drive the main shaft of the overdrive unit at a ratio of 0.7:1.

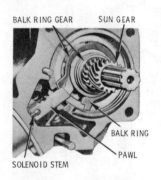

(A) Engine driving.

(B) Pawl engaged.   **(C) Coasting.**

Fig. 7. Pawl and balk ring positions.

The overrunning clutch is uncoupled when in overdrive because the main shaft of the overdrive is turning faster than the output shaft of the transmission. The engine can now drive the rear wheels or the rear wheels can drive the engine. There is no free-wheeling action when in overdrive.

The pawl can be disengaged under two conditions. One is when the car speed drops below approximately 22 mph. At this speed or below, the governor switch opens and de-energizes the solenoid, permitting the return spring to pull the pawl out of the slot in the balk ring. Too, the driver may shift the overdrive back to direct drive at any road speed by pressing the accelerator to the floor, thereby actuating the kickdown switch.

This action opens the circuit to the solenoid, permitting the return spring to exert a pull on the pawl. At the same time, the kickdown grounds the ignition system causing the engine to misfire long enough to permit the pawl to be pulled out of the balk ring. Normal ignition is restored as soon as the pawl moves out of the slot, and the car is now in direct drive. The actual time of ignition interruption is equal to that required for one revolution of the crankshaft.

If the solenoid should energize when the car is coasting up through 28 mph, with the engine idling (such as might occur on a down-hill grade), the sun gear will be rotating clockwise (from the rear) and the balk ring will be in the position shown in Fig. 7C. The pawl cannot engage under this condition. To place the unit in overdrive, it will be necessary to speed the engine up to the point where the sun gear reverses its direction of rotation. The balk ring will then move counterclockwise, allowing the pawl to be forced into the slot.

When the overdrive control handle is pulled out, the car cannot be placed in overdrive at any speed. This lockout is accomplished by the shift rail moving the sun gear into engagement with the lock-up teeth on the planet carrier (Fig. 6C). This locks the planetary gearing as one unit, mechanically connecting the output shaft of the transmission to the main shaft of the overdrive. This action is necessary to drive the car in reverse or when pushing the car to start the engine. Otherwise, the overrunning clutch would prevent power flow through the unit with the elements running backwards or with the rear wheels trying to transmit power to the engine through the drive shaft.

Service

Troubles may originate in either the mechanical portion of the overdrive unit or in the electrical control system. Therefore the control system should always be checked before disassembling the overdrive. Figs. 8, 9, 10, and 11 show the electrical systems of typical overdrive units.

When unsatisfactory overdrive operation is experienced, look for one of the following conditions:

1. Blown fuse in the governor-solenoid circut.
2. Loose terminals on any of the connecting wires.
3. Incorrect terminal locations of connecting wires.
4. Circuits grounded by water, dirt, or worn insulation.
5. Defective contacts in the solenoid.
6. Insufficient travel or defective contacts in the kickdown switch.
7. Excessive end play in the governor shaft.
8. Improper adjustment of the control springs in the governor.
9. Burned contacts in the governor.
10. Damaged governor cap and contacts.
11. Rubber cover over governor damaged or missing, allowing dirt and water to enter governor mechanism.
12. Shift rod misadjusted.

If none of these checks indicate trouble, the unit should be disassembled for inspection and repair. Follow the manufacturer's instructions for the specific unit being serviced.

CLUTCHES

The clutch used in cars with manual transmissions is of the dry-disc type, and consists of the clutch disc, pressure plate, and the clutch release bearing. A typical centrifugal-type clutch assembly is shown in Fig. 12. Certain models of cars use a diaphragm-type clutch similar to the one in Fig. 13. Either type of clutch is actuated by a clutch pedal and a series of mechanical links.

Centrifugal-Type Clutch

With the clutch pedal in the engaged position (not depressed), the clutch disc facings are clamped between the friction surface on

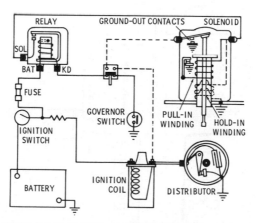

Fig. 8. Diagram of the overdrive electrical system used on 1964 Chevelles.

637

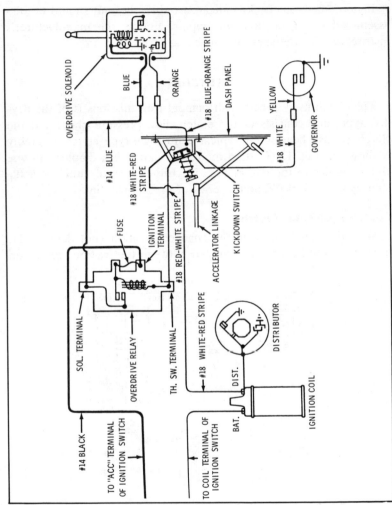

Fig. 9. Diagram of the overdrive electrical system used on 1964 Fords and Mercurys.

the engine flywheel and the face of the clutch pressure plate by the pressure of the clutch springs. When the clutch pedal is depressed, the release yoke or fork is moved on its pivot, applying pressure to the release (throw-out) bearing sleeve or collar. The rotating race of the throw-out bearing presses against the clutch release levers and moves them on their pivots. Since the outer end of the release levers are fastened to the clutch cover, the pressure plate is moved back from the clutch disc, compressing the clutch springs and allowing the engine flywheel and clutch elements to rotate independently of each other.

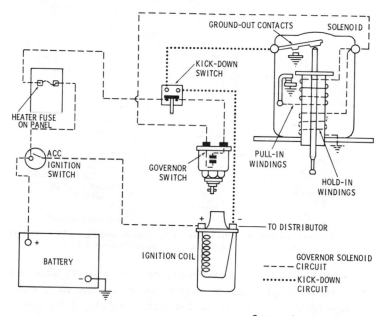

Courtesy American Motors Corp.

Fig. 10. Diagram of the overdrive electrical system used on 1964 American Motors Corp. cars.

The throw-out yoke moves only on its pivot which is fastened to the flywheel housing by means of a bracket or transverse shaft. All parts of the clutch assembly, except the throw-out bearing and

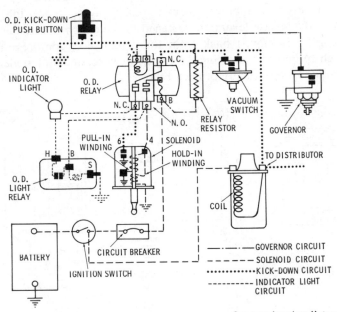

Fig. 11. Diagram of the overdrive electrical system used on 1964 American Motors Corp. cars equipped with Twin-Stick.

collar, rotate with the flywheel when the clutch is engaged. When the clutch is disengaged, the clutch disc will come to rest if the transmission is in neutral or the car is standing still. If the car is in gear and moving, the clutch disc will be rotating, being driven through the transmisison by the rear wheels.

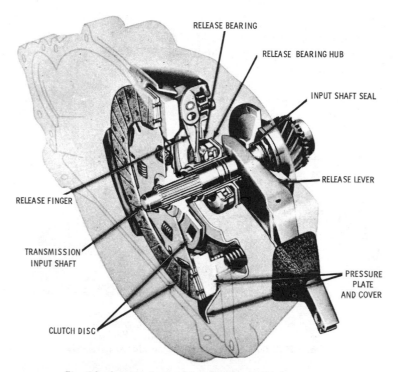

Fig. 12. A typical centrifugal-type clutch assembly.

Diaphragm-Type Clutch

The operating principle of a diaphragm-type clutch differs from that of the centrifugal type only in the method by which the pressure plate is held against the clutch disc. Instead of helical clutch springs, a disk-shaped diaphragm is used to supply the pressure to hold the clutch disc against the flywheel facing. The diaphragm is positioned between the cover and the pressure plate so that the diaphragm spring is nearly flat when the clutch is engaged.

Service

Several things can affect good clutch operation. Therefore, before performing any major clutch operations, preliminary inspections should be made to determine if the trouble is actually in the clutch proper.

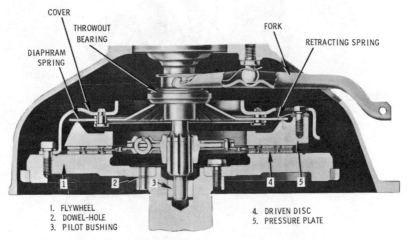

Fig. 13. A typical diaphragm-type clutch assembly.

1. FLYWHEEL
2. DOWEL-HOLE
3. PILOT BUSHING
4. DRIVEN DISC
5. PRESSURE PLATE

The following checks should be made:

1. With the engine running, hold the clutch pedal approximately ½ inch from the floor mat and shift between first and reverse gears several times. If the shifting is smooth, the clutch is fully releasing. If the shifting is not smooth, adjustment of the clutch is necessary.
2. Check the clutch pedal bushings for binding or excessive wear.

3. Check the throw-out yoke for proper installation on the ball stud or pivot pin. Lack of lubrication on the yoke can cause it to be pulled off the ball, or can cause it to bind on the pivot pin.
4. Check for bent, cracked, or damaged cross-shaft levers, support brackets, and other parts of the clutch linkage.
5. Check for loose or damaged engine mounts which may allow the engine to shift its position causing a bind in the clutch linkage. Check to make sure proper clearance is present for all parts of the clutch linkage to operate without interference.

The adjustments to be made on the clutch while it is in the vehicle are total travel of the clutch pedal (necessary on some models only) and clutch pedal free play. Improper adjustment is one of the most frequent causes of clutch failure and can, in some cases, be one of the contributing factors to transmission failure.

The total travel is that distance the pedal moves from its bumper stop position to its fully depressed position. An example of the measurements to make for determining total travel is shown in Fig. 14 for a 1964 Chevelle. Here, measurement A is subtracted from measurement B to determine total travel. If the total travel is less than the specifications (6½″ in this case), the bumper stop is trimmed until the correct travel is obtained. If the bumper stop is excessively worn or missing, the pedal will be abnormally high. Always check total travel before checking free play.

Clutch pedal free play is an adjustment that must be made from time to time on all cars equipped with a manual transmission. This adjustment is for the amount of free clutch pedal travel before the throw-out bearing makes contact with the release fingers. This measurement will vary slightly from model to model, but the usual free play specified is around ½ inch. This adjustment is made on most cars by lengthening or shortening one of the linkage rods equipped with adjusting nuts. On same makes, the rod itself is turned into or out of a threaded fitting to obtain the correct length. A locknut is provided to lock the adjustment after it is made. On

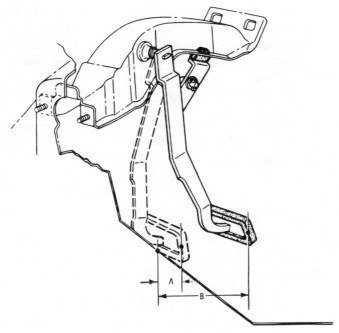

Fig. 14. Measurements to determine total pedal travel.

other cars, the adjusting rod is threaded on one end and has two nuts, one being loosened while the other is tightened to change the length of the rods. After the correct adjustment is made, both nuts are tightened to effectively lock the adjustment.

Fig. 15 shows an example of the clutch linkage and adjustments found on 1964 Ford cars. The total pedal travel is adjusted on

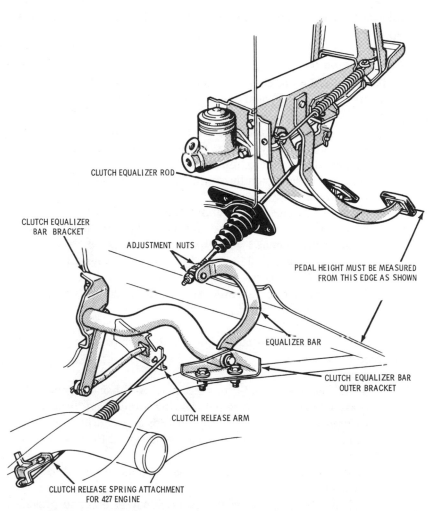

CLUTCH EQUALIZER ROD

CLUTCH EQUALIZER
BAR BRACKET

ADJUSTMENT NUTS

PEDAL HEIGHT MUST BE MEASURED
FROM THIS EDGE AS SHOWN

EQUALIZER BAR

CLUTCH EQUALIZER BAR
OUTER BRACKET

CLUTCH RELEASE ARM

CLUTCH RELEASE SPRING ATTACHMENT
FOR 427 ENGINE

Fig. 15. 1964 Ford clutch linkage and adjustments.

this particular linkage by moving the pedal bumper and bracket up or down.

Clutch Removal

To remove the clutch for inspection and repair, the following steps are necessary on most cars:

1. Remove the transmission, following the procedure outlined by the manufacturer for the particular car being serviced.
2. Remove the flywheel housing cover.
3. Disconnect the clutch linkage and any retracting springs at the clutch release fork.
4. Remove the release (throw-out) bearing and sleeve.
5. Mark the clutch cover and flywheel to insure that they will be correctly matched when they are reassembled.
6. Remove the bolts holding the cover to the flywheel, loosening each bolt (in succession) a few turns until the cover is free.
7. Remove the clutch assembly (cover, disc, and pressure plate) from the clutch housing.

With the clutch cover, clutch disc, and pressure plate removed, proceed as follows:

1. Mark the cover and pressure plate so that they may be reassembled in their original position to maintain balance.
2. Compress the cover using an arbor or drill press, as in Fig. 16, or by using a special tool designed for this purpose (Fig. 17).
3. With the assembly under pressure, remove the throw-out lever eyebolt nuts.
4. Release the pressure on the cover slowly in order to prevent the springs from flying out.

Fig. 16. Compressing the clutch cover to permit disassembly.

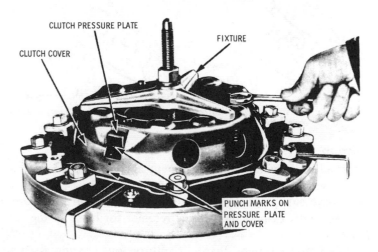

Fig. 17. Using a special tool to compress the clutch cover for disassembly.

5. Lift the cover off the pressure plate to expose all parts for inspection and cleaning. **NOTE: It is important to make a notation of the location of the parts on some clutch assemblies.** (See Fig. 18.)

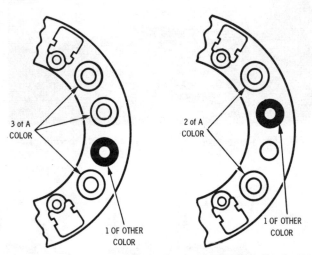

Courtesy Chrysler-Plymouth Div., Chrysler Motors Corp.

Fig. 18. The pressure springs must be replaced in the proper order in certain Chrysler-made clutch assemblies.

Inspection

Clean all parts with a suitable solvent and inspect carefully for excessive wear or distortion. **WARNING: The throw-out bearing on some cars is prelubricated and should not be cleaned with a solvent.** Inspect the bearing retainer for loose spring clips and rivets.

Throw-Out Bearing—Inspect the throw-out bearing assembly for burrs. If any are found, they should be removed with fine crocus cloth. Also inspect the input shaft to the transmisison and remove any scoring with crocus cloth. Coat the bearing retainer with a thin film of lithium-base grease. Hold the inner race of the throw-out bearing and rotate the outer race while applying pressure to it. If the rotation is rough or noisy, replace the bearing.

Most throw-out bearing failures are the result of improper clutch pedal adjustments. Failure can also be caused by the throw-out lever contact points being out of plane. If one side of the throw-out bearing assembly is worn more than the other side, either the lever is bent or is not centered on the flywheel housing bracket. Misalignment between the engine and transmission can also cause throw-out bearing failure.

Pressure Plate—Inspect the pressure plate surface for burn marks, scores, or ridges. Minor imperfections can be removed if care is taken to maintain the flatness of the pressure plate. If the plate is badly heat checked, deeply scored, or warped more than 0.005 inch, it should be replaced along with the cover assembly.

Clean the surfaces of the pressure plate and flywheel with a suitable solvent, such as carbon tetrachloride, to make sure the surfaces are free of any oil film. **CAUTION: Do not use cleaners having a petroleum base, and do not immerse the pressure plate in the solution.**

Clutch Disc—Inspect the clutch disc facings for oil or grease. **NOTE: Eliminate the source of any oil or grease before replacing the disc.** An excessive amount of grease in the pilot bushing in the throw-out bearing hub will eventually find its way to the disc facings. Too high a lubricant level in the transmission or a plugged transmission vent will force lubricant from the transmission out past the input shaft and onto the clutch facings.

Inspect the clutch disc for worn or loose facings. Check the disc for distortion and for loose rivets at the hub. Check for broken springs. Replace the disc if any of these defects are present.

CAUTION: Do not drop or contaminate the new disc with oil or grease while installing it.

Pressure Springs—It is advisable to test the pressure springs when the clutch is dismantled after considerable service, or if there has been considerable slippage. Slippage creates heat which may cause the springs to lose their specified load. Discard any spring that does not meet the minimum requirements.

Cover Plate—Check the cover plate for distortion by laying it on a perfectly flat and smooth surface. If the cover shows signs of being warped, replace with a new unit.

Release Levers—Replace any release levers that are badly worn on the tips. Correct the cause of this abnormal wear (insufficient clutch free pedal play, damaged throw-out bearing, worn or damaged threads on eyebolts or adjusting nuts, binding which prevents free back-and-forth movement, etc.).

Reassembly

To reassemble the clutch, coat the sides of the driving lugs and edges of the pressure plate openings with a thin film of lithium-base grease. **Do not apply excessive lubricant.**

Place the pressure springs in their proper place and in their proper sequence (in some clutches) to maintain the proper clutch balance. Place the cover over the springs, matching the punch marks made when the clutch was disassembled. Slowly compress the springs, using an arbor or drill press (or special tool), making sure the bolts are guided through the holes in the cover.

Screw the adjusting nuts on the protruding bolts until the nuts are flush with the top of the bolts. Slowly release the pressure on the cover. Depress the throw-out levers several times to properly seat the parts.

Either torque the fastening nuts to specifications, or adjust the throw-out levers by the use of a feeler gauge and spacers. Follow the manufacturer's instructions if the clutch is the type in which the throw-out levers must be adjusted.

Before installing the clutch assembly in the car, make sure the mounting surfaces of the transmisison and flywheel housing are free of dirt, paint, and burrs. Place the clutch disc and pressure plate assembly in position on the flywheel and start the attaching bolts to hold the assembly in place. **Take care not to drop the parts or to contaminate them with oil or grease.** Align the clutch disc and tighten the fastening bolts evenly to specifications.

Place the throw-out bearing and hub on the throw-out lever and coat the inside of the bearing retainer lightly with lithium-type grease. **Do not grease the bearing hub.** (Pack the throw-out bearing with grease if it is not of the prelubricated type.)

Install two guide pins in the lower mounting holes of the flywheel housing and move the transmission forward on these pins until it is tightly positioned against the flywheel housing. Install the upper mounting bolts. Remove the guide pins and install the lower mounting bolts. Torque all bolts to specifications.

Install any other bolts that may have been removed, such as those that attach the extension housing to the engine rear support. Remove the jack from under the transmission and connect the parking brake cable (if disconnected). Install the overdrive solenoid (if so equipped) and connect the gear shift rods and speedometer cable. Adjust the linkage of the gear shift rods and adjust the free travel of the clutch pedal.

CLUTCH-SYSTEM TROUBLES AND REMEDIES

Symptom and Possible Causes	*Possible Remedy*
Clutch Chatter	
(a) Worn or damaged clutch disc.	(a) Replace clutch disc.

Symptom and Possible Causes	*Possible Remedy*

(b) Grease or oil on disc facings.

(b) Replace clutch disc.

(c) Improperly adjusted cover assembly.

(c) Remove and recondition.

Clutch Slipping

(a) Burned, worn, or oil-soaked facings.

(a) Replace clutch disc.

(b) Insufficient pedal free play.

(b) Adjust pedal free play.

(c) Weak or broken pressure springs.

(c) Recondition cover assembly.

Difficult Gear Shifting

(a) Excessive pedal free play.

(a) Adjust pedal free play.

(b) Worn or damaged clutch disc.

(b) Replace clutch disc.

(c) Improperly adjusted cover assembly.

(c) Remove and recondition.

Clutch Noisy

(a) Dry clutch linkage.

(a) Lubricate as necessary.

(b) Worn throw-out bearing.

(b) Replace throw-out bearing.

(c) Worn clutch disc.

(c) Replace clutch disc.

(d) Worn release levers.

(d) Recondition cover assembly.

(e) Worn or dry pilot housing.

(e) Lubricate or replace bushing.

(f) Dry pressure plate lugs in cover.

(f) Lubricate lightly.

CHAPTER 25

Automatic Transmissions

All automatic transmissions used on modern cars have the same general operating principles. The construction features are also similar, although parts from one type cannot usually be used in a transmission of a different manufacture.

Most automatic transmissions in use today are a combination of a torque converter and a two-speed planetary gear system. Torque multiplication is obtained hydraulically through the converter, and mechanically through the planetary gears. A cross-section of a typical automatic transmission is shown in Fig. 1. Other transmissions are shown in Figs. 2 and 3.

The combination of the torque converter and planetary gears provides a high startnig ratio for acceleration from a stop and up steep grades. The torque converter portion provides torque multiplication for proper performance and smooth operation; it functions as a fluid coupling at normal road loads, and at normal and higher speeds. The transmission consists of six (6) basic sections:

1. Torque converter.
2. Oil pump.
3. Planetary gears and controls.

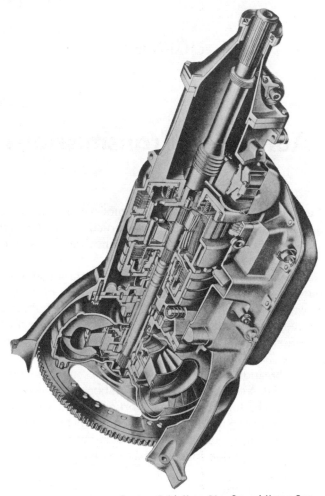

Fig. 1. Cross-section of a typical automatic transmission. This particular unit is a Super Turbine "300" used on some 1965 Buicks.

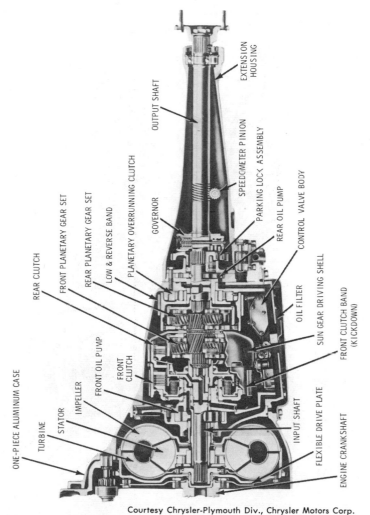

EXTENSION HOUSING

OUTPUT SHAFT

SPEEDOMETER PINION

PARKING LOCK ASSEMBLY

REAR OIL PUMP

CONTROL VALVE BODY

GOVERNOR

REAR CLUTCH

FRONT PLANETARY GEAR SET

REAR PLANETARY GEAR SET

LOW & REVERSE BAND

PLANETARY OVERRUNNING CLUTCH

OIL FILTER

SUN GEAR DRIVING SHELL

FRONT CLUTCH BAND (KICKDOWN)

FRONT OIL PUMP

FRONT CLUTCH

ONE-PIECE ALUMINUM CASE

IMPELLER

STATOR

TURBINE

INPUT SHAFT

FLEXIBLE DRIVE PLATE

ENGINE CRANKSHAFT

Courtesy Chrysler-Plymouth Div., Chrysler Motors Corp.

Fig. 2. Cross-sectional view of a TorqueFlite transmission for a 1964 Plymouth V8.

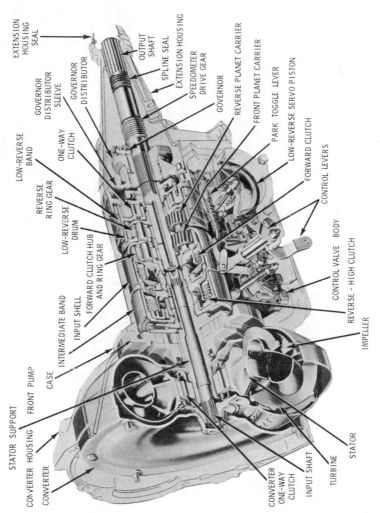

EXTENSION HOUSING SEAL

OUTPUT SHAFT

SPLINE SEAL

EXTENSION HOUSING

SPEEDOMETER DRIVE GEAR

GOVERNOR

REVERSE PLANET CARRIER

FRONT PLANET CARRIER

PARK TOGGLE LEVER

LOW-REVERSE SERVO PISTON

FORWARD CLUTCH

CONTROL LEVERS

CONTROL VALVE BODY

REVERSE - HIGH CLUTCH

IMPELLER

GOVERNOR DISTRIBUTOR SLEEVE

GOVERNOR DISTRIBUTOR

LOW-REVERSE BAND

ONE-WAY CLUTCH

REVERSE RING GEAR

LOW-REVERSE DRUM

FORWARD CLUTCH HUB AND RING GEAR

INPUT SHELL

INTERMEDIATE BAND

CASE

FRONT PUMP

STATOR SUPPORT

CONVERTER HOUSING

CONVERTER

CONVERTER ONE-WAY CLUTCH

INPUT SHAFT

TURBINE

STATOR

Fig. 3. Cross-section of a C4 dual-range automatic transmission used on some 1964 Fords.

4. Reverse clutch.
5. Governor.
6. Valve body.

TORQUE CONVERTER

The torque converter is connected to the engine flywheel and serves as a fluid (hydraulic) coupling through which engine torque is transmitted to the input shaft. The torque converter steps up (multiplies) engine torque whenever operating conditions are such that more torque is needed than the engine alone can supply. The torque converter consists of three (3) basic sections:

1. Converter pump.
2. Variable pitch stator.
3. Converter turbine.

Converter Pump

The function of the converter pump (Fig. 4) is to convert the power from the engine into a flow of oil to drive the converter turbine. The converter pump operates as a centrifugal type, picking up oil at its center and discharging oil at its rim.

Variable Pitch Stator

The variable pitch stator is supported by the stator shaft and is located between the converter turbine and the converter pump, as shown in Fig. 5. The stator is equipped with a free-wheeling (over-running) clutch. When this clutch is held stationary, the direction of the oil flow from the turbine is changed to the proper angle for smooth entrance into the converter pump. As the speed of the turbine approaches the pump speed, the direction of the oil flow changes until it no longer opposes the pump rotation. The stator

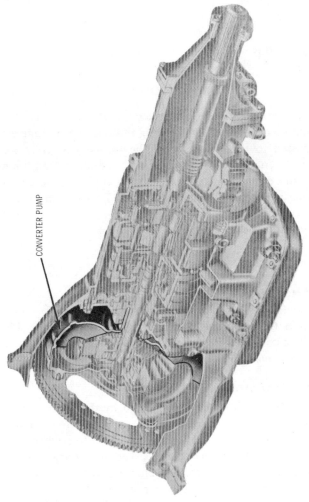

CONVERTER PUMP

Courtesy Buick Motor Div., General Motors Corp.

Fig. 4. The converter pump in a typical torque converter.

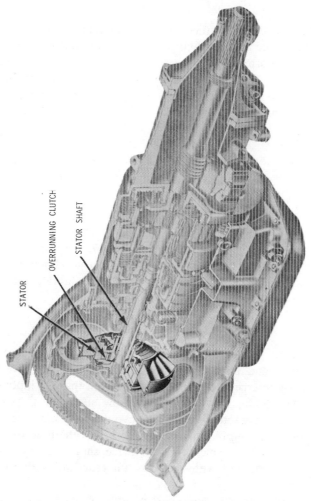

STATOR

OVERRUNNING CLUTCH

STATOR SHAFT

Courtesy Buick Motor Div., General Motors Corp.

Fig. 5. Variable pitch stator and supporting shaft.

will free-wheel under this condition so that it will offer little or no interference to the flow of oil between the turbine and converter pump. For normal operation in the Drive range, the stator blades are at a low angle. For increased torque, the stator blades are changed to a greater angle. This will provide more power for acceleration or increased road load.

Converter Turbine

The function of the converter turbine (Fig. 6) is to convert the energy present in the moving oil from the pump into torque to turn the input shaft.

OIL PUMP

A gear-type oil pump, shown in Fig. 7, supplies oil to fill the converter, to operate the forward and reverse clutches, to release the low band, and to circulate the oil for lubrication and heat transfer.

PLANETARY GEARS AND CONTROLS

The planetary gear set consists of an input sun gear, low sun gear, short and long pinions, a reverse ring gear, and a planet carrier. By referring to Fig. 8, it can be seen that the input sun gear is splined to the input shaft. The low sun gear is part of the forward clutch assembly, and will revolve freely until the low band is applied. The input sun gear is meshed with three long pinions which, in turn, are meshed with three short pinions. The short pinions are meshed with the low sun gear and with the reverse ring gear.

The input sun gear and short pinions always rotate in the same direction. Application of either the low band or the reverse clutch determines whether the output shaft rotates forward or backward.

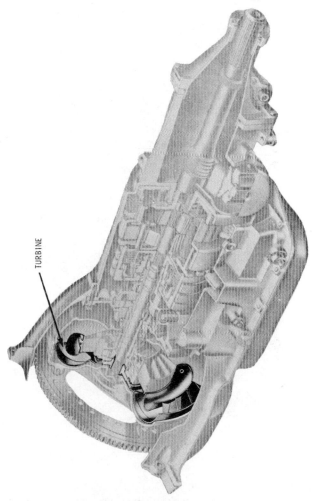

TURBINE

Fig. 6. The converter turbine.

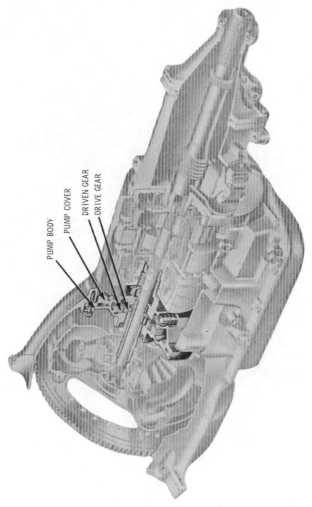

PUMP BODY

PUMP COVER

DRIVEN GEAR

DRIVE GEAR

Courtesy Buick Motor Div., General Motors Corp.

Fig. 7. The oil pump.

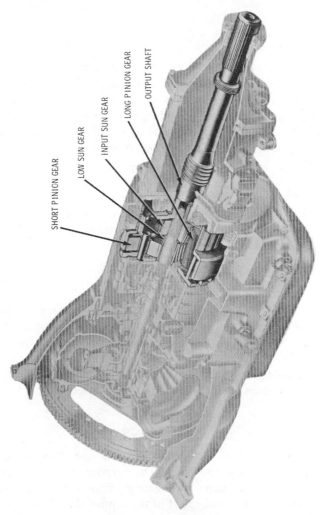

SHORT PINION GEAR

LOW SUN GEAR

INPUT SUN GEAR

LONG PINION GEAR

OUTPUT SHAFT

Fig. 8. The planetary gear set.

663

Forward Clutch

The forward clutch assembly consists of a drum, piston, springs, piston seals, and a clutch pack. These parts, shown in Fig. 9, are all retained within the drum by the low sun gear and flange assembly. When oil pressure is applied to the piston, the clutch plates are forced together, connecting the clutch drum to the input shaft through the clutch hub. This action causes the low sun gear to rotate with the input shaft.

Low Band

The low band, also shown in Fig. 9, surrounds the forward clutch drum. The band is hydraulically applied by the low servo piston, and released by spring pressure.

REVERSE CLUTCH

The reverse clutch assembly (Fig. 10) consists of a piston, inner and outer seal, cushion spring, coil springs, clutch pack, and pressure plate. All these parts are retained inside the case by a retaining ring. When oil pressure is applied to the piston, the clutch plates are forced together, holding the reverse ring gear stationary. This action causes reverse rotation of the output shaft.

GOVERNOR

The governor is located to the rear of the transmission case and is driven by the output shaft. The purpose of the governor is to generate a speed-sensitive modulating oil pressure that increases up to a certain rotational speed of the output shaft. Thus, the governor determines or affects the shift points, main-line oil pressure, and down-shift timing.

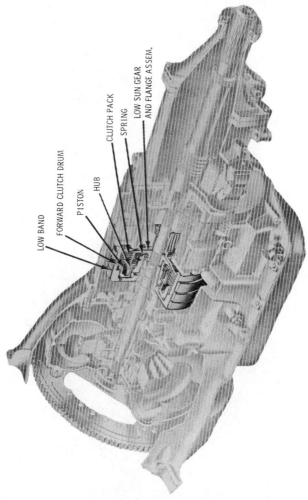

LOW BAND

FORWARD CLUTCH DRUM

PISTON

HUB

CLUTCH PACK

SPRING

LOW SUN GEAR AND FLANGE ASSEM.

Courtesy Buick Motor Div., General Motors Corp.

Fig. 9. Forward clutch and low band assembly.

665

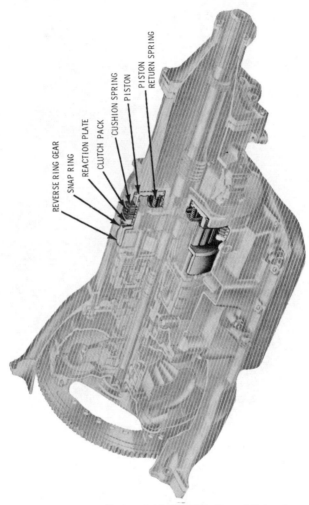

REVERSE RING GEAR

SNAP RING

REACTION PLATE

CLUTCH PACK

CUSHION SPRING

PISTON

PISTON RETURN SPRING

Courtesy Buick Motor Div., General Motors Corp.

Fig. 10. Reverse clutch assembly.

VALVE BODY

The valve body assemblies are located at the bottom of the transmission. These units can be removed from some transmisisons by merely removing the oil pan. In other transmisisons it is necessary to remove the entire transmission to gain access to the valve body assembly. The purpose of the valve body is to direct the pressurized oil to the proper location to actuate the various clutches, bands, etc. This is accomplished by controlling the oil flow through the passages by means of spring-loaded and mechanically-actuated valves.

GEARSHIFT CONTROLS

Selection of the desired driving range is made by either a selector lever mounted on the steering column, a dash-mounted push-button assembly, or by a console-mounted selector lever.

TRANSMISSION OIL COOLER

Most cars equipped with an automatic transmisison have a transmisison oil cooler. Transmission fluid is circulated through lines to a unit in the bottom of the car radiator. Here the heat carried by the transmission fluid is transferred to the coolant in the radiator. Thus, the fluid returning to the transmission is at a much lower temperature.

SERVICE

In-car service of most automatic transmissions consists of periodic checking of the fluid level, adjustment of the control linkage, adjustment of throttle and downshift linkage, and band adjust-

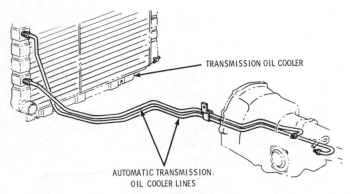

TRANSMISSION OIL COOLER

AUTOMATIC TRANSMISSION.
OIL COOLER LINES

*Fig. 11. Transmission fluid is circulated through a transmission oil cooler
on most cars equipped with an automatic transmission.*

ments. Due to the variations in the many makes and models of
automatic transmissions, it is suggested that any service to be
performed on these units follow the procedures outlined in the
manufacturer's service manuals.

Transmission removal and reconditioning must be performed
according to the instructions in the manufacturer's service manual.
**These units are extremely complex and only trained per-
sons should attempt removal and repair.**

TOWING AND STARTING PRECAUTIONS

Starting

Some cars equipped with automatic transmissions can be started
by pushing and some cannot. Always consult the owner's manual
or service manual to determine if a particular make and model can
be started in this manner. In general, jumper cables to an auxiliary
battery should be used if possible. If this method is impractical, and
the particular make and model of car is capable of being started

by engaging the transmisison while the car is moving, **always push the car to start it—do not tow it.** The sudden surge when the car starts may cause a rear-end collision with the towing vehicle.

Towing

Cars with automatic transmissions should be towed with the rear-end off the ground, when possible. Some makes and models can be towed for short distances with the transmission in neutral, others cannot. Check the owner's or service manual. When long-distance towing is necessary, or when the transmission is faulty, **always** tow with the rear-end off the ground or with the propeller (drive) shaft removed.

AUTOMATIC-TRANSMISSION TROUBLES AND REMEDIES

The following troubles and their possible causes and remedies are general in nature and do not necessarily apply to all makes and models. They are listed only as a possible aid in determining the cause of trouble in automatic transmissions and to suggest a possible remedy.

Symptom and Possible Cause   *Possible Remedy*

Harsh Engagement

(a) Engine idle speed too high.

(a) Adjust idle speed to recommended rpm.

(b) Hydraulic pressure too high or too low.

(b) Check fluid level. Check hydraulic pressure and adjust to specifications.

(c) Low-reverse band out of adjustment.

(c) Adjust.

Symptom and Possible Causes	*Possible Remedy*
(d) Faulty or leaky valve body.	(d) Perform pressure tests to determine cause. Correct as necessary.
(e) Faulty low-reverse servo, band, or linkage.	(e) Inspect servo for damaged seals or for binding. Repair as necessary.
(f) Worn or damaged front and/or rear clutch.	(f) Inspect clutches and repair or replace as required.

Delayed Engagement

(a) Low fluid level.	(a) Refill to correct level with the recommended fluid.
(b) Incorrect control linkage adjustment.	(b) Adjust control linkage.
(c) Oil filter clogged (if so equipped).	(c) Replace filter.
(d) Hydraulic pressure too high or too low.	(d) Make hydraulic pressure tests and adjust to specifications.
(e) Faulty or leaky valve body.	(e) Make pressure tests to determine cause and correct as necessary.
(f) Clutches or servos sticking or not operating.	(f) Remove valve body and make air pressure tests. Repair as necessary.
(g) Worn or faulty front and/or rear clutch.	(g) Inspect clutch and repair or replace as necessary.
(h) Faulty front pump.	(h) Make hydraulic pressure tests. Adjust or repair as necessary.

Symptom and Possible Causes	*Possible Remedy*
(i) Air bubbles in fluid.	(i) Inspect for air leaks into the suction passages of the front pump.

Runaway or Harsh Upshift or Kickdown

(a) Low fluid level.	(a) Refill to correct level with recommended fluid.
(b) Incorrect throttle linkage.	(b) Adjust throttle linkage.
(c) Incorrect hydraulic pressure.	(c) Make hydraulic pressure tests and adjust to specifications.
(d) Kickdown band out of adjustment.	(d) Adjust kickdown band.
(e) Faulty or leaky valve body.	(e) Make hydraulic pressure tests to determine cause and repair as necessary.
(f) Faulty governor.	(f) Inspect governor and repair as necessary.
(g) Clutches or servos sticking or not operating.	(g) Remove valve body and make air pressure tests. Repair as necessary.
(h) Kickdown servo, band, or linkage faulty.	(h) Inspect servo for sticking, for broken seal rings, for binding in linkage, or for faulty band lining.
(i) Worn or faulty front clutch.	(i) Inspect clutch and repair or replace as necessary.

Symptom and Possible Causes	Possible Remedy
No Upshift	
(a) Low fluid level.	(a) Refill to correct level with recommended fluid.
(b) Incorrect throttle linkage adjustment.	(b) Adjust throttle linkage.
(c) Kickdown band out of adjustment.	(c) Adjust kickdown band.
(d) Incorrect hydraulic pressure.	(d) Make hydraulic pressure tests and adjust to specifications.
(e) Governor sticking.	(e) Remove and clean governor. Replace if necessary.
(f) Faulty or leaky valve body.	(f) Make pressure tests to determine cause and repair as necessary.
(g) Clutches or servos sticking or not operating.	(g) Remove valve body and make air pressure tests. Repair as necessary.
(h) Faulty rear oil pump.	(h) Make hydraulic pressure tests and adjust or repair as necessary.
(i) Kickdown servo, band, or linkage faulty.	(i) Inspect servo for sticking, for broken seal rings, for binding linkage, or for a faulty band lining. Repair as necessary.
(j) Worn or faulty front clutch.	(j) Inspect clutch and repair or replace as necessary.

Symptom and Possible Causes   *Possible Remedy*

No Kickdown or Faulty Downshift

(a) Incorrect throttle linkage adjustment.

(a) Adjust throttle linkage.

(b) Incorrect control linkage adjustment.

(b) Adjust control linkage.

(c) Incorrect kickdown band adjustment.

(c) Adjust kickdown band.

(d) Incorrect hydraulic pressure.

(d) Make hydraulic pressure tests and adjust to specifications.

(e) Governor sticking.

(e) Remove and clean governor. Repair or replace as necessary.

(f) Faulty or leaky valve body.

(f) Make pressure tests to determine cause and repair as necessary.

(g) Clutches or servos sticking or not operating.

(g) Remove valve body and make air pressure tests. Repair as necessary.

(h) Kickdown servo, band, or linkage faulty.

(h) Inspect servo for sticking, broken seal rings, binding linkage, or faulty band lining. Repair as necessary.

(i) Overrunning clutch not holding.

(i) Repair overrunning clutch as necessary.

Erratic Shifting

(a) Low fluid level.

(a) Refill with recommended fluid.

Symptom and Possible Causes	*Possible Remedy*
(b) Air bubbles in fluid.	(b) Inspect for air leakage in the front pump suction linkage.
(c) Incorrect throttle linkage adjustment.	(c) Adjust throttle linkage.
(d) Incorrect control linkage adjustment.	(d) Adjust control linkage.
(e) Incorrect hydraulic pressure.	(e) Make hydraulic pressure tests and adjust to specifications.
(f) Governor sticking.	(f) Remove and clean governor. Replace if necessary.
(g) Oil filter clogged.	(g) Replace oil filter.
(h) Faulty valve body.	(h) Make pressure tests to determine cause and correct as necessary.
(i) Clutches or servos sticking or not operating.	(i) Remove valve body and perform air pressure tests. Repair as required.
(j) Faulty rear and/or front oil pump.	(j) Make hydraulic pressure tests and adjust or repair as necesary.

Slips in Forward Drive Positions

(a) Low fluid level.	(a) Refill with recommended fluid.
(b) Air bubbles in fluid.	(b) Inspect for air leaks in the front pump suction passages.

Symptom and Possible Causes	*Possible Remedy*
(c) Incorrect throttle linkage adjustment.	(c) Adjust throttle linkage.
(d) Incorrect control linkage adjustment.	(d) Adjust control linkage.
(e) Hydraulic pressure too low.	(e) Make hydraulic pressure tests and adjust to specifications.
(f) Valve body faulty or leaky.	(f) Make pressure tests to determine cause and correct as necessary.
(g) Clutches or servos sticking or not operating.	(g) Remove valve body and make air pressure tests. Repair as necessary.
(h) Worn or faulty front and/or rear clutch.	(h) Inspect clutch and repair or replace as necessary.
(i) Overrunning clutch not holding.	(i) Repair overrunning clutch as necessary.

Slips in Reverse Only

(a) Low fluid level.	(a) Refill with recommended fluid.
(b) Air bubbles in fluid.	(b) Inspect for air leakage in front pump suction passages.
(c) Incorrect control linkage adjustment.	(c) Adjust control linkage.
(d) Incorrect hydraulic pressure.	(d) Make hydraulic pressure tests and adjust to specifications.

Symptom and Possible Causes

(e) Low-reverse band out of adjustment.

(f) Faulty or leaky valve body.

(g) Front clutch or rear servo sticking or not operating.

(h) Low-reverse servo, band, or linkage faulty.

(i) Faulty front oil pump.

Possible Remedy

(e) Adjust low-reverse band.

(f) Make pressure tests to determine cause and repair as necessary.

(g) Remove valve body and make air pressure tests. Repair as necessary.

(h) Inspect servo for damaged seals, binding linkage, or faulty band lining. Repair as necessary.

(i) Make hydraulic pressure tests and adjust or repair as necessary.

No Drive

(a) Low fluid level.

(b) Hydraulic pressure too low.

(c) Oil filter clogged.

(d) Valve body faulty or leaky.

(e) Faulty front oil pump.

(a) Refill with recommended fluid.

(b) Make hydraulic pressure tests and adjust to specifications.

(c) Replace oil filter.

(d) Make pressure tests to determine cause and correct as necessary.

(e) Make hydraulic pressure tests, and adjust or repair as necessary.

Symptom and Possible Causes	*Possible Remedy*
(f) Clutches or servos sticking or not operating.	(f) Remove valve body and and make air pressure tests. Repair as necessary.

Drives in Neutral

(a) Incorrect control linkage adjustment.	(a) Adjust control linkage.
(b) Valve body faulty or leaky.	(b) Make pressure tests to determine cause and repair as necessary.
(c) Rear clutch inoperative.	(c) Inspect clutch and repair as necessary.

Drags or Locks

(a) Kickdown band out of adjustment.	(a) Adjust kickdown band.
(b) Low-reverse band out of adjustment.	(b) Adjust low-reverse band.
(c) Kickdown and/or low-reverse servo, band, or linkage faulty.	(c) Inspect servo for sticking, broken seal rings, binding linkage, or faulty band linings. Repair as necessary.
(d) Front and/or rear clutch faulty.	(d) Inspect clutch and repair or replace as necessary.
(e) Planetary gear sets broken or seized.	(e) Inspect gear set and replace as required.
(f) Overrunning clutch worn, broken, or seized.	(f) Inspect clutch and repair or replace as necessary.

Symptom and Possible Causes

Possible Remedy

Transmission Overheats

(a) Low fluid level.

(a) Refill with recommended fluid.

(b) Kickdown band adjustment too tight.

(b) Adjust kickdown band.

(c) Low-reverse band adjustment too tight.

(c) Adjust low-reverse band.

(d) Faulty cooling system.

(d) Inspect transmission cooling system, clean and repair as necessary.

(e) Faulty front and/or rear oil pump.

(e) Inspect oil pump for incorrect clearance, and repair as necessary.

(f) Insufficient clutch clearance in front and/or rear clutch.

(f) Measure clutch-plate clearance and correct as necessary.

CHAPTER 26

Drive Shafts and Universal Joints

Power from the engine is coupled through the transmission to the rear wheels by means of a drive shaft and universal joints. The universal joints are necessary because the rear wheels (and axles) move up and down with relation to the body. If a hinged joint were not provided, the drive shaft would be bent or would break as the rear wheels and axles move up and down.

DRIVE SHAFTS

The drive shaft on modern cars may be a one-piece or a two-piece unit, depending on the make and model.

One-Piece

An example of a one-piece drive shaft is shown in Fig. 1. This type has two universal joints and a splined slip yoke to allow the drive shaft to expand and contract endways as the rear-axle assembly moves up and down.

All drive shafts, whether of the one- or two-piece variety, are balanced units. This balance must be preserved if vibration-free driving is to be experienced. Therefore, mud or grease should not be allowed to accumulate or the balance will be destroyed. Special care must be taken if the car is to be undercoated. The entire drive shaft should be covered with paper or cloth before the undercoating is applied to the underbody of the car.

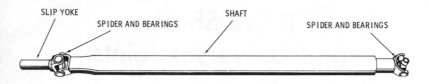

Courtesy Oldsmobile Div., General Motors Corp.

Fig. 1. The one-piece drive shaft used on some 1963 Oldsmobiles are typical of other one-piece assemblies.

Two-Piece

A two-piece drive shaft is shown in Fig. 2. This type consists of a front and rear unit, a center bearing support, three universal joints, and a splined slip yoke. This type has the advantage of shorter unsupported sections of the rotating portions and thus reduces the tendency for the drive shaft to whip at high speeds.

The front and rear drive shafts are connected to each other by a slip yoke and a constant-velocity type of universal joint. The center bearing support is attached to a cross member that is fastened to the side rails of the frame or body.

UNIVERSAL JOINTS

There are three general types of universal joints that may be found on modern cars. These are the cross-and-yoke type, the ball-and-trunnion type, and the constant-velocity type (shown in Fig. 5).

680

Cross-and-Yoke Type

The cross-and-yoke type of universal joint (Fig. 3) is found on the majority of cars. The lubrication of this kind of joint was necessary at periodic intervals in older-model cars, but most later models are factory packed with grease to last indefinitely. The only time they are to be lubricated is if they are disassembled for service.

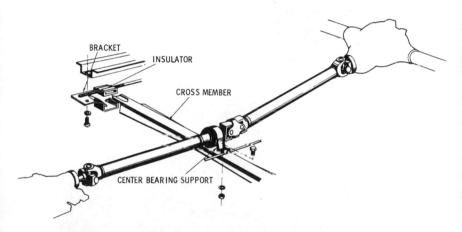

BRACKET

INSULATOR

CROSS MEMBER

CENTER BEARING SUPPORT

Courtesy Oldsmobile Div., General Motors Corp.

Fig. 2. A two-piece drive shaft is used on many cars.

Ball-and Trunnion Type

The ball-and-trunnion type of universal joint (Fig. 4) is used on certain models of Chrysler-made cars. This type features ball-bearing construction and is also usually prelubricated for life or until disassembled for service. This type is usually protected from dust, dirt, and water by a rubber boot.

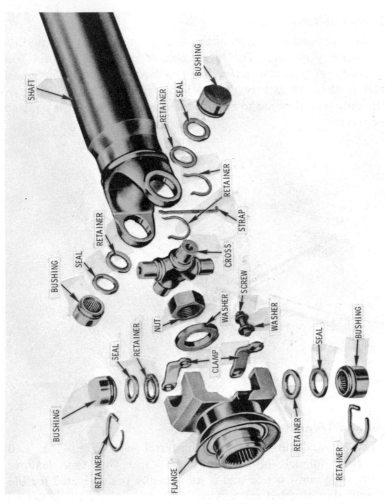

Courtesy Chrysler-Plymouth Div., Chrysler Motors Corp.

Fig. 3. A cross-and-yoke type of universal joint.

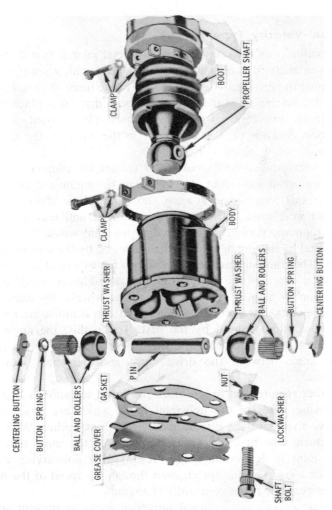

Courtesy Dodge Div., Chrysler Motors Corp.

Fig. 4. A ball-and-trunnion type of universal joint.

Constant-Velocity Type

A peculiarity of the conventional universal joint is that it causes the driven shaft to rotate at a variable speed with respect to the shaft doing the driving. This variation is in the form of an acceleration and deceleration of the rotational speed that takes place twice during each revolution of the driven shaft. The amount of such fluctuation depends on the difference in the angle of the driving shaft to the angle of the driven shaft.

This variation of rotational speed cannot be eliminated by a simple universal joint, but its effect can be minimized by using two universal joints—one at each end of the drive shaft. If only one joint were used between the transmission and rear axle, the acceleration and deceleration caused by the joint would be resisted on one end by the engine and on the other end by the inertia of the vehicle. The combined action of these two forces would place great stress on all parts of the power train and, in addition, would result in a nonuniform force being applied to the wheels. By using two universal joints, however, the second joint can compensate for the speed fluctuations caused by the first. To do this, the angle between the transmission shaft and the drive shaft must be the same as the angle between the drive shaft and the shaft into the differential.

Another requirement to minimize the speed variation is that the two driving yokes of the universal joints which are attached to the drive shaft must be displaced 90° from each other. With this arrangement, the first joint is accelerating at the same time the second joint is decelerating. This results in a nonvarying wheel speed for a given engine speed, even though the speed of the drive shaft between the two is constantly changing.

The use of two conventional universal joints to prevent speed fluctuations is satisfactory as long as the driving angles are small.

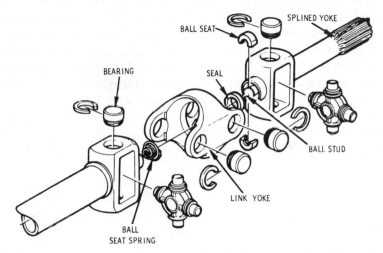

BALL SEAT

SPLINED YOKE

BEARING

SEAL

BALL STUD

LINK YOKE

BALL
SEAT SPRING

Courtesy Buick Motor Div., General Motors Corp.

Fig. 5. A constant-velocity type of universal joint.

For larger driving angles, however, the constant-velocity type of joint (Fig. 5) is more satisfactory. The design of this unit is such that speed fluctuation is entirely eliminated, providing a smooth, vibration-proof ride. On most cars, these joints do not require lubrication unless disassembled for service.

DRIVE-SHAFT ANGULARITY

The angles through which the universal joints on each end of the drive shaft operate must be very nearly the same. If these angles are different, operation is rough and an objectionable vibration is produced. In addition, the universal joints are designed to operate safely and efficiently within certain angles. If the design angle is exceeded, the joint may break or otherwise be damaged.

685

The front universal-joint angle is actually the angle between the transmission output shaft centerline and the centerline of the drive shaft which connects to it. This angle is determined by the design of the body assembly and is not likely to change. Therefore, this is not adjustable. However, the angle at the rear universal joint can change and must be adjusted. This adjustment is made by rotating the rear axle assembly in some way. The method used varies from car to car. Some provide a means of lengthening or shortening the upper control arms with shims at the frame bracket ends. Other cars provide adjustment with shims being placed between the rear springs and differential housing spring plates. One make of car provides cam-type adjusters located at each rear upper control arm-to-differential carrier attaching point. Refer to the manufacturer's service manual for the specific procedure for adjusting the drive shaft rear joint angle.

SERVICE

Drive shafts and universal joints require little service, other than periodic lubrication for those units that are not permanently lubricated. Failure of the joints and slip yoke does occur occasionally, and makes necessary the removal of the entire assembly to make the repair.

Drive Shaft Removal

One-Piece Type—To remove a one-piece shaft, proceed as follows:

1. Remove both U-bolts or clamps from the pinion yoke.
2. Mark the relation of the slip yoke and the drive flange so that they may be installed in their original positions. This maintains the balance of the assembly. Some manufacturers

provide a key to prevent installing in any but the correct position.

3. Disconnect the front universal joint from the transmission flange and slide the drive shaft to the rear until the front slip yoke clears the transmission housing and seal.

> **CAUTION: Do not allow the drive shaft to drop or hang loose on the vehicle from either joint during removal. Wire it up to the underbody.**

Two-Piece Type—A two-piece drive shaft must be removed as a unit. Proceed as follows:

> **Note: During handling out of the car, the assembly must be supported in as straight a line as possible to avoid jamming or bending any of the parts.**

1. Remove the bolts from the center bearing attaching plate.
2. Remove the U-bolts (or clamps) from the rear universal joint. Mark both the flange and the shaft to insure assembly in the same position.

> **CAUTION: If the rear universal-joint bearings are not retained on the spider (cross) by a connecting strap, use tape or wire to secure the bearings.**

3. Support the rear end of the drive shaft to avoid damage to the constant-velocity joint, and slide the complete assembly to the rear until the slip yoke slides out of the splines in the transmission output shaft.
4. Protect the oil seal surface on the slip yoke by taping or wiring a cloth over the entire front universal joint.

5. Slide the entire drive-shaft assembly to the rear and out from under the vehicle. **Do not bend the constant-velocity joint to its extreme angle at any time.**

Universal-Joint Service

Cross-and-Roller Type—To service a cross-and-roller type of universal joint, proceed as follows:

1. Remove the retainers that hold the bearings in the yoke and drive shaft.
2. Place the joint in a vise or press.
3. Select a socket (from a socket-wrench set) with an **outside** diameter slightly smaller than that of the outside diameter of the joint bearings. Select another socket with an **inside** diameter slightly larger than the outside of the bearings.
4. Place the sockets at oposite bearings so that the smaller socket becomes a bearing driver and the larger socket becomes a bearing receiver as the jaws of the vise come together (Fig. 6).
5. Close the vise jaws until the spider (cross) contacts the yoke. Take the drive shaft from the vise and remove the one bearing with pliers.
6. Reverse the sockets and press the opposite bearing out in the same manner.
7. Remove the spider from the yoke. Remove the remaining two bearings in the same manner.
8. Clean the parts in kerosene, mineral spirits, or other suitable solvent, and dry with compressed air.
9. Inspect the bearing surfaces of the spider. The surface should be smooth and free from pits or ripples. If either are present, or if the dust seal retainers are damaged, replace the spider assembly.

10. Inspect the bearings. All bearings should have a uniform appearance and should roll freely inside the bushings. If they do not, or if they have operated on a worn spider, they should be replaced.
11. Force recommended lubricant (usually wheel-bearing grease) between the rollers in all four bushings. Fill the reservoirs (if present) in the ends of the cross.

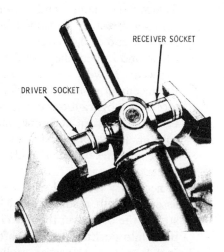

Fig. 6. Disassembly of a cross-and-roller type of universal joint.

12. Place the cross in the drive-shaft yoke and insert the roller bushing assemblies in the yoke.
13. Press the roller and bushing assemblies into the yoke while guiding the spider into both bushings.
14. Press until the bushing retainers can be installed in the grooves in the bushings.
15. Position the remaining two bushings on the spider and install the retainer strap (if so equipped) to hold them in place during installation in the vehicle.

Ball-and-Trunnion Type—To service a ball-and-trunnion type universal joint, proceed as follows:

1. Straighten the tabs on the grease cover, and remove it and the gasket. See Fig. 4.
2. Push the body back to expose the trunnion pin. Remove the parts from both ends of the trunnion pin.
3. Remove the clamps and loosen the dust cover. Remove and save the breather (polished jute) located between the shaft and rear end of the cover.
4. Clean and inspect the trunnion pin and raceways in the body for wear. If wear can be felt, the body should be replaced. Replacement of either the pin or the body requires a special tool and a hydraulic press to push the pin out of the shaft.
5. Clean all parts in kerosene, mineral spirits, or other suitable solvent. If the pin, body, and boot have not been removed, make sure the boot and body are clean inside as well as outside.
6. If necessary to install a new boot, coat all parts of the joint assembly with recommended lubricant. Without using tools, stretch the boot over the pin (Fig. 7) and work it through the body into position on the shaft.
7. Install a thrust washer, rollers, ball, button spring, and thrust button on each end of the trunnion pin and position the body over the pin assembly.
8. Position the boot on the drive shaft, with the breather (polished jute) parallel to the shaft. Install and tighten the clamp.
9. Position the boot on the joint body and install the clamp.
10. Lubricate the universal joint with the correct amount of recommended lubricant applied evenly in both raceways, one-half of the grease back of the trunnion pin and one-

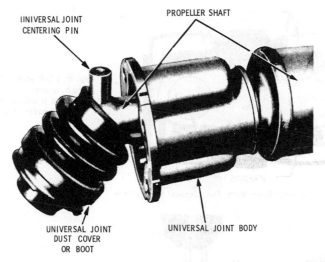

UNIVERSAL JOINT
CENTERING PIN

PROPELLER SHAFT

UNIVERSAL JOINT
DUST COVER
OR BOOT

UNIVERSAL JOINT BODY

Courtesy Chrysler-Plymouth Div., Chrysler Motors Corp.

Fig. 7. Sliding the boot over the ball head and pin.

half between the pin and cover. **Do not use more than the specified amount and do not place grease inside the boot.**

11. Install the gasket on the grease cover, and position the cover on the body with tabs at the grooves. Bend the tabs to tighten the cover in place.

Constant-Velocity Type—To service a constant-velocity type of universal joint, proceed as follows:

1. Mark all yokes before disassembly so they may be reassembled in their original positions to maintain proper balance. Fig. 8 shows the method of using punch marks to insure correct reassembly.

691

Drive Shafts and Universal Joints

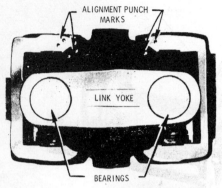

ALIGNMENT PUNCH MARKS

LINK YOKE

BEARINGS

Fig. 8. Link yoke showing punch marks to properly align the units when they are reassembled.

Courtesy Buick Motor Div., General Motors Corp.

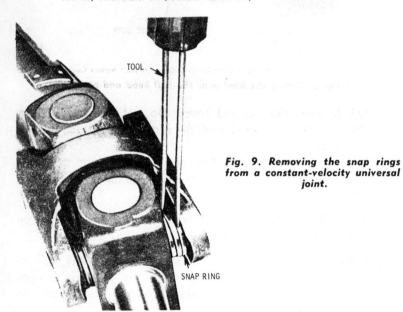

TOOL

Fig. 9. Removing the snap rings from a constant-velocity universal joint.

SNAP RING

Courtesy Buick Motor Div., General Motors Corp.

NOTE: For ease of disassembly, remove the bearings from the link yoke first.

2. Remove the snap rings from the bearings. These rings are on the inside of the link yoke and can be removed with a special tool, as shown in Fig. 9.

Fig. 10. Pressing out a bearing.

Courtesy Buick Motor Div., General Motors Corp.

3. Press out the bearings with a hydraulic press and special fixture as shown in Fig. 10.
4. Install a special guide through the bearing hole in the link yoke and over the journal end of the spider. This guide aligns the spider while removing the opposite bearing (Fig. 11).
5. Remove the bearing.

6. Repeat this procedure to remove other bearings until the unit is disassembled to the point desired or until the spider can be slipped out of the link yoke.

7. To remove the ball-stud seat, position the drive-shaft yoke in a vise so that the seat is accessible.

Fig. 11. *Pressing opposite bearing out, using guide over spider.*

Courtesy Buick Motor Div., General Motors Corp.

8. Pry out the seal with a screwdriver, and remove the seal washer, ball seat, seat washer, and ball-seat spring. See Fig. 12.

9. Inspect the ball stud and seats for scores or wear. Replacement kits are available for worn seats. A damaged ball stud requires replacement of the splined yoke, of which it is a part.

10. Clean out the seat cavity and pack with recommended lubricant.

11. Install the ball-seat spring, small end first. Install seat washer, seats, and seal washer. Apply Permatex to the outer diameter of the seal and install the seal with its lip toward the seat.
12. Stake the seal lightly and evenly in four places. Take care not to damage or distort the seal.
13. Pack the cavity around the ball stud with recommended lubricant.

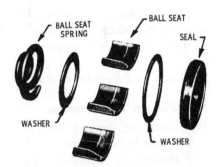

Fig. 12. Ball-stud seat assembly.

Courtesy Buick Motor Div., General Motors Corp.

14. Replace any worn or damaged parts in the constant-velocity joint. Repair kits containing a spider, 4 bearings, and 4 snap rings are available. **Always install a complete repair kit.**
15. Make certain that all the rollers are present in the bearings, that the bearings are properly packed with recommended lubricant, and that the seals are in position.
16. Reassemble the constant-velocity joint, taking care to prevent the bearing needles from becoming dislodged or burring the edge of the spider journals. Move the spider back and forth while pressing the bearings into position to make certain the spider journals engage the bearings squarely to avoid damage

and binding. If binding exists, remove the bearings and spider and examine for dislodged rollers or damaged journals.

17. Strike the yoke with a hammer to fully seat the snap rings against the yoke. Turn the spider to make certain it is free.

DRIVE-SHAFT AND UNIVERSAL-JOINT TROUBLES AND REMEDIES

The following symptoms, their possible causes, and their possible remedies are general and do not necessarily apply to all makes and models of cars.

Symptom and Possible Causes   *Possible Remedy*

Shudder on Acceleration

(a) Loose or missing bolt at center bearing support.

(a) Tighten bolts.

(b) Improperly adjusted rear joint angle.

(b) Adjust joint angle.

(c) Incorrect front joint angle.

(c) Shim under transmission support mount to bring to correct angle.

(d) Improper yoke phasing.

(d) Check for correct yoke phasing and correct if required.

Roughness or Vibration at All Speeds

(a) Center bearing support rubber damaged.

(a) Replace rubber.

(b) Improper yoke phasing.

(b) Check for correct yoke phasing and correct if required.

Symptom and Possible Causes	*Possible Remedy*
(c) Bent shaft.	(c) Replace shaft.
(d) Dented shaft.	(d) Replace shaft.
(e) Tight universal joints.	(e) Strike yokes with hammer to free up. Replace if unable to free up or if joint feels rough when rotated by hand.
(f) Worn universal joints.	(f) Replace worn joints.
(g) Undercoating on shaft.	(g) Remove from shaft.
(h) Incorrect U-bolt torque.	(h) Torque to specifications.
(i) Incorrect rear joint angle.	(i) Check and adjust to correct angle.
(j) Tire unbalance.	(j) Balance wheels.
(k) Drive shaft unbalanced.	(k) Balance shaft or replace.
(l) Excessive grease in dust boot.	(l) Remove all grease and repack with correct amount.
(m) Worn trunnion pin.	(m) Replace pin.

Roughness on Heavy Acceleration

(a) Constant-velocity joints worn.	(a) Replace as necessary.
(b) Seat spring broken or set.	(b) Repair as necessary.

Roughness at Low Speeds and Light Loads

(a) Improperly adjusted joint angles.	(a) Adjust angles.

Whine or Whistle

(a) Defective center support bearing.	(a) Replace bearing.

Symptom and Possible Causes   *Possible Remedy*

Squeak

(a) Lack of lubricant or worn constant-velocity joint centering ball.

(a) Lubricate or replace ball-socket assembly.

Knock or Click

(a) Joint or shaft hitting frame.

(a) Shim up or replace center bearing mount.

(b) Worn constant-velocity joint centering ball.

(b) Replace.

(c) Loose upper or lower control-arm bushing bolts.

(c) Tighten bolts.

(d) Damaged center bearing support rubber.

(d) Replace rubber.

(e) Stones or gravel in frame tunnel.

(e) Remove stones or gravel.

Scraping Noise

(a) Shaft rubbing on parking-brake cable.

(a) Correctly position brake cable.

CHAPTER 27

Rear-Axle Assemblies

The rear-axle assembly on modern cars consists of four main sub-assemblies—the axle drive shafts with related parts, a differential with ring gear, a drive pinion and carrier, and the axle housing. All of these subassemblies, except the axle housing, can be serviced without removing the entire assembly. The operating principles and general construction features of the rear-axle assemblies are the same or similar for all passenger cars. Minor variations in design, however, make necessary consulting the manufacturer's service manual for specific service procedures.

Two general types of differentials are available on most cars—the conventional standard design, or the newer antislip type. Fig. 1 shows the construction details of a standard differential, while Fig. 2 shows a typical antislip type.

REAR-AXLE SERVICE

The rear axles support the weight of the car through either roller bearings (Fig. 3) or ball bearings (Fig. 4) enclosed in the outer axle-housing tubes. These bearings usually receive their lubrication

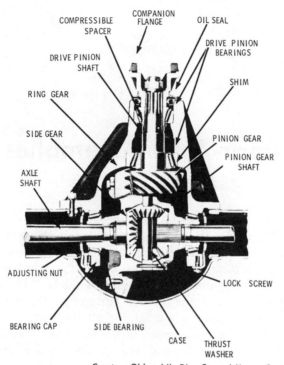

COMPRESSIBLE SPACER

COMPANION FLANGE

OIL SEAL

DRIVE PINION BEARINGS

DRIVE PINION SHAFT

SHIM

RING GEAR

SIDE GEAR

PINION GEAR

PINION GEAR SHAFT

AXLE SHAFT

ADJUSTING NUT

LOCK SCREW

BEARING CAP

SIDE BEARING

CASE

THRUST WASHER

Courtesy Oldsmobile Div., General Motors Corp.

Fig. 1. The construction features of a typical standard differential.

from the lubricant in the differential, although it may be necessary to pack them when a new one is installed.

Rear-Axle Removal

The method of removing an axle shaft varies from car to car. Special tools are required in some cases. The procedure in general, however, is as follows:

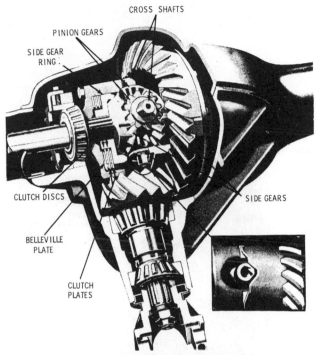

CROSS SHAFTS

PINION GEARS

SIDE GEAR
RING

CLUTCH DISCS

BELLEVILLE
PLATE

CLUTCH
PLATES

SIDE GEARS

Courtesy Oldsmobile Div., General Motors Corp.

Fig. 2. An antispin differential.

1. Lift the car, allowing the rear-axle assembly to hang with the wheels just clear of the floor.
2. Remove the wheel and tire from the brake drum.
3. Remove the nuts or bolts that secure the brake drum to the axle flange, and remove the brake drum.
4. Remove the wheel-bearing retainer plate. Take care not to disturb the brake carrier plate. One or two nuts or bolts can usually be installed to hold this unit in place.

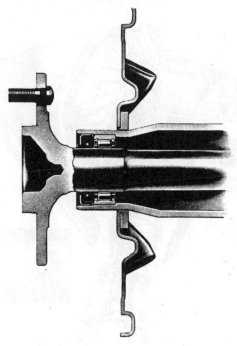

Fig. 3. Roller-type rear-axle bearings used on some cars.

5. Pull the axle-shaft assembly out of the housing. To remove the axle on some cars, it is necessary to install a special puller (Fig. 5). In certain other cars a "C" lock must be removed to free the axle shaft. Check the manufacturer's service manual for specific instructions.

Wheel Bearing Replacement

The wheel bearing will come out with the axle shaft on some makes of cars, but will remain in place in the axle housing in

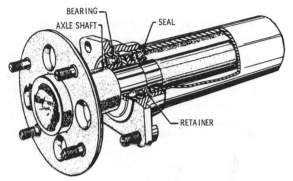

Courtesy Buick Motor Div., General Motors Corp.

Fig. 4. A ball-type bearing is used on the outer end of some axle housings.

others. The type bearing that remains on the axle shaft can be replaced as follows:

1. Nick the bearing retainer in 3 or 4 places with a cold chisel, as in Fig. 6, to loosen it. The retainer will then slip off.

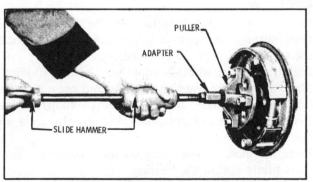

Courtesy Buick Motor Div., General Motors Corp.

Fig. 5. A special puller being used to remove an axle shaft.

703

2. Press the bearing off the shaft with a special puller designed for this purpose. Take care not to damage or burr the oil-seal surface of the axle shaft. **NOTE: Whenever an axle shaft has been removed, a new oil seal should be installed.** New seals (for some cars) should be soaked in SAE 10 motor oil for ½ hour before installing.

Fig. 6. Removing the axle shaft bearing retainer.

3. Inspect the machined surface of the axle shaft and axle housing for rough spots or other damage which would affect the sealing action of the new seal.
4. Lightly coat the wheel-bearing bores with ball-joint grease, place the retainer plate on the axle and press the new wheel bearing on the axle. **Do not attempt to press both the bearing and inner retainer ring on the axle shaft at the same time.**
5. Press the inner retainer ring on the shaft until the retainer seats firmly against the bearing.
6. Install the new oil seal. Coat the outside diameter with oil-resistant sealer before it is installed. **Do not put sealer on the sealing lip.**

7. Place new gaskets (if so equipped) on each side of the brake backing plate, and carefully slide the axle shaft into the housing. **Care must be taken during this operation so as not to damage the oil seal.**

8. Start the axle splines into the side gear of the differential, and push the shaft in until the bearing bottoms in the housing.

9. Install the bearing retainer plate and nuts (or bolts) that secure it. Tighten to specifications. (On certain cars, the axle is held in place by a "C" washer in the differential.)

10. Install the brake drum and the drum retaining nuts.

11. Install the wheel and tire on the drum.

STANDARD DIFFERENTIALS

Complete servicing of a standard differential is possible without removing the unit from the vehicle. The only exception to this is if the differential housing itself must be replaced. The procedure to follow varies with the make and model of car and requires the use of special tools. For this reason, the mechanic should refer to the manufacturer's service manual for specific instructions.

Gear Tooth Contact

The contact between the pinion gear teeth and the ring gear teeth is critical in all differentials. Either shims or adjusting nuts are provided to move the ring gear sideways so that it is closer to or farther from the pinion gear. Shims are also provided to move the pinion gear endways on its shaft to bring it closer to or farther from the ring gear. These adjustments are shown in Fig. 7.

Tooth contact patterns are used to determine if the contact between the teeth is correct. The pattern obtained is compared to normal and abnormal patterns and the indicated corrective adjustment is made. In order to interpret the patterns correctly, it is necessary to be familiar with the nomenclature (Fig. 8) used to identify certain portions of the gear teeth.

To check the gear tooth contact, paint the gear teeth with a suitable gear marking compound, such as a paste made with dry red lead and oil. A mixture that is too wet will run and smear,

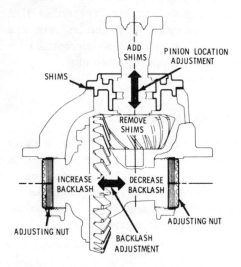

Fig. 7. Pinion and drive gear adjustments to correct tooth contact.

while too dry a mixture cannot be pressed out from beneath the teeth. Rotate the ring gear back and forth while holding a cloth or rope around the drive pinion flange to load the gears slightly.

Certain types of contact patterns on the ring gear indicate incorrect adjustment. Typical patterns and the necessary corrections are shown in Fig. 9. Rear-axle noise caused by incorrect adjustment can often be eliminated or reduced by readjusting the gears.

Gear tooth runout can sometimes be detected by an erratic pattern on the teeth. However, a dial indicator should be used to measure the amount of runout, if such a condition is suspected.

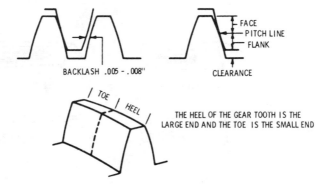

BACKLASH .005 - .008''

FACE
PITCH LINE
FLANK

CLEARANCE

TOE

HEEL

THE HEEL OF THE GEAR TOOTH IS THE
LARGE END AND THE TOE IS THE SMALL END

Fig. 8. Gear tooth nomenclature.

LOCKING DIFFERENTIAL

Locking-type differentials, variously called *Positraction, Sure-Grip, Positive Traction, No-Spin, Anti-Spin, Twin-Grip, Safe-T-Track*, etc., consist of a different type of differential case assembly used in place of the conventional assembly. Rear-axle components are the same as those used with conventional differentials.

The primary advantage of a locking differential is that it reduces the possibility of the car becoming stuck under adverse driving conditions. When only one rear wheel is on a slippery surface, the car can still move forward because both rear wheels tend to rotate at the same speed. This feature allows the wheel on the dry surface to provide the necessary traction.

Another advantage of a locking differential is that bumps do not adversely affect rear wheel action. With a conventional transmission, when one rear wheel bounces clear of the road, it spins momentarily. When this rapidly spinning wheel contacts the road again, the sudden shock may cause the car to swerve. This is also hard on the entire drive train and on the tires. With a locking

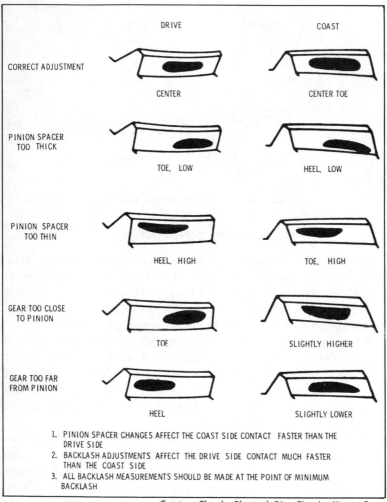

Fig. 9. Tooth contact patterns.

differential, the free wheel continues to rotate at the same speed as the wheel on the road, thereby minimizing the shock and resultant swerve.

The locking differential has pinion gears and ring gears which operate in a manner similar to those in a conventional differential. However, the locking type has clutch packs installed back of each ring gear. These clutch packs are preloaded by springs to provide internal resistance to the differential action within the case itself. The purpose of these preloaded clutch packs is to hold the ring gears to the side of the case, which tends to cause the axle shafts to rotate together.

CAUTION: A car equipped with a locking differential will always have both rear wheels driving. Care must be used when servicing, because if only one rear wheel is raised off the floor, and the rear axle is driven by the engine, the wheel on the floor will drive the car off the stand or jack.

All locking-type differentials require special lubricant. **Never use lubricant other than this special kind (or its equivalent), even for adding, or a severe clutch chatter may result when turning corners.** If the wrong type of lubricant is accidentally added, it will be necessary to completely drain the differential, flush with light engine oil, then fill with the special lubricant.

REAR-AXLE NOISE DIAGNOSIS

Where a rear-axle is suspected as being noisy, it is advisable to make a thorough test to determine if the noise is actually caused by the rear-axle assembly, or if it is caused by the tires, road surface, front wheel bearings, engine, or transmission.

Tire Noise

Tire noise may easily be mistaken for rear-axle noise, even though the noisy tires may be located on the front wheels. Tires worn unevenly or with saw-tooth variations may produce vibrations that seem to come from elsewhere in the vehicle.

Tire noise changes with different road surfaces—rear-axle noise does not. Temporarily increase the tire pressure to 50 lbs. (for test only) and drive the car. If the noise has changed materially, the noise is caused by the tires. Rear-axle noise usually disappears when coasting under 30 mph. Tire noise continues, but with a lower tone as the car speed is reduced.

Road Noise

Brick, stone, or rough concrete roads cause noise that may be mistaken for tire or rear-axle noise. Driving on a different type of road, such as smooth asphalt, will quickly show if the noise is caused by the road surface. Road noise is usually the same whether the car is driving or coasting.

Front Wheel Bearing Noise

Loose or rough front wheel bearings can cause noise that is often confused with rear-axle noise. However, front wheel bearing noise does not change when comparing drive and coast.

Engine and Transmission Noise

A noise in the engine or transmission is often confused with rear-axle noise. To determine which unit is actually causing the noise, observe the approximate car speeds and conditions under which the noise is most pronounced. Stop the car in a quiet place, and with the transmission in neutral, run the engine slowly up and down through the engine speeds at which the noise was formerly most pronounced. If the noise is heard under these conditions, the engine or transmission is at fault, not the rear axle.

Rear-Axle Noise

If a careful test of the car shows that the noise is not caused by any of the external items just described, it is then reasonable to assume the noise is from the rear-axle assembly. Noise from this area may be caused by a faulty drive shaft or rear wheel bearings, faulty differential or pinion-shaft bearings, misalignment between universal joints, worn differential side and/or pinion gear, or by a ring-and-pinion gear set that is either mismatched or improperly adjusted.

Rear Wheel-Bearing Noise—A rough rear wheel bearing produces a vibration or growl which continues with the car coasting while the transmisison is in neutral.

Differential Side- and Pinion-Gear Noise—The differential side and pinion gears seldom cause noise since their movement is relatively slight during straight-ahead driving. Noise produced by these gears will be most pronounced on turns.

Pinion-Bearing Noise—Rough pinion bearings cause a continuous low-pitched whirring or scraping noise starting at a relatively low speed.

Ring- and Pinion-Gear Noise—The noise produced by this set of gears usually is apparent whether driving, coasting, or floating.

(a) *Drive Noise* is most evident during constant acceleration through the speed range.

(b) *Coast Noise* is most evident when the car is allowed to coast through the speed range with the throttle closed but with the car in gear.

(c) *Float Noise* is most evident while just barely holding the car speed constant on a level road at any given speed.

(d) *Drive, Coast, and Float Noises* will be very rough and irregular if the differential or pinion-shaft bearings are rough, worn, or loose, and will vary in tone with car speed.

Index

Index

Index

Height-control valve, 337, 338
High-tension ignition wire, 116, 125
Holley distributor, 105
Honing, cylinder, 557-559
Hose, brake, 292, 293
Hot spark plugs, 47, 48
Hydraulic
  brake
    bleeding, 284-287
    fluid, 283, 284
    hose, 292, 293
    line, 292, 293
    master cylinder, 287-289
    system, 280, 281
    wheel cylinder, 289-292
  valve lifters, 590-603

I

Idle
  arm, steering, 358
  speed adjustment, 496-501
  vent-valve linkage, 488
Ignition
  coil, 110, 111, 125, 148-152
  scope, 156-172
  tests, 140
    insulation, secondary, 167
    primary circuit, 118-124, 146-147
    resistance, secondary, 164-166
    secondary circuit, 124-126
  timing, 126, 135-138

Ignition—cont'd
  transistor, 127-135
  troubleshooting, 132-135
  wire
    high-tension, 116, 125
    primary resistance, 109, 110
Indicator, oil-pressure, 539, 540
Inflation, tire, 249-254
Insulation
  ignition secondary, 167
  resistance, condenser, 76, 77
Installation, spark-plug, 45
Integral-type power steering, 375-384

K

King-pin inclination, 397-400
Knock, engine, 23, 24

L

Lead
  fouling, spark-plug, 39, 40
  sulfuric acid batteries, 50
Line, brake, 292, 293
Linkage
  accelerator-pump, 486-488
  choke, 490, 491
  fast-idle cam, 490, 491
  idle vent-valve, 488
  power-valve, 488
  secondary-throttle, 488

Index

Index

Storage
  battery, 49-66
  tank, air, 340
Suspension
  air, 336-341, 343-345
  front, 321-345
  rear, 441, 442
Sway bar, 324, 328
Switch, ignition, 108, 109

T

Tank, overflow, 525
Testers, engine, 138-140
Thermostat, 521-523
Three-speed transmission, 622-625
Throttle
  linkage, 473, 474, 482, 483, 488
  valve, carburetor, 464
Tie-rod ends, 358
Timing, ignition, 126, 135-138
Tire
  inflation, 249-254
  maintenance, 249-256
  noise, 710
  repair, 256-270
  rotation, 254-256
  tubeless, 259-270
  tube-type, 256-258
Toe-in, 350-354, 404-407, 426, 427
Torque converter, 657-660
Torsion bar, 325, 330-336

Transistor ignition, 127-135
  troubleshooting, 132-135
Transistorized alternator regulator, 232, 233
Transmission
  automatic, 653-678
  governor, 106, 107
  manual, 622-631
    four-speed, 625-628
    three-speed, 622-625
  noise, 711
  oil cooler, 667
Troubleshooting, 9-24
  charging system, 20, 21
  cooling system, 19, 20
  fuel system, 21, 22
  starter, 10-11
Tubeless tires, 259-270
Tube-type tires, 256-258
Tune-up, 25-32
Turbine, converter, 660
Turn signals, 236-239
Turning
  angles, 346-350
  radius, 404

U

Universal joints, 680-685
  ball-and-trunnion, 681, 690, 691
  constant velocity, 684, 685, 691-696
  cross-and-yoke, 681, 688, 689
Unloader, choke, 491